Saga

of the

Vacuum Tube

Saga of the Vacuum Tube

by

Gerald F. J. Tyne

Research Associate

Smithsonian Institution

Prepared under grants from the Antique Wireless Association
and the Smithsonian Institution,
Division of Electricity and Nuclear Energy

Edited by Diana D. Menkes
Editorial Coordinator: Elliot N. Sivowitch

PROMPT
PUBLICATIONS

International Standard Book Numbers:
Soft Cover: 0-672-21470-9
Hard Cover: 0-672-21471-7
Library of Congress Catalog Card Number: 77-83684

Printed in the United States of America.

Preface

The object of this book is to record the history of the evolution of the thermionic vacuum tube, to trace its complex genealogy, and to present essential facts to assist in the identification of such tubes made prior to 1930.

Development of the vacuum tube was an international accomplishment and often involved international controversies. Since an invention is a device based on prior discovery and contrived to meet a need, the precise moment at which invention occurs, and by whom it is made, is frequently open to question. This gives rise to disputes. In the days of the natural philosopher such arguments were usually confined to the annals of scientific societies. With the coming of the technologist and the establishment of the patent system, commercial interests in industrial laboratories were sufficiently great to make priority disputes the subject of long-drawn-out court actions. These patent suits have placed on record many developmental details which would not otherwise be available to the historian.

The growing interest in vacuum tube history and in tube collecting has prompted me to update the original "Saga of the Vacuum Tube" by ten years—to 1930. This revision affords the opportunity to fill in some gaps in the earlier record, gaps caused by wartime interruption in the exchange of scientific and technological information.

My avid interest in collecting information pertinent to vacuum tubes dates back to the time I first saw an Audion, in 1913. In the intervening years I have known many pioneers, including Dr. Lee de Forest, Edwin Smythe, George Clark, Henry McCandless, and others who aided and abetted this cause by generously giving me samples of their work and many personal papers. I have heard their reminiscences. In the course of research abroad, I have had the privilege of listening to the reminiscences of pioneers in France, England, Holland, and Germany, who gave me free access to their records and personal journals. Throughout the book I have used only information which is supported by evidence.

Tracing the genealogy of the vacuum tube was no less an international endeavor than its development. To establish a progressive line of development required years of intensive research in the archives of Bell System companies, General Electric research laboratories, Westinghouse Electric and Manufacturing Company, Marconi Wireless Telegraph Company of America, and Radio Corporation of America in this country. Similar research was done in the archives of Marconi Ltd., Marconi Osram, and Standard Telephones and Cables Ltd. in England, Telefunken and Siemens A.G. in Germany, and Philips in Holland. The cooperation of these companies was reflected in the fine assistance given by Lloyd Espenschied, W. C. White, George H. Clark, Peter Kailus, and E. H. Smythe in this country; D. N. Corfield, George Jessup, S. R. Mullard, and Capt. H. J. Round in England; R. Hahn and Drs. W. D. Brill and Walter Schottky in Germany; Drs. D. Boer and his assistants, C. F. M. Jansen, H. Bergman, M. A. Sijmons, and G. Copal, in Holland.

The story of development in France is complete because of the personal assistance of Dr. Ing. Robert Champeix, noted author and historian, who made available to me his records of French tube development (see the reference footnote to Chapter 19).

For research in museums abroad I am grateful for the help of Don Chilton, Gerald R. M. Garratt, J. A. Chaldecott, and Mrs. Edna Coles of the Science Museum and Library, London; Dr. Wolfgang Maurer of the Deutsches Museum; and Torlief Lindtveit and Edvard Farner of the Norsk Teknisk Museum.

Jacob Verwer, curator of the historical museum at the Technological University of Delft, which houses the largest display of vacuum tubes in the world, has assisted me beyond the call of duty, has accompanied me as interpreter for appointments in Holland and Germany, and has contributed many rare tubes to my collection.

I am indebted to Bernard Finn and Elliot Sivowitch, historians at the National Museum of History and Technology of the Smithsonian Institution, for encouragement and assistance in bringing to publication this segment of the story of industrial archaeology.

I wish to thank Josephine Ciullo and June and Eileen Mullen for long hours of typing, and Charles W. McCue of the Video Production Service for many of the photographs. From the Smithsonian editorial staff—I am grateful to Diana Menkes for diligently reading and editing the manuscript and to Rosemary Regan for typing the final draft.

To Dr. I. D. Okamura of the Retina Associates of Boston, I wish to express my thanks for nineteen years of sight. His skillful surgery made my continued research possible.

Special thanks to my wife, Gertrude, colleague and alter ego in this work. Her enthusiastic help has made every tedious step a lively partnership in effort.

GERALD F. J. TYNE

Photo Credits

AEG-Telefunken Firmenarchiv: 12-6.

Bell Telephone Laboratories: 3-10, 3-11, 6-4, 6-5, 6-6, 6-7, 6-10, 6-18, 6-22, 6-24, 6-25, 6-26, 6-27, 6-28, 6-29, 8-16, 8-17, 8-23, 8-24, 8-28, 9-9, 9-29, 10-4, 10-6, 11-1, 11-20, 11-22, 11-25, 11-27, 11-28, 12-4, 12-29, 14-11, 14-15, 14-21, 14-23, 17-1.

Robert Champeix: 21-33.

Clark Historical Library: 4-10, 4-11, 12-22, 12-23.

Compagnie des Lampes: 10-2, 10-7, 10-8.

De Forest Radio Telephone & Telegraph Company: 4-12, 4-16.

Deutsches Museum, Munich: 1-2, 2-8, 2-10.

Edison National Historic Site: 2-1, 2-4.

Lloyd Espenschied: 7-17.

General Electric Company: 8-2, 8-6, 8-7, 8-9, 8-10, 8-18, 8-19, 8-22.

Robert F. Gowen: 7-7, 7-26, 7-27.

H. M. Stationery Office (copyright): 3-1, 3-4, 8-4, 11-17.

Marconi Wireless Telegraph Company Ltd.: 11-8, 11-9, 11-15.

Norsk Teknisk Museum: 3-8B, 22-3, 22-4, 22-5, 22-6.

A. S. Paul: 12-47.

N. V. Philips Gloeilampenfabrieken: 13-3.

RCA: 4-14, 10-5, 16-6, 16-7, 16-8, 16-9, 16-10, 16-12, 16-13, 16-16, 16-18, 16-19, 16-22, 16-23, 16-24, 16-25, 16-26.

Walter Schare: 7-18.

Howard Schrader: 2-3.

Siemens A. G.: 21-1, 21-2, 21-6.

Siemens & Halske A. G.: 12-5, 12-8, 12-14.

E. H. Smythe: 4-1.

Technische Museum, Vienna: 5-7, 12-7.

Technological Museum of Delft: 20-1, 20-2, 20-3, 20-4, 20-6.

Thorn-A.E.I. Ltd.: 3-2.

R. McV. Weston: 3-6, 3-9, 4-15, 11-7, 11-10, 11-16, 11-18, 12-35.

Contents

Journal Abbreviations

Title of Journal	Abbreviation
Amateur Wireless and Electrics	Amat. Wireless
American Journal of Physics	Amer. J. Phys.
Annalen der Physik	Ann. Phys.
Annales de Chimie et de Physique	Ann. Chim. Phys.
Annales des Postes, Télégraphes et Téléphones	Ann. Post. Télégr. Téléph.
Archiv für Elektrotechnik	Arch. Elektrotech.
Archiv für Geschichte der Mathematik, der Naturwissenschaften, und der Technik	Arch. Gesch. Math. Naturwiss. Tech.
Atti della Reale Accademie dei Lincei	Atti Accad. Lincei
Comptes Rendus de l'Académie des Sciences, Paris	Compt. Rend.
De Forest's Standby	
Electric (Club) Journal	Elect. J.
Electrical Communication	Elect. Commun.
Electrical Experimenter	Elect. Exper.
Electrical Review, Chicago	Elect. Rev. Chicago
Electrical Review, London	Elect. Rev. Lond.
Electrician	
Electronics	
Elektrische Nachrichtentechnik	Elekt. NachrTech.
Elektrotechnische Zeitschrift	Elektrotech. Z.
Engineering	
Europäischer Fernsprechdienst	Europ. Fernsprechdienst
Experimental Wireless (and the Wireless Engineer)	Exp. Wireless
General Electric Review	G.E. Rev.
Histoire de l'Académie Royale des Sciences de Berlin	Hist. Acad. Roy Sci. Berlin
Institution of Post Office Electrical Engineers, Papers	Inst. P.O.E.E.
Jahrbuch der drahtlosen Telegraphie und Telephonie	Jb. Draht. Telegr.
Jahrbuch der Radioaktivität und Elektronik	Jb. Radioakt.
Journal of the Franklin Institute	J. Franklin Inst.

Journal of the Institute of Electrical Engineers	J.I.E.E.
Journal of the Royal Society of Arts	J. Roy. Soc. Arts
Liebig's Annalen der Chemie	Liebig's Ann.
Lumière Électrique	Lumière Élect.
Modern Electrics	Mod. Elect.
Modern Wireless	Mod. Wireless
Monatsbericht der Akademie der Wissenschaften zu Berlin	Monatsber. Akad. Wiss. Berlin
Nature	
National Telegraph Review and Operator's Companion, N.Y.	Nat. Tel. Rev. Oper. Comp., N.Y.
Pacific Radio News	Pacif. Radio News
Philosophical Magazine	Phil. Mag.
Philosophical Transactions of the Royal Society	Phil. Trans.
Physical Review	Phys. Rev.
Physikalische Zeitschrift	Phys. Z.
Popular Radio	Pop. Radio
Popular Science Monthly (and the World's Advance)	Pop. Sci. Mon.
Popular Wireless	Pop. Wireless
Post Office Electrical Engineers Journal	P.O.E.E. J.
Proceedings of the American Institute of Electrical Engineers	Proc. A.I.E.E.
Proceedings of the Cambridge Philosophical Society	Proc. Cambridge Phil. Soc.
Proceedings of the Institute of Radio Engineers	Proc. I.R.E.
Proceedings of the Physical Society of London	Proc. Phys. Soc.
Proceedings of the Royal Institution	Proc. Roy. Inst.
Proceedings of the Royal Society	Proc. Roy. Soc.
Progrès et Sciences	Progr. Sci.
QST	
Radio Amateur News	Radio Amat. News
Radio Broadcast	
Radio Craft	
Radioélectricité	
Radio News	
Radio Nieuws	
Radio Review	Radio Rev.
Radio and Television News	Radio Telev. News
Radio World	
Rivista Italiana de Radio Tecnica	Riv. Ital. Rad. Tec.
Science Abstracts	Sci. Abstr.
Science and Invention	Sci. & Invent.
Scientific American	Sci. Amer.
Scientific American Supplement	Sci. Amer. Suppl.
Siemens-Zeitschrift	Siemens-Z.
Silliman's Journal	Silliman's J.
Sitzungsberichte der Physikalisch-medizinischen Sozietät in Erlangen	Sitzungsber. Phys. Med. Soz. Erlangen
Telefunken Festschrift	Telefunken Fest.
Telefunken Zeitung	Telefunkenztg
Transactions of the American Institute of Electrical Engineers	Trans. A.I.E.E.
U.S. Patent Office Gazette	U.S. Pat. Off. Gaz.

Verhandlungen der Deutschen Physikalischen Gesellschaft, Berlin	*Verhandl. Deut. Phys. Ges.*
Veröffentlichungen aus dem Gebiet der Nachrichtentechnik	*Veröff. NachrTech.*
Wireless Age	
Wireless Constructor	*Wireless Constr.*
Wireless Magazine	*Wireless Mag.*
Wireless World (and Radio Review)	*Wireless World*

Introduction

This book is a revision and expansion of a series of articles bearing the same title, "The Saga of the Vacuum Tube," which appeared in *Radio News* during the period 1943–1946. It is a detailed record— now extended from 1920 to 1930—of scientific research, pioneer inventions, development by industrial research teams, and applications and productions of the tube; it carries with it the parallel story of infringements, restrictive litigation, circumvention of patents, and claims of priority. It includes the story of science and industry combining forces to work on the tube to meet the military demands of World War I, and the step-by-step changes in the tube in the postwar era of radio in the 1920s, all of which affected the direction and urgency of its evolution.

This history is divided into three sections. The first covers briefly the scientific discoveries which are the foundation of this century's technology. The second describes tube development in various countries up to 1920, with the United States subdivided into four chapters to assist the reader in segregating the concurrent lines of development of major companies and independent producers. The third section continues the work in each of the countries up to 1930, and here again the United States is subdivided into four chapters covering the work of various companies.

Significant differences in this revised history, in addition to the years covered, are the following: the story of early scientific development has been curtailed, more information on European development is included, almost 300 illustrations have been added, about 275 brand names of U.S. independent tubes are listed alphabetically, an error in the original series has been corrected, and a change has been noted in the history of development of the Audion.

The error was one of nomenclature: the French TM-type tube was earlier referred to as the S tube, thus perpetuating the error in *Text Book on Wireless Telegraphy* (Vol. II, 1919), by Rupert Stanley, the only source available on the subject at that time. Research of contemporary French records disclosed no name other than TM for this tube. No explanation for the misnomer S ever surfaced.

The change in the history of the Audion is important. Shortly after the publication of the original series of articles, H. W. McCandless, who made all of the early Audions, gave me his shop records and correspondence pertaining to Audions. These records disclose that de Forest had duplicates of the Fleming valve made late in 1905, and he experimented with them before applying for a patent on the Audion. These original records are now in the Smithsonian Institution, bound in a volume entitled "The Story of McCandless and the Audion," by G. F. J. Tyne.

Response to the original "Saga" indicated that there was international interest in collecting vacuum tubes, an interest that has intensified with the advent of the transistor. However, since manufacturers never preserved samples of tubes for posterity, there exist so few specimens of early tubes that the rare survivals barely suffice to illustrate even a general line of development in this country. In Europe early specimens are even rarer because of the destruction of two wars. Despite this major handicap in collecting, this is the saga of the thermionic tube as a physical entity rather than as a circuit element. Emphasis is on its appearance and structure. Inventors, manufacturers, brand names, designations, electrical parameters, and clues for identification are supported by hundreds of photographs of tubes, chiefly from the author's tube collection, long regarded as one of the foremost ever assembled.

Information is presented to assist in identification of tubes made prior to 1930, particularly in answer to the questions about when a tube was made, where, why, and by whom. In answer to the question of how a tube was made, accounts of procedures in manufacture are added only when such information will aid in identification. The stories of pirates, picaresque entrepreneurs, and domestic and international intrigue are included of necessity for historical accuracy and continuity.

Chapter 1

Electrical Developments Prior to 1880

The modern thermionic vacuum tube is the result of an evolutionary process which has extended over a period of more than 250 years. Scientists in the fifteenth century studied electrical phenomena in the belief that if electricity could be understood, this great force of nature could be harnessed and utilized. Their research proceeded at a slow pace, partly because of inadequate support for scientific effort and inefficient communications. Few scientists were financially independent. Some had members of the nobility as patrons, but in many cases the scientist was only one step above the court jester, and was expected to perform spectacular experiments for the entertainment of the patron and his guests. Fortunately for such scientists, the era of static electricity lent itself to the production of flamboyant displays. When not entertaining, these scientists did serious work and disseminated the results of their progress by correspondence with other workers in the field. Letters, however, took a long time to travel.

In the seventeenth century the establishment of scientific societies provided a forum for direct interchange and discussion. The first such society of any importance was the Accademia dei Lincei, founded in 1603 at Rome. Then came the Accademia del Cimento, which existed from 1657 to 1667. In 1645 a small society came into being, which in 1660 became the Royal Society of London. The Académie des Sciences in Paris made its appearance in 1666. While these societies provided for the interchange of ideas within a country, the language barrier still hampered international exchange. In addition, the downfall of feudalism and the disintegration of the Holy Roman Empire had resulted in sweeping changes in the social and political systems of Europe. Countries were being torn by internal strife and external war. These factors are important to our story, because they had a disastrous effect on intellectual unity. The rise of nationalism tended to discourage the attributing of credit where credit was due. The resultant dissension in the scientific world presents a multifaceted picture which sometimes defies evaluation.

In studying the evolution of the thermionic vacuum tube, the complex interrelationships in the electricity-heat-vacuum field must be considered. Glazebrook's *Dictionary of Applied Physics* defines *thermionics* as the term "applied to the phenomena associated with the discharge of electricity from hot bodies." While we usually think of thermionics in connection with electron emission in a vacuum, the term as defined is much broader and includes phenomena taking place under atmospheric conditions, such as ionization of air by emission from hot bodies and flames. It is in this broader sense that we shall consider thermionics.

The earliest published reference to the interaction between heat and electricity is found in William Gilbert's famous work on magnetism usually referred to as *De magnete* (the first words of its page-long title). In this work of 1600 Gilbert writes, "Moreover the spirit of the amber which is called forth is enfeebled by heat . . . ," and later, "It is manifest indeed that the effluvia [charge] are destroyed by flame and igneous heat; and therefore they attract neither flame nor bodies near a flame."[1]

The first important experimenter in the field was Otto von Guericke, of Magdeburg, who made contributions along two lines in the seventeenth century. He invented both the "electrical machine" (electrostatic generator) and the air pump. His electrical machine, shown in Fig. 1-1, was a simple sulfur ball mounted on an axle and arranged to be rotated by hand. The hand of the operator held against the rotating ball generated the charge. One of his air pumps, preserved in the Deutsches Museum at Munich, is shown in Fig. 1-2. Von Guericke made many experiments with the machine shown in Fig. 1-1 as a power source. He observed that a body once attracted to an "excited electric" was then repelled by it and not again attracted until it had been touched by some other object.[2] He also noted one exception to this: if the attracted (charged) body came near a flame, it could again be attracted by the "electric" without having touched any other body.

A host of investigators made modifications and improvements in both the electrical machine and the air pump. In England Robert Boyle, with his associate Denis Papin, improved the air pump; Francis Hauksbee, somewhat later, improved the electrical machine. It has been estimated that von Guericke could obtain pressures as low as 0.8 torr after several hours operation by relays of strong men. Boyle obtained vacuums of the same order of magnitude, but in less

Fig. 1-1. Right: Otto von Guericke's "electrical machine." Left: operator using charged sulfur ball to repel feather. (Reproduced from *Experimenta Nova Magdeburgica de vacuo spatio*, Amsterdam, 1672.)

time and with less effort with his improved pump. After Boyle and Papin there appears to have been little further improvement for many years. Electrical investigators used existing pumps. Unfortunately, however, few made any attempt to measure and record the vacuums attained or noted in their writings the kind of pump used. Hauksbee, using a two-cylinder pump of the Boyle-Papin type, was one of the few who recorded pressures. His records indicate that he

Fig. 1-2. One of von Guericke's air pumps, now in the Deutsches Museum, Munich.

obtained pressures as low as 1.6 torr.[3] Jean-Antoine Nollet, in the middle of the eighteenth century, recorded pressures as low as 3.3 torr.[4]

Hauksbee improved on von Guericke's electrical machine by substituting for the heavy sulfur ball a hollow glass globe with which higher rotational speed would be attained. After the work of Hauksbee at the beginning of the eighteenth century there came a hiatus in the development of the electrical machine. Workers in the electrical field in France and England reverted to the use of a glass rod excited by rubbing with cloth or fur as a source of electricity.

Investigators as early as 1722 had been attempting to make mercurial air pumps. Such pumps would not require the mechanical valves which imposed limitations on the mechanical pumps. Examples of mercury pumps were those of Swedenborg (1722), Baeder (1784), Hindenburg (1787), Patten (1824), and Geissler of Bonn (1855). Geissler's first pump could reduce pressure to about 0.1 torr, and after some improvements by Geissler and others his pump could achieve 0.01 torr. Later modifications introduced by Toepler enabled investigators to get as low as 0.006 torr. In 1865 Dr. Herman Sprengel introduced a different form of mercury pump, variations and modifications of which could produce vacuums of 5×10^{-4} torr.[5]

During the eighteenth century others were studying the interactions between heat and electricity. Among these, two Frenchmen, Charles du Fay and his successor, the Abbé Nollet, are of importance. Charles du Fay, a brilliant man of catholic tastes, was the only member of the French Académie who made contributions to all six fields into which science was divided by that body. He was one of the originators of the two-fluid theory of electricity, which postulates the existence of two electric "fluids," which du Fay called "vitreous" and "resinous." Bodies having the same fluid repelled each other; those having different fluids attracted each other. When the fluids combined they neutralized each other.

In 1733, du Fay began his work in electricity. During that and the succeeding year he had six *memoires* published by the French Académie. In his second *memoire* du Fay described an experiment which is worthy of note. He observed that the flame of a candle could not be electrified at all and was not attracted by an electrified body. He added the following:

> This singularity merits a close examination, in which we will perhaps enter into the question of leakage; but of this we can assure ourselves, for the present, that this [phenomenon] is not due to the heat or the burning; for a red-hot iron and a glowing coal, placed on the glass table, becomes it [is electrified] exceedingly.[6]

After du Fay's death in 1739 Nollet carefully repeated his experiments and after many meticulous tests decided that du Fay's conclusions were incorrect. He found that a white-hot piece of iron dissipated the "virtue" (charge) very quickly, and that the result was the same when the iron had cooled to a red heat. As the temperature of the iron decreased, the rate of dissipation became less and reached zero when the iron became cold.[7]

While Nollet was pursuing his researches in France, scientists in the Germanic states were working to improve the "electrical machine." J. H. Winckler (1745) conceived the idea of using a fixed cushion to replace the operator's hand,[8] G. M. Bose (1745) added the "prime conductor," an elementary form of capacitor,[9] and Andreas Gordon (1746) substituted a glass cylinder for the glass globe.[10] John Canton of England (1762) improved Winckler's cushion by coating it with an amalgam of mercury and tin.[11] These improvements resulted in much higher outputs, both in voltage and energy.

The next important step was the discovery, in 1745, by E. G. von Kleist, of the "Leyden jar," the progenitor of the modern high-voltage capacitor. A number of such jars, connected in parallel, could be assembled into what was then called a "battery." When this battery was charged to a high voltage by an electrical machine it could be used as an energy source in spectacular demonstrations. Fig. 1-3 shows a typical Leyden jar and Fig. 1-4 a "battery."

Using this new tool, other scientists in England and Germany continued experiments to determine the interactions between heat and electricity. In 1756 Franz Aepinus in Germany discovered that when tourmaline crystals were heated to about 150 °F the crystals became electrified.[12] This was the first time that such an effect had been observed. In 1777 Tiberio Cavallo, while making an experiment

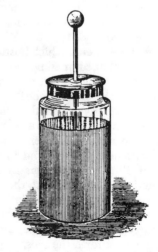

Fig. 1-3. Leyden jar.

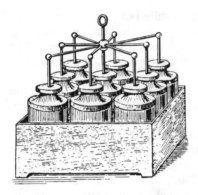

Fig. 1-4. A battery of Leyden jars.

to show that hot air is a conductor of electricity, attempted to discharge a battery of Leyden jars. He reported that the battery could be discharged if a red-hot iron was brought close to the battery terminals but not if a piece of red-hot glass was used, "whence we may infer that hot air is not so good a conductor as has been imagined or else that air heated by iron (perhaps from its ignited particles) is stronger with respect to its conducting power, than when heated by the red-hot glass."[13] The parenthetical "perhaps from its ignited particles" is the keynote of the difference between his explanation and that of his predecessors.

Thus far we have considered only the work done in Europe, but developments were also taking place in America. Every schoolboy knows of Benjamin Franklin's experiments, although many know only that he flew a kite with a key on the string. Franklin first became interested in electricity in the mid-1740s. He pursued the subject with much diligence and made many experiments. So revolutionary and conclusive were his findings that his contemporaries abroad were amazed. By May 25, 1747, Franklin had evolved the one-fluid theory of electricity, which postulated that "electric fire" is a common element contained in all bodies.[14] If by artificial means more electricity is added to the body, it is said to be charged *plus* or positively; if some of the normal electricity is removed, it is said to be charged *minus* or negatively. At this time he proposed the use of a sharp-pointed conductor for drawing off the electricity from a charged body. Franklin's experiments had convinced him that lightning was an electrical discharge, and in some papers attached to a letter of July 29, 1750, to one of his British friends, he proposed the use of elevated pointed rods with their lower ends connected to ground to draw off the charge accumulated on clouds in order to prevent lightning discharges.[15] Later he obtained experimental confirmation of this theory by means of the famous kite experiment. In these same papers he set forth the most important properties of the elementary particles of electricity with such clarity and correctness that he is considered by some to be the discoverer of the "atom of electricity"— the electron.[16]

Beginning about 1800 with the publication of the work of Galvani and Volta, the emphasis in electrical research shifted to the field of galvanism and voltaic electricity, where the technique was essentially that of low impedances. We find little done in the next few decades which had any direct bearing on the field of thermionics. Not until the tools of voltaic electricity were developed to the point where comparatively high voltages and greater energies became available from low-impedance sources was any great amount of work done in the high-impedance field of thermionics.

Michael Faraday was one of the first workers whose investigations of electrical phenomena involved both low- and high-impedance fields. In 1838 he studied the conduction of electricity by solids, liquids, and gases, his work on gases including observations both at atmospheric pressure and at reduced pressure. He observed that the passage of current through a tube containing a rarefied gas resulted in the gas becoming luminous. As the rarefaction was increased, the luminous column broke up into striations, with a dark space between the glow at the negative electrode and the luminous column. This occurred at about 10 torr. As the pressure was further reduced, the dark space became longer. Faraday's observations indicated that the lowest pressure he obtained was greater than 1 torr.[17]

In 1849 Augustus de la Rive, in the course of some experiments to determine the nature and cause of the aurora borealis, constructed a discharge tube in which one of the electrodes was a soft iron bar and the other was a copper ring concentric with the bar.[18] When the air pressure in the tube was reduced to 3–5 torr, an electrostatic generator was used to set up a luminous discharge between the electrodes. When a strong magnet was applied to the outer end of the bar, the discharge was seen to rotate.

In 1851 Professor Heinrich Buff published a paper on the electrical conditions existing in flames.[19] He concluded that gaseous bodies which have been rendered conducting by strong heating were capable of exciting other bodies, solid as well as gaseous, electrically. He used a glass tube closed at one end into which were introduced two small strips of platinum. Heating the glass to the softening point produced no results, but applying the flame of a spirit lamp to the strips resulted in a current flowing between the strips, the flow being from the hotter to the colder.

Edmond Becquerel in 1853 began a series of experiments on the electrical conductivity of gases. Previous experimenters had worked with heat and electricity, or with rarefied gases and electricity; Becquerel was the first to combine heat, rarefaction, and electricity in

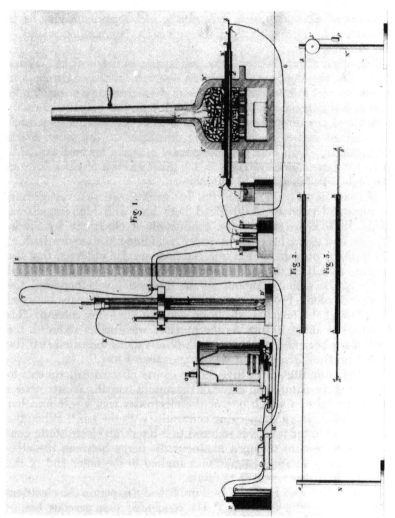

Fig. 1-5. Becquerel's apparatus and electrode systems. (Reproduced from *Ann. Chim. Phys.*, 1853, *39.*)

the same experiment. The arrangement of the apparatus used is shown in Fig. 1-5. Three different electrode systems were available, and the one marked "Fig. 2" is of the most interest. It consists of a platinum tube, 65 centimeters long and 2 centimeters in diameter, with a platinum wire stretched along its axis. A'–B' is a refractory-earth tube into which the electrode system is introduced. This tube was heated by the fire of the furnace and served to keep the platinum electrodes free from contamination by the flame. An arrangement of glass tubes and stopcocks (imperfectly shown in the illustration) permitted Becquerel to seal off the platinum tube A–B and introduce various gases into it, or to evacuate it by means of a mechanical air pump. The highest vacuum he was able to obtain was 3–4 torr. This combination was, in effect, *the first thermionic diode.*

The results of the experiments conducted with this apparatus enabled Becquerel to draw the following conclusions.[20]

1. Gases become conductors only at or above the temperature of red heat, and as the temperature increases so does the conductivity.
2. At such temperatures gases are conductors even when a low voltage is applied.
3. The relative dimensions of the electrodes have an effect on the conductivity of the gas, the conductivity increasing rapidly with the surface of the negative electrode.
4. The resistance of the gas varies with the applied voltage and with the current through it; that is, Ohm's law does not apply.
5. Below red heat, the pressure of the gas has little effect, there being no conduction at low voltages. Above red heat, rarefaction of the gas increases the conductivity.

Since the heat was applied externally, in order to heat the gas it was also necessary to heat the electrodes. It is reasonable to assume that the outer tube was hottest, the gas was next hottest, and the central wire was the least hot, especially since part of such heat as it may have absorbed from the gas would have been conducted along the wire to its outer ends. We know now that the effects noted by Becquerel were due to ionic conductivity in the gas produced by the heat, and also that there was thermionic emission from the electrodes, especially at the highest temperatures (white heat) attained.

Becquerel was at a loss to explain these phenomena. If gases were truly conductors (in the same way that metals are), then removing a portion of the conducting material by rarefaction should have increased, not decreased, their resistance. He could not understand why, since the pressure of the rarefied gas remained constant, the increased temperature should facilitate the flow of current through the gas, except on the hypothesis that at the temperature of red heat and above, material particles become detached from the electrodes and move through the rarefied medium, establishing a continuous circulation of electricity. He considered such a hypothesis to be untenable at the existing state of science, "for until now no experiment has proved the emission of metallic particles on the part of the electrodes."[21] Had he been audacious enough to accept it, and continue his work to justify it, he might have become the "father of thermionics." His work apparently did not become widely known for many years, for little credit is given him in later treatises on the conduction of electricity through gases.

Studies of the discharge of electricity through gases were made by numerous scientists over the next two decades, but neither the element of heat nor heated electrodes were introducd. Julius Plücker, among others who worked with cold-cathode tubes, observed that if the exhaustion was carried far enough (to about 0.001 torr), the glow disappeared and the glass walls of the tube exhibited a green fluorescence.[22] It was soon ascertained that this fluorescence was the result of something emanating from the cathode. E. Goldstein thought it was a form of radiation and, in 1876, called it "cathode rays."[23] Sir William Crookes suggested that these rays consisted of electrified particles of some very attenuated form of matter, which he dubbed "radiant matter."[24]

William Hittorf, in 1869, began his studies of the conduction of electricity through gases using cold-cathode devices. In his earlier work he used a Geissler pump with minor modifications and a phosphorous pentoxide trap as a drying agent. He introduced the practice of freeing the glass from occluded gases by heating the glass envelope "as far as the glass will stand it,"[25] and sealing it off before stopping the pump. It was only after ten years of work that Hittorf began experimenting with hot-cathode tubes. It is evident that he obtained thermionic emission in considerable quantity before 1883, using a cathode heated by an auxiliary battery. In 1884, while working with a hot-cathode tube, he noted that if the hot cathode was connected to the negative pole of the battery of a few cells while the positive pole was connected to the anode, a considerable current flowed. If the battery connections were reversed, there was no flow of current even when the battery was increased to two hundred cells.

REFERENCES

1. W. Gilbert, *De magnete, magneticisque corporibus* . . . (London: Peter Short, 1600), pp. 53, 59.
2. Otto von Guericke, *Experimenta nova Magdeburgica de vacuo spatio* . . . (Amsterdam, 1672), pp. 147–150.
3. Francis Hauksbee, *Physico-mechanical Experiments on Various Subjects* . . . (2nd ed., London, 1719), pp. 95–97.
4. J. A. Nollet, *Recherches sur les causes particulières des phénomènes électriques et sur les effets nuisibles ou avantageux qu'on peut en attendre* (Paris: Frères Guerin, 1749), pp. 235–236.
5. S. P. Thompson, "The Development of the Mercurial Air-Pump," *J. Roy. Soc. Arts*, 1887, 36:21–49.
6. Nollet, *Recherches*, p. 212.
7. *Ibid.*, pp. 214–215.
8. J. H. Winckler, *Gedanken von den Eigenschaften, Wirkungen, und Ersachen der Elektricität nebst einer Beschreibung zwo neuer elektrischen Maschinen* (Leipzig: Breitkopfs, 1744). See also the French translation, *Essai sur la*

nature, les effets et les causes de l'électricité, avec une description de deux nouvelles machines à électricité (Paris: Jorry, 1748), pp. 9–11 and Plt. I. See also Phil. Trans., 1744/1745, 43:166–169 (read Nov. 22, 1744).

9. G. M. Bose, Tentamina electrica in academiis regiis Londinensi et Parisina primum habita, omni studio repetita quae novis aliquot accessionibus locupletavit (Wittenberg: Io. Ioach. Ahlfeldium, 1744). See also Recherches sur la cause et véritable téorie de l'électricité (Wittenberg, 1745).

10. A. Gordon, Versuch einer Erklaerung der Elektricität (2nd ed., Erfurt: Nonne, 1746), Plt. I.

11. J. Canton, "A Letter from John Canton to Benjamin Franklin," Phil. Trans., 1762, 52:457–461 (read Feb. 4, 1762).

12. F. Aepinus, "Mémoires concernant quelques nouvelles expériences électriques remarqueables," Hist. Acad. Roy. Sci. Berlin, 1756, pp. 105–121. See also Aepinus, Recueil des différents mémoires sur la tourmaline (Petersburg, 1762).

13. T. Cavallo, A Complete Treatise of Electricity in Theory and Practice with Original Experiments (London: Dilly, 1777), p. 307.

14. I. B. Cohen, ed., Benjamin Franklin's Experiments: A New Edition of Franklin's Experiments and Observations on Electricity (Cambridge, Mass.: Harvard University Press, 1941), pp. 171, 175–176.

15. Ibid., pp. 212–214.

16. R. A. Millikan, "Franklin's Discovery of the Electron," Amer. J. Phys., 1948, 15:319.

17. M. Faraday, Experimental Researches in Electricity, 3 vols. (London, 1839–1855; reprint New York: Dover, 1965), Sect. 1526 ff.

18. A. de la Rive, "On the Cause of Aurora Borealis," Phil. Mag., 1849, 35:446–449. See also Compt. Rend., Oct. 15, 1849, and Silliman's J., May 1850, p. 451.

19. H. Buff, "Ueber die electrische Beschaffenheit der Flame," Liebig's Ann., 1851, 30:1–16. See also Nat. Tel. Rev. Oper. Comp., 1853, 1:161, and Phil. Mag., 1852, 3:145–148.

20. E. Becquerel, "Recherches sur la transmission de l'électricité au travers des gaz à des températures élevées," Ann. Chim. Phys., 1853, 39:355–402.

21. Ibid., p. 395.

22. J. Plücker, "Ueber die Enwirkung des Magneten auf die elektrischen Entladungen in verdünnten Gasen," Ann. Phys., 1858, 103:104. See also Phil. Mag., 1858, 16:130.

23. E. Goldstein, "Vorlaufig Mittheilungen über elektrische Entladungen in verdünnten Gasen," Monatsber. Akad. Wiss. Berlin, May 1876, pp. 284–285.

24. W. Crookes, "On a Fourth State of Matter," Proc. Roy. Soc., 1880, 30:469–472. See also Nature, 1880, 22:153–154, Ann. Chim. Phys., 1881, 23:378–384, and Compt. Rend., 1880, 91:108–111.

25. W. Hittorf, "Ueber die Elektricitätsleitung der Gase," Ann. Phys., 1869, 136:4.

Chapter 2

The Engineer Enters the
Picture, 1880-1900

Even as Hittorf pursued his scientific researches, the characteristics of a kindred device were being investigated by those in the engineering field, beginning with Thomas A. Edison. In 1879 Edison succeeded in making a commercially practicable incandescent lamp. While practicable, it was far from perfect. Edison soon observed that as the time of operation increased, the light output of the lamp was reduced by a blackish deposit on the interior of the glass bulb. He found this deposit to be carbon and theorized that by some electrical process carbon had been removed from the filament and carried to the wall of the bulb. He called this process "electrical carrying," and he initiated a series of experiments to find a way to prevent its occurrence. The first experiment was undertaken on February 13, 1880, and Edison's notebook record of it is shown in Fig. 2-1. Other experiments followed, involving multiple auxiliary electrodes of different materials, magnets, and so forth.

In the course of these investigations, two other things of importance were observed. First, in some instances there was found on the glass, in the plane of the filament, a line on which the deposit was very light. Such a bulb is shown in Fig. 2-2. Second, the leg of the filament which was connected to the positive pole of the supply circuit was the one which "cast the shadow." It appeared as though the opposite leg, which was connected to the negative pole, was throwing off minute particles of filament material which traveled outward in straight lines and were deposited everywhere on the glass except where it was screened by the positive leg of the filament.

In order to study this condition further, Edison had made some

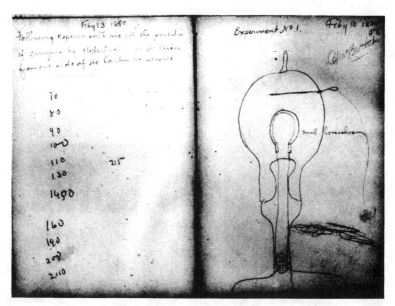

Fig. 2-1. Edison's notebook entry for experiment 1.

lamps which contained a metallic shielding plate between the legs of the filament. One of these bulbs is shown in Fig. 2-3. Edison found that when this plate was connected to the positive leg of the incandescent filament a current would flow across the vacuous space; no

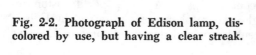

Fig. 2-2. Photograph of Edison lamp, discolored by use, but having a clear streak.

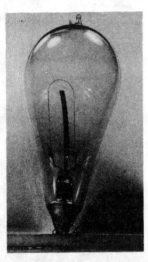

Fig. 2-3. Edison-effect lamp.

current would flow if it was connected to the negative leg. Edison thought this device could be used to indicate variations of potential on a lighting circuit by measuring the current in the plate-filament circuit. The notebook record of his instructions for such a trial is shown in Fig. 2-4. The arrangement worked satisfactorily,[1] and Edison applied for a patent on his "Electrical Indicator" on November 15, 1883. In this patent he noted that "This current [across the vacuous space] I have found to be proportional to the degree of incandescence of the conductor [filament] or the candlepower of the lamp."[2]

The International Electrical Exhibition was held in Philadelphia in the fall of 1884, and Edison's indicator lamp was on display. In connection with this exhibition the newly formed American Institute of Electrical Engineers held its first meeting. At Edison's request Professor Edwin J. Houston presented a paper entitled "Notes on Phenomena in Incandescent Lamps."[3] In this paper Houston referred to the peculiar high-vacuum phenomena observed by Edison in some of his incandescent lamps and described some of Edison's experiments.

Among those present, and taking an active part in the discussion which followed the presentation of the paper, was William Preece (later Sir William Preece, engineer-in-chief of the British General Post Office), who was extremely interested in this new phenomenon. He announced that he intended to exercise his "persuasive eloquence" upon Edison to induce him to give him one of these lamps, and said, "When I go back to England I shall certainly make an illustration before our Society there, and then make careful inquiry into it."[4] How he succeeded and what he did will be told later.

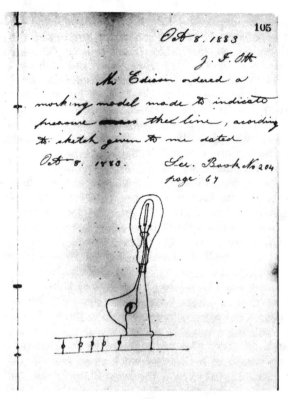

Fig. 2-4. Edison notebook entry showing scheme for using the Edison-effect lamp as a voltage indicator.

Edison formed the New York Edison Illuminating Company to carry out his system of incandescent lamp lighting. In 1881 he organized the Edison Electric Light Company of London for the same purpose. Early in 1882 John Ambrose Fleming (who was later knighted) was appointed electrician to the new London company and later became its scientific adviser. He was thus brought into close touch with the many problems which arose in the use of incandescent lamps. He, like Edison, noted that when the lamps were discolored in service there was frequently a line of less discoloration on one side, in the plane of the filament. This he termed a "molecular shadow." His first mention of it came in a paper read before the Physical Society of London on May 26, 1883.[5] This paper was more or less a brief summary, to precede a full discussion, which was not presented until some two years later, on June 27, 1885.[6]

In the interim, Preece had returned from the United States with the fruits of his persuasive eloquence, in the form of several Edison-

effect lamps. He duplicated Edison's experiments and made quantitative measurements of the Edison effect, presenting the results to
the Royal Society on March 26, 1885.[7] It is in this paper that the
expressions "blue effect" (later blue glow) and "Edison effect" first
appear.[8] Preece observed that in the presence of the blue effect
(caused by the ionization of residual gas in the bulb) current could
be caused to flow in either direction across the vacuous space. He
also confirmed Edison's observation that the current through the
vacuous space was proportional to the degree of incandescence of
the lamp. This last observation had been, of course, given in Edison's
application for a patent, which was issued on October 21, 1884.

It is uncertain how Fleming first learned of the Edison effect: it
may have been from Preece, from the Edison patent, or from some
other publication. But apparently after his 1885 paper, mentioned
above, he began to study the Edison effect in his work on molecular
shadows. On February 14, 1890, he presented a discourse before the
Royal Institution entitled "Problems in the Physics of an Electric
Lamp."[9] He again discussed molecular shadows and the reason for
their formation. He also reviewed the work of Edison and of Preece
and showed that a single Clark cell (electromotive force = 1.43
volts), if connected with its positive pole to the cold electrode, was
capable of sending a sensible current across the vacuous space.

On March 27, 1896, Fleming reported to the Physical Society of
London the results of his further work along these lines.[10] He further demonstrated that even if the lamp filament was energized by

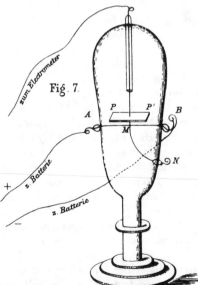

Fig. 2-5. Elster and Geitel tube.
(Reproducd from *Ann Phys.*, 1887,
31.)

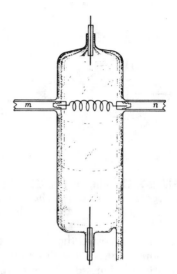

Fig. 2-6. One of Hittorf's tubes. (Reproduced from *Ann. Phys.*, 1883, 20.)

alternating current of 80–122 cycles per second, the current flowing in the circuit to the cold electrode was unidirectional, regardless of which side of the filament was connected through the galvanometer to the cold electrode; that is, the lamp functioned as a rectifier.[11] There the matter rested for a number of years.

While these advances were being made in the engineering field, Hittorf continued his researches. Other scientists entered the field. Johann Elster and Hans Geitel had begun, about 1880, an investigation of the asymmetric conductivity of flames. This led to a study of the electrification of gases by incandescent wires. Fig. 2-5 shows one of their experimental bulbs. They described the vacuum they used as "the best possible, such as Crookes used in his famous experiments."[12] They found the same type of unilateral conductivity as had Edison.

In continuing his work with cold-cathode tubes, Hittorf found that his original precautions to attain the highest possible vacuum were nullified by the evolution of gas from the electrodes during his experimental work. The electrodes became hot as a result of the high energies of the gaseous discharge, and the occluded gases released thus impaired the vacuum. To overcome this difficulty he used a cathode which could be maintained at a high temperature by external means during the process of exhaustion. Fig. 2-6 shows one of Hittorf's tubes. The experiments performed were essentially those of Becquerel, except that Hittorf used higher voltages and better vacuums and could heat one electrode at a time.

Arthur Schuster in 1884 advanced the idea that cathode rays were composed of negatively charged particles moving at high speeds.[13]

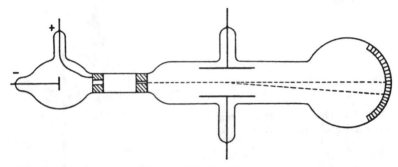

Fig. 2-7. Drawing of J. J. Thomson's tube for determining e/m (electron charge/electron mass). The scale shown at the right is made of paper, glued to the outside of the bulb.

He also suggested that these negative particles came from the dissociation of gas molecules into positive and negative portions. The positively charged portions would be attracted to the negatively charged cathode and the negatively charged portions repelled.

In 1894 J. J. Thomson first attempted to measure the velocity of the cathode rays, but his experimental method gave erroneous results.[14] In 1895 the French physicist Jean Perrin demonstrated that the cathode rays were negatively charged.[15] In 1897 Thomson reported a new series of experiments which did much to promote general acceptance of the idea that the cathode ray consisted of a stream of negatively charged particles.[16] Fig. 2-7 is a drawing of one of his experimental tubes, and Fig. 2-8 is a photograph of the tube. The cathode beam in this tube was acted upon by electrostatic and magnetic forces, the values of the fields being adjusted to counteract

Fig. 2-8. Thomson e/m tube.

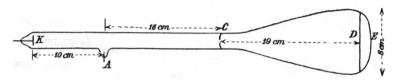

Fig. 2-9. Drawing of the Braun tube. (Reproduced from *Ann. Phys.*, 1897, *60*.)

each other so that the beam of charged particles remained unde-flected. From the calculated values of the two fields Thomson could then compute the ratio of the charge carried by each particle to its mass.

The first application of cathode rays to "engineering" measure-ments was made by Ferdinand Braun and reported in 1897.[17] A dia-gram of his apparatus is given in Fig. 2-9, and Fig. 2-10 is a photo-graph of one of his tubes. In Fig. 2-9, K is the cathode, and A is the anode, which is inserted in a side tube so as not to be in the path of the rays; C is a diaphragm with a circular hole, about 2 millimeters in diameter. The jet of rays issuing from this hole and traveling down the axis of the tube is cylindrical. D is a mica plate which is coated, on the side facing the jet of rays, with a mineral substance chosen for high fluorescence when bombarded by cathode rays. The screen thus shows a bright luminescent spot when the tube is excited. This spot may be deflected in any direction by means of an electro-static or a magnetic field. As originally used by Braun it was a one-dimensional deflection of the spot of light which was viewed through a rotating mirror. The deflection of the spot was accomplished magnetically.

In 1899 Jonathan Zenneck made certain improvements in the de-sign of Braun's tube.[18] The modified tube is shown in Fig. 2-11. The

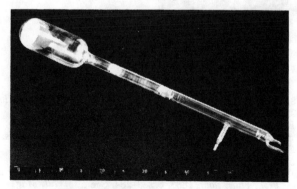

Fig. 2-10. The original Braun tube.

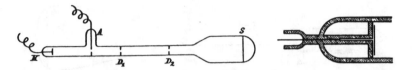

Fig. 2-11. Drawing of Zenneck's modification of the Braun tube. The tube assembly is at left, and details of the cathode at right. (Reproduced from *Ann. Phys.*, 1899, 69.)

anode A is a disk with a small hole in the center through which the cathode ray beam passes; D_1 and D_2 are small metal plates with circular central holes placed to cut off any divergence of the beam. Zenneck produced a deflection of the beam in one plane by the current to be measured and applied a linear time deflection at right angles to the first deflection. The result was a pattern which could be photographed with an ordinary camera. Owing to the low screen brilliance and low emulsion speeds of that era, an exposure time of 10 minutes was needed, and thus only repetitive phenomena could be photographed. Such photographs became known as oscillograms. One of the earliest photographs made by Zenneck is shown in Fig. 2-12.

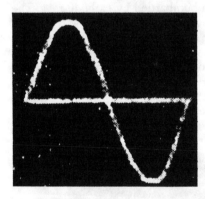

Fig. 2-12. One of the earliest oscillograms made by Zenneck. (Reproduced from *Ann. Phys.*, 1899, 69.)

REFERENCES

1. F. J. Sprague, letter dated Dec. 22, 1883, to W. J. Hammer, *Electronics*, Jan. 1933, 6:15.
2. T. A. Edison, U.S. Patent No. 307,031, issued Oct. 21, 1884.
3. E. J. Houston, "Notes on Phenomena in Incandescent Lamps," *Trans. A.I.E.E.*, 1884, 1:1–8.
4. *Ibid.*, p. 6.
5. J. A. Fleming, "On a Phenomenon of Molecular Radiation in Incandescent Lamps," *Proc. Phys. Soc.*, 1883, 5:283–284. See also *Phil. Mag.*, 1883, 16: 48–49.

6. J. A. Fleming, "On Molecular Shadows in Incandescent Lamps," *Proc. Phys. Soc.*, 1885, *7*:178–181. See also *Phil. Mag.*, 1885, *20*:141–144.

7. W. H. Preece, "On a Peculiar Behaviour of Glow Lamps when Raised to High Incandescence," *Proc. Roy. Soc.*, 1885, *38*:219–230.

8. *Ibid.*, pp. 222, 229.

9. J. A. Fleming, "Problems in the Physics of an Electric Lamp," *Proc. Roy. Inst.*, Feb. 14, 1890. See also *Sci. Amer. Suppl.*, 1890, *30*:12204–12206.

10. J. A. Fleming, "A Further Examination of the Edison Effect in Glow Lamps," *Proc. Phys. Soc.*, 1896, *14*:187 ff. See also *Phil. Mag.*, 1896, *42*: 52–102.

11. Fleming, *Phil. Mag.*, 1896, *42*:99.

12. J. Elster and H. Geitel, "Ueber die Elektrisierung der Gase durch glühende Körper," *Ann. Phys.*, 1887, *31*:120.

13. A. Schuster, "Experiments on the Discharge of Electricity through Gases. Sketch of a Theory," *Proc. Roy. Soc.*, 1884, *37*:317–339. See also *Sci. Amer. Suppl.*, 1884, *13* (No. 451):7201–7202.

14. J. J. Thomson, "On the Velocity of the Cathode Rays," *Phil. Mag.*, 1894, *38*:358–365.

15. J. Perrin, "Nouvelles propriétés des rayons cathodiques," *Compt. Rend.*, 1895, *121*:1130–1134.

16. J. J. Thomson, "Cathode Rays," *Phil. Mag.*, 1897, *44*:293–316.

17. F. Braun, "Ueber ein verfahren zur Demonstration und zum Studium des zeitlichen Verlaufes variabler Ströme," *Ann. Phys.*, 1897, *60*:552–559.

18. J. Zenneck, "Eine Methode zur Demonstration und Photographie von Strömcurven," *Ann. Phys.*, 1899, *69*:838–853. See also *Elektrotech. Z.*, 1899, *20*:288.

Chapter 3

The Beginnings of Thermionics in
Communications, 1900-1910: *Great Britain*

While the work covered in the preceding chapters was being accomplished, the development of the infant branch of the communications art, the wireless telegraph, was steadily progressing. The earliest utilization of thermionic tubes took place in this branch and was the work of John Ambrose Fleming in England.

In 1899 Fleming became technical adviser to Marconi's Wireless Telegraph Company, Ltd., and in 1900 he assisted in preparations for the experiments which were to lead to the establishment of transatlantic wireless telegraph communication. At first he worked on transmitting apparatus and later on receiving equipment. At that time the only detectors of wireless signals were of the imperfect contact type—coherers, microphones, and the like. The mechanical delicacy and erratic behavior of these devices led to the development of the magnetic detector, which was reliable and stable and not thrown out of adjustment by the operation of nearby transmitters. Unfortunately, its sensitivity was low, and the detector continued to be the weakest element of the system.

Fleming went to work on developing a different type of detector. Since he was the victim of a progressive deafness, he sought a device which could operate a mechanism by which signals would be recorded and translated by the eye rather than by ear. The most sensitive current-indicating instrument in use at that time was the d'Arsonval mirror galvanometer, which operated only on unidirectional current. Fleming wanted to utilize this sensitivity, but to do so he had to rectify the high-frequency oscillations of the incoming signal. He tried such rectifiers as were commercially available for low-frequency use, but the results were nil. He then recalled the work he had done many years before on the Edison effect and decided to find out by experiment whether the known rectifying action at low frequencies would also exist at the high frequencies of the oscillations used in wireless telegraphy. Accordingly, in October 1904—but let us read his own account of the discovery—

> . . . I was pondering on the difficulties of the problem when my thoughts recurred to my experiments in connection with the Edison effect.
>
> "Why not try the lamps?" I thought.
>
> Then and there I determined to see if they would serve the purpose. I went to a cabinet and brought out the same lamps I had used in my previous investigations. My assistant helped me to construct an oscillatory circuit with two Leyden jars, a wired wood frame, and an induction coil. We then made another circuit, in which we inserted one of the lamps and a galvanometer, afterwards tuning it to the same frequency as the first circuit.
>
> It was about five o'clock in the evening when the apparatus was completed. I was, of course, most anxious to try the experiment without further loss of time. We set the two circuits some distance apart in the laboratory and I started the oscillations in the primary circuit.
>
> To my delight I saw the needle of the galvanometer indicate a steady direct current passing through, and found that we had in this peculiar kind of electric lamp a solution to the problem of rectifying high frequency wireless currents. The missing link in wireless was found—and it was an electric lamp.[1]

Fig. 3-1 shows one of these lamps now preserved in the Science Museum in London. Fleming gave the name "Oscillation Valve" to the Edison-effect lamp used as described above, and today all

Fig. 3-1. One of Fleming's Edison-effect valves used in his first high-frequency experiments.

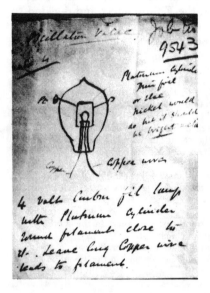

Fig. 3-2. Fleming's first order to Edison and Swan Electric Light Co. for experimental valves to be used as wireless detectors.

types of thermionic vacuum tubes except cathode-ray tubes are still known in Britain as "valves." In fact, all such electron-discharge tubes are in general considered by the British as lineal descendants of the Fleming valve.

Immediately after these first experiments Fleming ordered from Edison and Swan United Electric Company some new lamps, the first to be designated as oscillation valves. The sketch which he gave to Edison and Swan specifying the construction to be used is shown in Fig. 3-2. As will be seen from this illustration, these lamps operated with a 4-volt carbon filament and had a platinum cylinder which surrounded the filament supported by leads through the wall of the bulb.

Fleming applied for patents on the oscillation valve and its use in Great Britain, Germany, and the United States. His British patent application was filed November 16, 1904; the complete specification was filed August 15, 1905, and the patent was granted September 21, 1905 (Patent No. 24,850 of 1904). In this and in his United States and German patents he specified that the vacuum in the bulb should be the highest possible in order to get complete rectification.[2] To aid in getting this vacuum he specified that the bulb should be heated by external means during the pumping process in order to free it from occluded gases.

It cannot be emphasized too strongly that Fleming did not invent the device to which he gave the name oscillation valve. What he did was apply the Edison-effect lamp, patented by Edison in 1884, to the

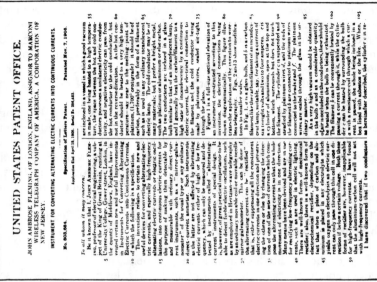

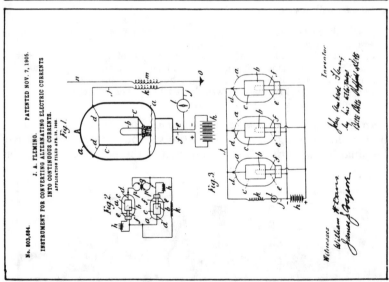

Fig. 3-3. Fleming's U.S. Patent No. 803,684 on his oscillation valve.

rectification of high-frequency oscillations. Actually he was not the first to use a vacuum tube as a rectifier. Ahead of him was Arthur Wehnelt with his pure thermionic tube and its oxide-coated cathode, devised and patented in Germany. (More about Wehnelt later.) Unfortunately, Fleming in his patent applications claimed as his invention not only the device itself but its use as a rectifier without limitations as to frequency. These false claims contributed to his American patent being adjudged void at a much later date. Fig. 3-3 shows the drawing which formed a part of his U.S. patent application. Observe that it shows only one battery. This fact should be noted carefully for later comparison with the work of de Forest on the Audion.

Immediately after his work on the first oscillation valves, Fleming had Edison and Swan make some new valves in which the filament was of treated carbon of such a size that it could be brought to its operating temperature by a 12-volt battery. These valves were of the types marked A, B, and D in Fig. 3-4.[3] The anode was a sheet-metal cylinder surrounding but not touching the filament. This cylinder was supported by a platinum wire sealed through the glass bulb. The bulbs were exhausted according to Fleming's specifications, and these valves were used in wireless work.

On February 8, 1905, Fleming read to the Royal Society of London a paper wherein he described his experiments to determine the apparent conductivity of the vacuous space. He described one of these valves as follows:

> A bulb containing a 12-volt carbon filament rendered brightly incandescent by a current of 2.7 to 3.7 amperes was employed. The filament was surrounded by an aluminum cylinder. The length of the carbon filament was 4.5 cms, its diameter 0.5 mm, and surface 70 square mm. The aluminum cylinder had a diameter of 2 cms, a height of 2 cms, and a surface of 12.5 square cms. The filament was shaped like a horse-shoe, the distance between the legs being 5 mm.[4]

In this paper Fleming reported the use of a separate insulated battery for sending current across the vacuous space, the negative terminal of the battery being connected to the negative terminal of

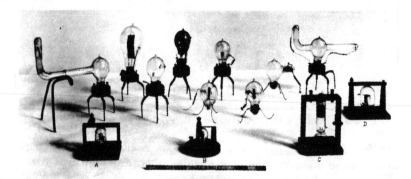

Fig. 3-4. Group of Fleming valves preserved at the Science Museum, London.

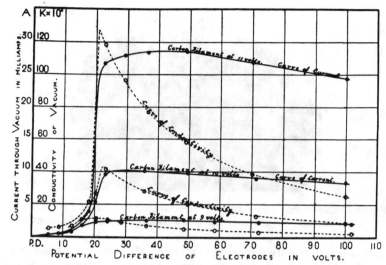

Fig. 3-5. Characteristic curves of Fleming valves. (Reproduced from *Proc. Roy. Soc.*, 1905, 74.)

the filament. He also gave data from which the curves shown in Fig. 3-5 were plotted. He described experiments using an alternating current potential on the anode. He further explained how two valves might be used to rectify both halves of the oscillations in order to get greater output. On March 23, 1906, Fleming presented another paper, this time before the Physical Society of London, which discussed a number of experiments showing that oscillation valves could be used to make quantitative determinations of high-frequency oscillations.[5]

On June 15, 1905, shortly after presenting the Royal Society paper mentioned above, Fleming sent to Marconi at Poldhu, Cornwall, five

Fig. 3-6. Early type of Fleming valve using cylindrical plate.

Fig. 3-7. The Marconi-Fleming valve receiver. Two valves are used with
a quick-changeover switch for quick transfer in case of burnout.

of his oscillation valves for trial in service.[6] Marconi at once began to
use these valves; a photograph of one of the earliest types is shown
in Fig. 3-6. Many of these valves were made in 1905 and 1906 for use
in combination with a special form of receiving circuit—a receiver
known as the Marconi-Fleming valve receiver (Fig. 3-7).

Fleming described the valves first used commercially as follows:

> The valves first supplied were made with carbon filaments and with sheet
> nickel cylinders or collecting plates, the filament being of such size that it
> requires about 12 volts to bring it to an incandescence corresponding to

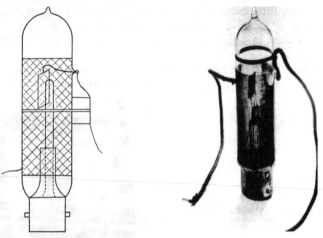

(A) *Drawing.* (*Reproduced from*   (B) *Photograph.*
Fleming's Thermionic Valve, *Lon-*
don, 1919.)

Fig. 3-8. The shielded Fleming valve.

Fig. 3-9. Commercial form of Fleming valve, as used in Marconi-Fleming valve receiver.

3.0 watts per candle. . . . It was, in fact, soon found that for radiotele-graphic purposes a small 4 volt lamp, made with a metal cylinder embracing but not touching the filament, was as effective as a detector as a large lamp, and required as a heating battery only a couple of portable cells.[7]

Because of the effects of nearby electrically charged bodies on the action of the valves, it was sometimes necessary to shield them by a covering of copper gauze which was grounded. A drawing and a photograph of such a valve, reproduced from one of Fleming's books, are shown in Fig. 3-8. Figs. 3-9 and 3-10 are commercial forms of Fleming valves, made for British Marconi by Edison and Swan. Fig. 3-11 shows five forms of Fleming valves which are believed to have been used by the Marconi Wireless Telegraph Company of America. Most of these have trapezoidal anodes, some with spring tension devices to position the filaments, which are of the inverted-V type.

After the first applications of his valve to the rectification of high-frequency oscillations, Fleming began to study the valve character-

Fig. 3-10. Another commercial form of the Fleming valve.

Fig. 3-11. Fleming valves used by Marconi Wireless Company of America.

istics in detail. Some of the valves had filaments of tungsten. He measured the characteristics with varying anode potential, supplied by a separate battery which had its negative terminal connected to the negative terminal of the filament. He found that the curves were

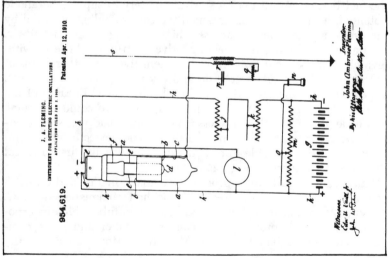

Fig. 3-12. Fleming valve circuit shown in U.S. Patent No. 954,619.

different for different filaments and for different degrees of vacuum. Analysis of the data obtained suggested to him another means of using the valve as a detector. If the anode potential could be adjusted to cause the valve to operate on the bottom bend of the characteristic curve, then the superimposed signal oscillation would produce a larger change in the mean current across the vacuous space. This would bring about an increase in the sensitivity of the device as a detector.

Fleming applied on January 25, 1908, for a British patent on the use of the oscillation valve with a tungsten filament. This filament was operated from a comparatively high voltage battery with a large resistance in series with the negative terminal. The anode potential was adjusted by means of a potentiometer across the battery to obtain operation on the bend in the characteristic curve. The complete specification of this patent was filed on April 15, 1909, and a corresponding U.S. patent was issued in 1910.[8] The drawing of the circuit used is shown in Fig. 3-12.

The same type of bend in the characteristic curve had been shown by Fleming in his February 8, 1905, paper before the Royal Society, but no utilization of this phenomenon was mentioned. It is interesting to note that this arrangement is equivalent to that described in de Forest's paper on the two-electrode Audion delivered before the American Institute of Electrical Engineers (A.I.E.E.) in October 1906, a year and a half before. The difference between them lay in the fact that de Forest used a separate battery to supply the anode potential, whereas Fleming obtained the corresponding potential by the use of a potentiometer across a higher-voltage filament battery.

In a practical sense the Fleming valve contributed little to wireless telegraphy at that time. It was less sensitive than other forms of detectors such as the electrolytic and crystal types, both of which appeared about the same time as the Fleming valve. Because of the Marconi Company's commercial policies, the valve could not come into general use. What usefulness it might have had was soon overshadowed by the development of a thermionic device of greatly increased sensitivity, the de Forest Audion. This was the first practical three-electrode thermionic tube.

During this decade little progress was made in England on cathode-ray tubes. J. T. MacGregor-Morris had commissioned A. C. Cossor, Ltd. to make for him a modified Braun tube which incorporated Zenneck's improvements.[9] This was smaller and more compact than the original tube, and MacGregor-Morris used it (Fig.

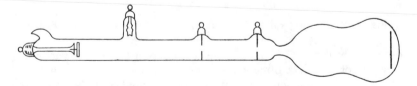

Fig. 3-13. Cathode-ray tube made by A. C. Cossor, Ltd. for
J. T. MacGregor-Morris in 1902.

3-13) in the determination of the maximum value of an alternating current.

REFERENCES

1. J. A. Fleming, "How I Put Electrons to Work in the Radio Bottle," *Pop. Radio*, Mar. 1923, 3:175–192.
2. J. A. Fleming, Patent No. 24,850 of Nov. 16, 1904, in Great Britain. Patent No. 803,684 of Apr. 12, 1905, in the United States. D.R.P. Nr. 186,084, Klasse 21A, Gruppe 68, of Apr. 12, 1905, in Germany.
3. R. P. Denman, *Catalogue of the Collections in the Science Museum—South Kensington. Electrical Communication II—Wireless Telegraphy and Telephony* (London: HMSO, 1925), p. 21. This catalogue entry describes these valves and tells the purpose for which they were used in Fleming's work.
4. J. A. Fleming, "On the Conversion of Electrical Oscillations into Continuous Currents by Means of a Vacuum Valve," *Proc. Roy. Soc.*, 1905, 74:476–487.
5. J. A. Fleming, "The Construction and Use of Oscillation Valves for Rectifying High Frequency Electrical Currents," *Proc. Phys. Soc.*, 1906, 20:177–185. See also *Phil. Mag.*, 1906, 6th Ser. 11:659–665.
6. *Transcript of Record of Proceedings in the Case of The Marconi Wireless Telegraph Company of America vs. De Forest Radio Telephone and Telegraph Company*, U.S. Circuit Court of Appeals, 2nd Circuit, Equity No. 12/31, Deposition of J. A. Fleming, p. 128.
7. J. A. Fleming, *The Thermionic Valve and Its Developments in Radio-telegraphy and Telephony* (London: Wireless Press, 1919), p. 62.
8. J. A. Fleming, Patent No. 13,518 of 1908, application date Jan. 25, 1908, issued Apr. 15, 1909, in Great Britain. The corresponding U.S. Patent is No. 954,619, application date Jan. 2, 1909, issued Apr. 12, 1910.
9. J. T. MacGregor-Morris, *Engineering*, 1902, 73:54.

Chapter 4

The Beginnings of Thermionics in Communications, 1900-1910: *United States*

In the United States Lee de Forest had become greatly interested in wireless telegraphy. His interest had been aroused during his undergraduate work at Yale University and continued during his years of graduate study. He received his PhD in 1899 after having submitted a thesis entitled "Reflections of Hertzian Waves from the Ends of Parallel Wires." After graduation he went to Chicago to work for the Western Electric Company and later for the magazine *Western Electrician.* While at Western Electric he became acquainted with Edwin H. Smythe, a telephone engineer with several inventions to his credit. De Forest and Smythe worked together after hours, trying to develop a new system of wireless telegraphy. De Forest had become very dissatisfied with the operation of coherers while at Yale and began to seek a better type of detector. He and Smythe developed a device which they called a "responder." In 1900, while testing the responder, de Forest noticed that when the induction coil of the transmitter used in the experiments was in operation, the gaslight in the room dimmed; when the coil ceased operation the light brightened. The gaslight was of the Welsbach-burner type. Further experiments made it obvious that the variations in the air pressure resulting from sound waves from the spark gap of the induction coil caused the dimming of the light—but de Forest and Smythe were imbued with an idea that influenced their thinking for a long time. Smythe's notes of one of their discussions of this phenomenon on September 20, 1900, are reproduced in Fig. 4-1. While the suggested method of utilization was never realized, the records are of academic interest and may well have been the foundation of later work by de Forest.

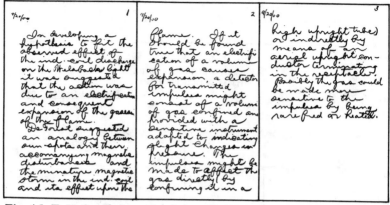

Fig. 4-1. E. H. Smythe's notebook record of the Welsbach-burner incident.

About 1903 de Forest, having broken with Smythe, began a search for a genuine response to electrical vibrations in the gas flame. On February 2, 1905, he applied for a patent on several varieties of Bunsen burner devices and bulbs enclosing heating elements to heat the enclosed air or (as he said) any other gas in the bulb.[1] For these flickering, unstable pieces of apparatus the patent specification included numerous claims and used such vague phraseology as "a self-restoring constantly receptive oscillation responsive device comprising in its construction a sensitive gaseous medium." Because of the diversity of arrangements shown (see Fig. 4-2), this application was subdivided into three applications: these were issued as Patent Nos. 867,876,[2] 867,877,[3] and 867,878.[4] There is no evidence that any of these devices ever worked.

Toward the latter part of 1905 C. D. Babcock, one of de Forest's assistants, brought to the office of H. W. McCandless & Company in New York a modified incandescent lamp which he told McCandless was a Fleming valve and asked that duplicates be made. McCandless was in the business of manufacturing small incandescent lamps, many of which were custom made for specific purposes. He accepted the job, and one of the diodes he produced is shown in Fig. 4-3. Subsequently McCandless received orders for other types of structures, all of which consisted of an incandescent lamp filament with cold electrodes of various shapes.

Although de Forest maintained steadfastly over the years and in all my conferences with him that he knew nothing of the Fleming valve prior to his invention of the Audion, the above history is a matter of record. Further substantiation of the McCandless records is found in de Forest's next patent application, filed December 9, 1905, for a "static valve."[5] It disclosed another Bunsen burner device,

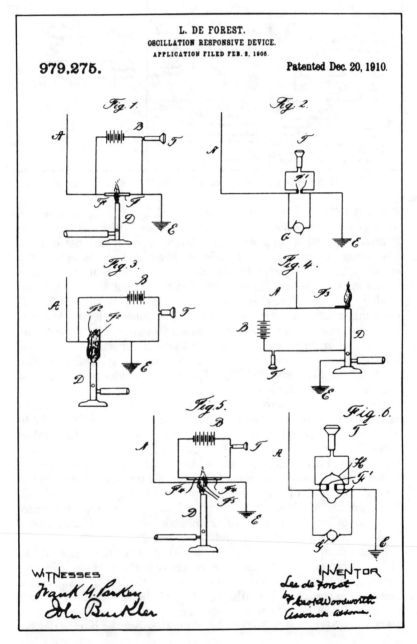

Fig. 4-2. Apparatus arrangement of de Forest's U.S. Patent No. 979,275.

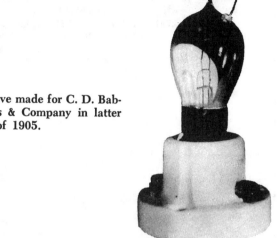

Fig. 4-3. Fleming valve made for C. D. Babcock by McCandless & Company in latter part of 1905.

the flame of which is described as having asymmetrical conductivity. This could act as a rectifier or one-way valve. The specification also disclosed an incandescent lamp with a cold electrode (Fig. 4-4A) which could be used for a similar purpose. It even states in the patent application that this incandescent lamp device had been fully described by J. A. Fleming in a paper published in the *Proceedings of the Royal Society of London*, March 16, 1905 (see Fig. 4-4B, lines 7–15). Apparently de Forest had done some experimental work with the Fleming valves which McCandless had duplicated for him.

In another patent application, originally filed January 18, 1906, then subdivided and refiled May 19, 1906, de Forest shows a two-electrode tube with a battery for heating the filament and a separate battery in the anode circuit (Fig. 4-5). This patent for an "oscillation responsive device" was issued November 13, 1906, as U.S. Patent No. 836,070.[6] This is the device which de Forest called the "two electrode Audion."

The first public announcement of the invention of the Audion was made by de Forest at the October 26, 1906, meeting of the A.I.E.E. in New York, in his paper entitled "The Audion: A New Receiver for Wireless Telegraphy."[7] His paper was discussed both at this meeting and at one which took place in Philadelphia November 12, 1906. The paper began with an account of the Bunsen burner experiments. He described his new invention as a detector for use in wireless telegraphy. It consisted of a partially evacuated glass bulb containing an incandescent lamp filament which was flanked by two platinum "wings," connected together and parallel to the plane of the filament, about 2 millimeters away from it on either side. In the

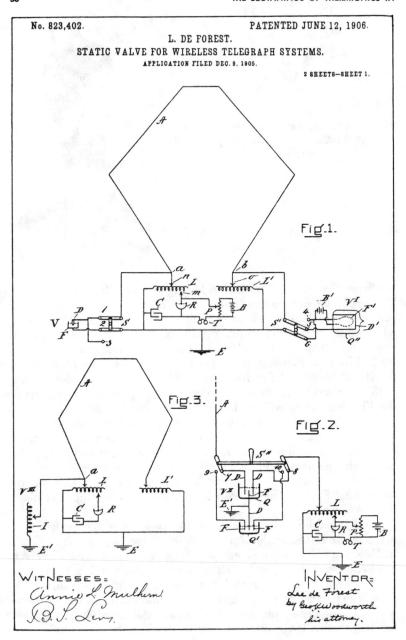

823,402   8

any electrical rectifier, asymmetric resistance, or "electric valve," electrolytic or otherwise, may be utilized in carrying out the above-stated objects of my invention, and I shall 5 now describe several forms of electric valve that are not electrolytic in nature.

The device V¹, (shown in Fig. 1,) connected between the antenna at the point b and earth, is an asymmetric resistance or electric valve 10 which has been fully described by J. A. Fleming in a paper published in the *Proceedings of the Royal Society of London*, March 16, 1905, to which reference may be had for a more complete description thereof than need be set 15 forth herein. Suffice it to say that the exhausted glass vessel Q" contains the filament F', heated to incandescence by the battery B', and a metal cylinder D', which surrounds said filament F'. This type of valve 20 passes positive electricity from the cold terminal D' to the heated terminal F' more readily than in the opposite direction, and hence when the switch S' makes contact, as shown in Fig. 1, with the contacts 5 and 6 25 positive static effects will pass to earth by way of the elements D' and F' of said valve, while if the connections be reversed by throwing the switch so as to contact with 4 and 5 negative static effects will pass to earth by 30 way of the elements F' and D' of said valve.

In Figs. 4 and 4ᵃ the valves V¹ᵛ and Vᵛ depend upon somewhat the same principle as the valve V¹. In these figures H is a lamp or Bunsen burner, the flame of which may be 35 made more conducting by the addition of sodium or other salts, and J is a conductor placed near said flame. M is a bunch of asbestos or mineral wool which may be attached to said conductor J. In these devices posi- 40 tive electricity passes more readily from the element J to the flame, and hence to earth E', than in the opposite direction. S''' is a reversing-switch whose function is the same as that of the switch S. 45

In Fig. 5 the device M' consists of mineral wool or asbestos placed between two plates and heated by the lamp H. This device is practically non-conducting when cold, but becomes a partial conductor when heated. 50 The oscillations developed in the antenna by the electromagnetic signal-waves will have but little tendency to pass to earth by way of the shunt a' M' E'; but heavy static charges induced in the antenna have an effect on the 55 device M' somewhat analogous to the phenomenon of coherence (although it is not a contact device) in that they increase the conductivity of said device, so that the latter becomes a very efficient static leak. The pas- 60 sage of the heated gases from the lamp H through the fibrous material of the device M' maintains said device in its sensitive high-resistance condition, and thereby prevents the shunting around to inductance L of the oscil- 65 lations intended to operate the responder.

In Fig. 3 I have shown still another static leak Vᵘᴵ, which I have effectively employed for the purpose of carrying my invention into effect.' In this figure the arrangement of re- 70 ceiving-circuits is the same as in Fig. 1, and from the point a I connect to earth E a shunt-circuit including the adjustable inductance-coil, I of iron or other paramagnetic material or of a non-magnetic material plated with a 75 paramagnetic material or of a non-magnetic material having a paramagnetic core. Such an inductance opposes enormous impedance to the passage of the high-frequency oscillations developed in the receiving system by 80 the electromagnetic signal-waves, but offers but little impedance to the passage of the slow frequency or practically unidirectional currents resulting from the static charges induced in said system by atmospheric electric- 85 ity, and hence eliminates the effect of said currents on the receiver.

By the term "static valve" as used in the specification and claims of this application I desire to be understood as meaning means 90 offering greater opposition to electric currents of one character than to electric currents of different character—such, for example, as the asymmetric resistances described in connection with Figs. 1, 2, 4, and 95 4ᵃ, the spiral I, described in connection with Fig. 3, and the coherer-like device M', described in connection with Fig. 5; but it is to be understood that the particular devices hereinbefore specifically described are merely 100 examples of a few of the static valves which may be employed for the purposes of the present invention.

I claim—

1. In a wireless-telegraph receiving system, the combination with an oscillation-de- 105 tector of an electrolytic static valve.

2. In a wireless-telegraph receiving system, an oscillation-detector and an electrolytic static valve so associated therewith as to protect the same from static effects. 110

3. In a wireless-telegraph receiving system, a receiving-antenna, an inductance included therein, a tuned receiving-circuit associated with said inductance, an oscillation-detector in said tuned receiving-circuit, and 115 means offering greater opposition to electric currents of one character than to electric currents of different character connected between the earth and a point in said antenna above the point of connection of said induc- 120 tance to said antenna.

4. In a wireless-telegraph receiving system, an oscillation-detector, and means offering greater opposition to electric currents of one polarity than to electric currents 125 of the opposite polarity so associated with said detector as to protect said detector from the effects of the currents of that polarity to which said means offers the greater opposition. 130

(B) Text.

text from de Forest's U.S. Patent No. 823,402.

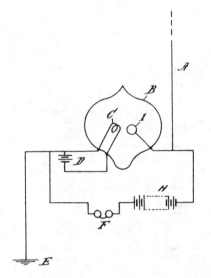

Fig. 4-5. First form of de Forest's two-electrode Audion. (Reproduced from U.S. Patent No. 836,070.)

paper de Forest referred to three types of filament: platinum, tantalum, and carbon.

At the discussion in Philadelphia on November 12, 1906, in response to a question from H. C. Snook, one of the members present, de Forest stated that he was using the tantalum filament entirely; he had never been able to use the tungsten filament but still thought tungsten might give better results than tantalum. He also said that some work had been done with filaments of the Wehnelt type, coated with salts of potassium and sodium, and that although their life had been short, they might yet be produced so as to excel the tantalum filament.

In this paper de Forest also referred to the work of Elster and Geitel: "Elster and Geitel, beginning in 1882 a systematic investigation of the ionization produced by incandescent metals, frequently employed an exhausted glass vessel containing an insulated platinum plate, stretched close to which passed a fine metallic filament brought to incandescence by an electric current." He also referred to the work of Fleming with an "Elster and Geitel tube" but stated that the action of the Audion was quite different from that of such an arrangement, and the Audion acted as a relay rather than as a rectifier.

We may assume he really believed this from his statements and diagrams of variations in the method of operation. Note the use of an external electrode connected to the antenna in Fig. 4-6, and the use of magnetic control by passing the high-frequency currents through a helix of wire wound around the bulb (Fig. 4-7) or through a flat coil brought close to the bulb with its axis perpendicular to the axis of the bulb. These arrangements involved no metallic connection

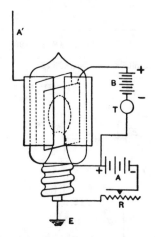

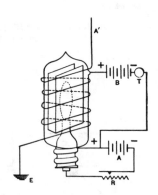

Fig. 4-6. The two-electrode Audion with external electrostatic control. (Reproduced from *Trans. A.I.E.E.*, 1906, 25.)

Fig. 4-7. The two-electrode Audion with electromagnetic control. (Reproduced from *Trans. A.I.E.E.*, 1906, 25.)

between the oscillatory circuit and the "wings" and hence could not be considered as rectifiers. The functioning of the Audion was attributed by de Forest to the influence of the electrostatic field on the motion of ions within the bulb in the case of the external electrode, and to the electromagnetic field on the motion of the ions within the bulb in the case of the external coils. He also attempted to explain the action of an external permanent magnet on the "flux" (space current) within the bulb.

The discussion which followed the paper showed that the exact principle of operation of the device was not clear even to de Forest. In response to a question from Percy Thomas at the New York discussion as to whether the action depended on the ionization of the residual gas or the particles coming from the electrodes themselves, de Forest replied: "I think that it is due to the ionization of the residual gases; the gases still exist in the lamp, because the vacuum is only that which obtains in all incandescent lamps."[8] In response to another question from H. C. Snook at Philadelphia de Forest stated: "If the exhausting process is carried too far, the Audion loses its sensitiveness. The gas particles rather than the particles of the metal dust are the carriers. I do not believe that the dust particles are controlling at all."[9]

Only the day before the presentation of this paper de Forest had filed another patent application (U.S. Patent No. 841,387) on an arrangement entitled "Device for Amplifying Feeble Electrical Currents."[10] This application disclosed an incandescent lamp with a

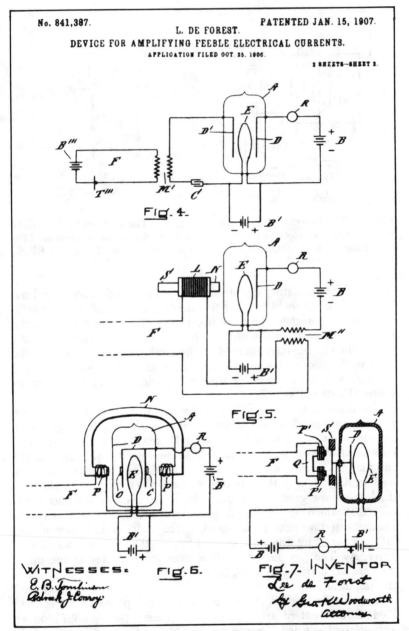

Fig. 4-8. The first three-electrode Audion patent. Note the
external connections.

carbon or metal filament which had two metal "wings" parallel to the plane of the filament, one on either side of the filament. This was not new, but the external connections and method of use were new. A lead from each "wing" was brought out independently (Fig. 4-8). The arrangement was said to depend for its operation on the electrostatic attraction between the filament and the "wing" which was connected to the antenna. While it might repeat, it is doubtful if it would amplify. This patent application contains the first mention of what Fleming later termed the "split cold electrode," and the device which the patent application covers is the first form of the three-electrode Audion.

Then de Forest reasoned that the bulb might work better if the second cold electrode were interposed between the filament and the anode, but he thought this would block the flow of "particles" from filament to anode. He decided to make the interposed electrode in such a form that this could not occur. He used a single wire bent back and forth in the shape of a gridiron. It is from this shape that the term "grid" is derived.

Accordingly, on November 25, 1906, he ordered from McCandless some tubes which embodied this wire grid between the filament and the anode. At this time de Forest was in deep legal and financial trouble. Three days after he placed this order with McCandless he was forced by his backers to resign from his position of vice-president and scientific director of the American De Forest Wireless Telegraph Company. He was given $1,000, half of which was taken by his lawyer, and the pending patents on the Audion (which the backers considered worthless) as severance pay. His preoccupation with this emergency makes it understandable that the new "grid type" Audions were not tested until December 31, 1906.[11] The tests were made by a high school boy named John V. L. Hogan, Jr. They were so successful that de Forest immediately got in touch with his patent attorney, George K. Woodworth, and a patent application was prepared and filed on January 29, 1907. The patent was issued on February 18, 1908, U.S. Patent No. 879,532[12]; the circuit which is disclosed is shown in Fig. 4-9.

The first public disclosure of the triode Audion was made by de Forest at the Brooklyn Institute of Arts and Sciences on March 14, 1907, in connection with his paper on "The Wireless Transmission of Intelligence." Immediately after this disclosure de Forest organized the De Forest Radio Telephone Company and its subsidiary, The Radio Telephone Company, to manufacture and market wireless apparatus on which he owned or controlled patent rights. Directly thereafter, the first grid-type Audion was manufactured for commercial use.

Only one receiving set equipped with two-element Audions was

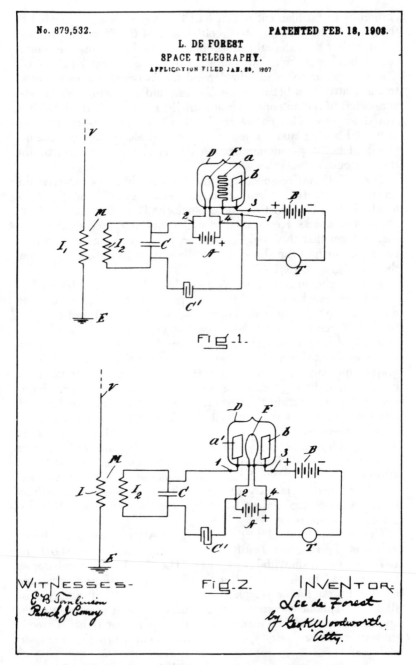

No. 879,532.   PATENTED FEB. 18, 1908.

L. DE FOREST
SPACE TELEGRAPHY.
APPLICATION FILED JAN. 29, 1907

Fig. 4-9. The first grid-type three-electrode Audion patent.

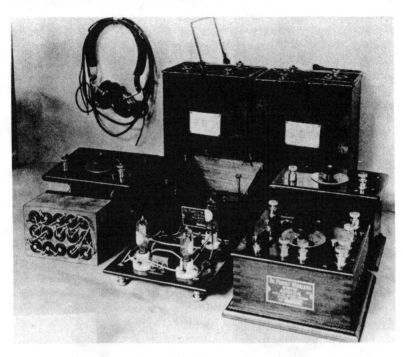

Fig. 4-10. Key West installation of two-electrode Audions, 1906.

Fig. 4-11. Panel mounting two-electrode Audions installed at
Key West, 1906.

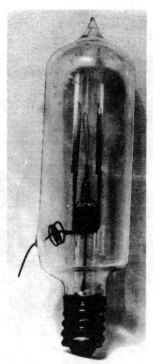
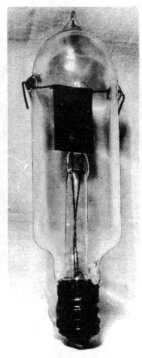

Fig. 4-12. Another type of   Fig. 4-13. The first grid-type
two-electrode Audion.   Audion.

ever sold, and this was installed at the U.S. Naval Radio Station at
Key West, Florida. A photograph of this installation is shown in
Fig. 4-10; a photograph of two of the Audions is given in Fig. 4-11.
Fig. 4-12 shows another two-electrode Audion with a different lead
arrangement. A photograph of the earliest structure of the grid-type
Audion is given in Fig. 4-13. Figs. 4-14 and 4-15 show two of the
earliest commercial triode Audions. The type shown in Fig. 4-14 was
incorporated in a number of sets of radiotelephone apparatus sold
to the U.S. Navy in 1907 by the Radio Telephone Company. When
the U.S. Fleet under the command of Admiral "Fighting Bob" Evans
made its memorable cruise around the world in 1907–1908, more
than twenty vessels were equipped with this de Forest apparatus.
Fig. 4-16 is a photograph of the battleship installations on the bridge
of the flagship, U.S.S. *Connecticut*. Fig. 4-17 shows the connections
of the Audion detectors used in this installation, and Fig. 4-18 shows
the Audion control box.

Comparison of Figs. 4-13, 4-14, and 4-15 shows that there was
little mechanical uniformity in the construction of the early triode

Fig. 4-14. Grid-type Audion used by the U.S. Navy in 1907–1908.

Fig. 4-15. Grid-type Audion once owned by Dr. J. A. Fleming, now in the Science Museum, London.

Audions. Up to 1915 all Audions were made by McCandless. No mechanical requirements were laid down by de Forest, and Mc-Candless changed the construction almost at will to simplify manufacture and reduce cost. Anodes were cut from sheet metal with ordinary hand scissors; sometimes the corners were left square, other times clipped off. At first anodes were supported by copper wires passed through holes near the upper corners and crimped in place. Later they were supported by wires hard-soldered to the sheet metal near the upper corners. In some cases the wires were soldered together near the middle of the top edge of the anode with one support wire bowed in an attempt to provide rigidity. Grids were made of copper wire, bent by hand around nails driven into a piece of wood. The final exhaust was accomplished by a Geissler pump, and the degree of vacuum was judged by the sound of the mercury as it fell through the glass tubing of the pump. There were no electrical requirements other than that the filaments be continuous. Consequently, each tube was an individual.

Only single-filament Audions with a life of 35 to 100 hours were made prior to 1908, when double-filament Audions were introduced. The free end of the second filament was insulated and brought out between the glass bulb and the shell of the candelabra base. When

Fig. 4-16. Lieutenant Weaver at the de Forest wireless telephone
installed on the flagship U.S.S. *Connecticut.*

the first filament burned out, the free end of the second filament was
stripped of insulation and wound around the base shell. It was held
in contact with the base by means of a rubber ring or by soldering if
the operator was willing to risk cracking the glass bulb.

About this time the bulb shape was changed from cylindrical to
spherical, in order to reduce the cost: spherical bulbs were readily
available in a lamp factory, while cylindrical ones were not. Fig. 4-19
shows an early spherical bulb. Some of these Audions bore a patent
marking on the screw base, "Pat. Nov. 8, 1904," which refers to U.S.
Patent No. 774,404 issued to Alfred Swan and covers an improved
method of constructing the base shell for an incandescent lamp; it
bears no relation to the Audion itself.

In 1909, in order to increase the conductivity of the tube and
obtain greater energy output, Audions were made with two grids
and two "wings," one set on either side of the filaments. These were
called "double Audions" and were sold at a higher price. The single-

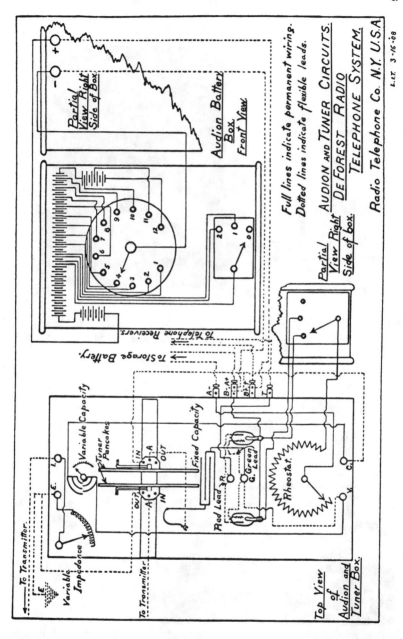

Fig. 4-17. Connections of Audion detector used on U.S. Navy ships
in 1907–1908.

Wireless. Telegraph
De Forest System.
From Radio Telegraph Co.
Audion Receiver. For
U.S.S. Culaoa. Req143-07 Bu
Contract. 171.   *1-18-08*

2380.

Fig. 4-18. Photograph of Audion detector in Fig. 4-17.

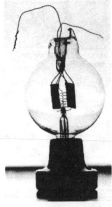

Fig. 4-19. A 1908 double-filament Audion.

Fig. 4-20. Double Audion, vintage 1909.

Fig. 4-21. A double Audion with separate leads from each grid and plate.

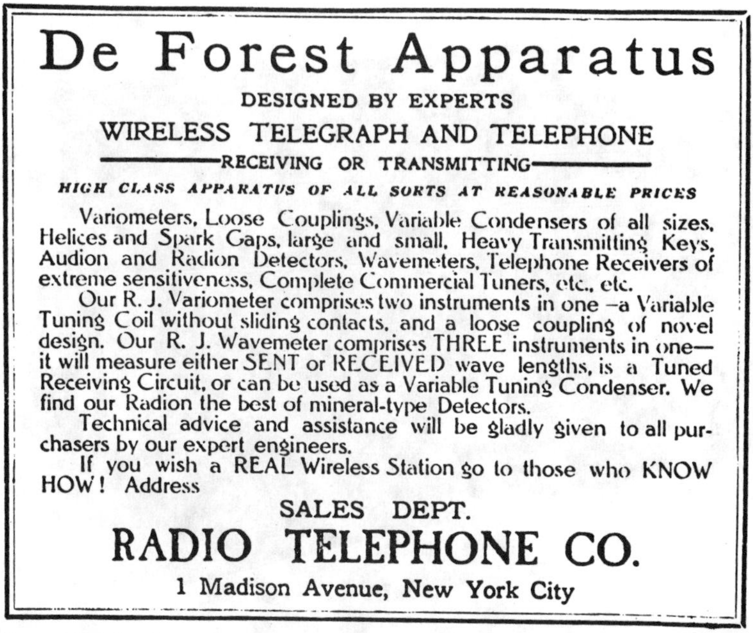

De Forest Apparatus

DESIGNED BY EXPERTS

WIRELESS TELEGRAPH AND TELEPHONE

RECEIVING OR TRANSMITTING

HIGH CLASS APPARATUS OF ALL SORTS AT REASONABLE PRICES

Variometers, Loose Couplings, Variable Condensers of all sizes, Helices and Spark Gaps, large and small, Heavy Transmitting Keys, Audion and Radion Detectors, Wavemeters, Telephone Receivers of extreme sensitiveness, Complete Commercial Tuners, etc., etc.

Our R. J. Variometer comprises two instruments in one –a Variable Tuning Coil without sliding contacts, and a loose coupling of novel design. Our R. J. Wavemeter comprises THREE instruments in one—it will measure either SENT or RECEIVED wave lengths, is a Tuned Receiving Circuit, or can be used as a Variable Tuning Condenser. We find our Radion the best of mineral-type Detectors.

Technical advice and assistance will be gladly given to all purchasers by our expert engineers.

If you wish a REAL Wireless Station go to those who KNOW HOW! Address

SALES DEPT.

RADIO TELEPHONE CO.

1 Madison Avenue, New York City

Fig. 4-22. The first advertisement for the Audion Detector. (Reproduced from *Mod. Elect.*, Sept. 1909.)

"wing" single-grid tube continued to be made. A double Audion is shown in Fig. 4-20. Some of these double Audions had separate leads from each grid and plate (Fig. 4-21). Audions were sold in two grades, the regular or S grade, and the extra-sensitive or X grade, the latter having a higher price. What was the difference between the grades? Walter Schare, who worked for de Forest at a later date, told me that if one of these tubes worked very well when it was tested, it was grade X; all other tubes were grade S. This statement is borne out by a letter sent by the De Forest Company to a disgruntled customer who complained that his order for X-grade tubes had not been filled. The letter states "X grade Audion bulbs cannot be wilfully made, but simply occur in the testing process and so their supply is beyond our control."

The first advertisement offering Audion detectors to the public appeared on page 288 in the September 1909 issue of *Modern Electrics* (Fig. 4-22 is a reproduction of this ad). The Radio Telephone Company had been advertising wireless apparatus since January 1909, but the September ad was the first to mention Audion detectors. Audions were sold as part of an assembly denoted the RJ4 Detector (Fig. 4-23). The designation RJ, meaning Radio Junior, was adopted for equipment developed for sale to wireless amateurs,

Fig. 4-23. The RJ4 detector. The tap switch at the left controls the plate voltage, that at the right is the off-on switch for the filament. The filament rheostat is mounted on the right-hand end of the box.

in contradistinction to the so-called professional equipment intended for commercial use.

Although the title of the patent on the first form of three-element Audion was "Device for Amplifying Feeble Electrical Currents," the Audion was for many years used only as a detector. At that time de Forest and his associates attempted to use the grid Audion as an amplifier at audio frequencies but they were unsuccessful. Judging from what John V. L. Hogan and de Forest told me of their early attempts, it seems probable that their failure was due to insufficient knowledge of the characteristics of the tube and to their use of high-frequency coupling to get audio-frequency amplification. It is also probably true that the grid-type Audion operated as the sensitive detector that it was by virtue of its inherent amplifying properties. The Audion was not used as an amplifier per se by de Forest or any-one else in the United States until some years later.

A tube containing a small amount of gas, such as the early Audi-ons, has sensitive spots (kinks) on its characteristic curves, particu-larly when operated at low anode voltages. These result from the ionization of small traces of gas, too small to make the tube break over into blue glow. This ionization causes a reduction in space

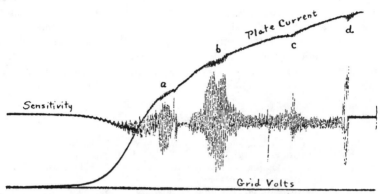

Fig. 4-24. Oscillographic study of a low-vacuum triode. (Reproduced from Proc. I.R.E., Dec., 1922.)

charge and results in greatly increased anode current. When operated on one of these kinks the tube has phenomenal sensitivity as a detector. Fig. 4-24 is an oscillographic study of such a tube.[13] The condition is an unstable one, as oldtimers who used the RJ4 detector will recall. The adjustment was critical because the RJ4 had no grid bias control; to find the kinks it was necessary to vary the filament current and plate voltage in small steps.

Development in the field of cathode-ray tubes in the early 1900s was forced by the urgent need of one experimenter, Harris J. Ryan, to find such a tube with a bigger screen. Ryan had found the use of existing tubes unsatisfactory because the maximum size available was about 3 inches in diameter. He requested Müller-Uri of Braunschweig, Germany, to make two tubes with screens as near 6 inches in diameter as possible. Since the glasswork of such a tube was quite difficult, the largest screen that could be provided proved to be 5 inches in diameter[14] (Fig. 4-25). These tubes were unsatisfactory in the beginning, giving an intermittent cathode-ray stream. The

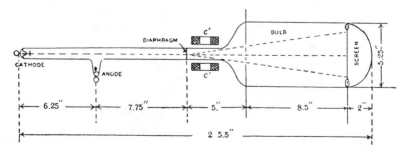

Fig. 4-25. Ryan's tube, as made by Müller-Uri.

trouble was eventually traced to corona and external leakage of the high-tension supply, which was derived from a motor-driven electrostatic generator. The trouble was corrected by the application of a thick jacket of solid insulation composed of hard rubber disks sealed with wax on the surface of the tube at the cathode and anode. Ryan used magnetic deflection coils on both axes and obtained a cyclographic figure on the screen which could be recorded photographically.

REFERENCES

1. Lee de Forest, "Oscillation Responsive Device," U.S. Patent No. 979,275, application date Feb. 2, 1905, issued Dec. 20, 1910.
2. Lee de Forest, "Oscillation Responsive Device," U.S. Patent No. 867,876, application date Feb. 2, 1905, issued Oct. 8, 1907.
3. Lee de Forest, "Art of Detecting Oscillations," U.S. Patent No. 867,877, application date Feb. 2, 1905, issued Oct. 8, 1907.
4. Lee de Forest, "Oscillation Detector," U.S. Patent No. 867,878, application date Feb. 2, 1905, issued Oct. 8, 1907.
5. Lee de Forest, "Static Valve for Wireless Telegraph Systems," U.S. Patent No. 823,402, application date Dec. 9, 1905, issued June 12, 1906.
6. Lee de Forest, "Oscillation Responsive Device," U.S. Patent No. 836,070, application date Jan. 18, 1906, issued Nov. 13, 1906.
7. Lee de Forest, "The Audion: A New Receiver for Wireless Telegraphy," Trans. A.I.E.E., 1906, 25:735–763; discussions on pp. 764–779.
8. Ibid., p. 769.
9. Ibid., p. 778.
10. Lee de Forest, "Device for Amplifying Feeble Electrical Currents," U.S. Patent No. 841,387, application date Oct. 25, 1906, issued Jan. 15, 1907.
11. G. L. Archer, History of Radio to 1926 (New York: American Historical Society, 1938), p. 92.
12. Lee de Forest, "Improvement in Oscillation Detectors," U.S. Patent No. 879,532, application date Jan. 29, 1907, issued Feb. 18, 1908.
13. E. L. Chaffee, "Oscillographic Study of Electron Tube Characteristics," Proc. I.R.E., Dec. 10, 1922, 10:449.
14. H. J. Ryan, "The Cathode Ray Alternating Current Wave Indicator," Trans. A.I.E.E., 1903, 22:539–552.

Chapter 5

The Beginnings of Thermionics in Communications, 1900-1910: *Continental Europe*

In Germany during this period, work was progressing along both scientific and technological lines. Arthur Wehnelt, in 1903, studied the effect of applying to a hot metallic cathode a coating of oxide of alkaline metals beginning with barium and calcium. The same year he published a paper describing a method of obtaining "negative ions" in great numbers from incandescent metallic compounds.[1] He used a platinum wire or strip coated with calcium or barium oxide as the cathode of a discharge tube. He found that there was a strong emission of negative ions when this cathode was brought to red heat. Further experiments of this nature were described by him in other papers in 1903 and 1904.[2] On January 15, 1904, Wehnelt applied for a German patent for such a discharge tube, containing an oxide-coated hot cathode, to be used as a rectifier for transforming single-phase and poly-phase alternating currents into direct currents.[3] No mention was made of any application at high frequencies or of wireless telegraph use.

In 1905 Wehnelt published two more papers, one entitled "An Electric Valve Tube."[4] In this paper he suggested the tube might be used for charging storage batteries or for supplying potential for the direct operation of Roentgen tubes. This paper was a short summary to be followed by a more complete exposition, but before the complete paper appeared, Wehnelt published another article which described a Braun-type tube fitted with a lime-coated hot cathode.[5] This tube is shown in Fig. 5-1.

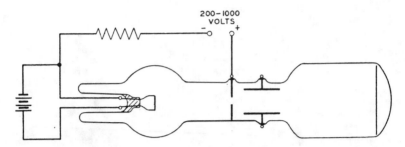

Fig. 5-1. Wehnelt's Braun-type tube with oxide-coated hot cathode.

The full paper, "An Electric Valve Tube," appeared in 1906.[6] Here, for the first time, Wehnelt showed that this tube could also be used as a rectifier of high-frequency currents (Wehnelt's tube is shown in Fig. 5-2). It should be noted that this was subsequent to the papers published by Fleming on the use of his valve as a rectifier of high-frequency oscillations. In fact, Wehnelt refers to Fleming in a footnote, in which he states that Fleming's work was "presumably stimulated" by Wehnelt's 1904 publication of his work and that the rectification of high frequencies was "self-evident" from the results

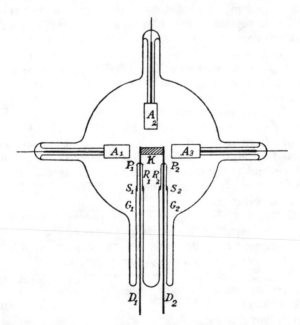

Fig. 5-2. Wehnelt's three-phase rectifier tube using oxide-coated hot cathode. (Reproduced from *Ann. Phys.*, 1906, *19*.)

he reported on power frequencies. The "self-evident" is questionable, since none of the other low-frequency rectifiers of that day would function at wireless telegraph frequencies. Until the 1906 paper, Wehnelt had never discussed the use of the tube at other than power frequencies.

During this period Robert von Lieben of Vienna was working on the problem of a telephone relay, or amplifier. Von Lieben, the son of wealthy parents, was born in Vienna in 1878. Although he grew up in intellectual surroundings, he always disliked formal education, preferring to educate himself in his own way. Very early in life he showed an aptitude for scientific investigation. At that time electrical engineering was a promising field, and it beckoned to von Lieben. He learned the practical phase of this work in the Siemens-Schuckert works in Nuremberg, and he went to the University of Göttingen for physical and chemical research under the renowned chemist and physicist Walther H. Nernst. Von Lieben's great versatility was evident from the time he began his research studies, but his aim to develop a telephone relay dominated his work. Professor Nernst said of him: "No problem impressed him so much as the construction of the telephone relay, or, more commonly expressed, a device which is capable of amplifying without distortion small changes in electrical currents."[7]

Returning from Göttingen in 1903, von Lieben set up his own physics laboratory in his parental home. In this laboratory during the years 1905–1910 his amplifying tube was created. Some time after he returned home in 1903 he also bought a telephone manufacturing business in Olmutz, Moravia, with the financial aid of his father. Here his association, first with Eugen Reisz and later with Sigmund Strauss, began. The manufacturing enterprise prospered and was sold to Telefonfabrik Berliner. Von Lieben, Reisz, and Strauss continued to work together.

In 1905 in his Vienna laboratory von Lieben checked Wehnelt's experiments with the oxide-coated cathode. Remembering the cathode-ray arrangement used by Braun in 1897, he hit upon the idea of constructing a telephone relay using this combination. He started by controlling the rays magnetically, and his work soon produced results. On March 4, 1906, he applied for a German patent on a device which he called a "cathode-ray relay."[8] The object of the invention was to enable current variations of small energy at the input terminals to release current variations of greater energy at the output terminals, with the frequency and waveform corresponding to that of the input. The patent states that the device is particularly suited to telephone applications such as "relaying of speech to great distances, cable telegraphy, wireless telephony, strengthening of speech, etc."[9] The relay and its circuit arrangements can be seen in Fig. 5-3, which shows magnetic control of the cathode rays, but the patent states that either electromagnetic or electrostatic control may be used.

In this tube, which was described as being "highly evacuated," von Lieben used a cathode which was in the form of a concave mirror covered with calcium oxide. This cathode was described as being heated by the battery b^1. The concave surface focused the cathode rays on the inner of two concentric hollow cylindrical anodes f and f^1 through the aperture o. The focus of the rays was altered by

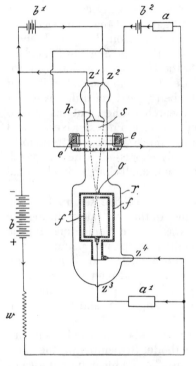

Fig. 5-3. Von Lieben high-vacuum cathode-ray relay of 1906, using magnetic field for beam defocusing. (Reproduced from D.R.P. Nr. 179,807.)

the input current flowing in the magnetic field coils e, which caused more or less of the cathode rays to impinge upon the inner cylinder and thus vary the inner anode current, which also flowed through the load device a^1. The battery b provided the energy in the anode circuit.

Even before this von Lieben patent was published, two other men, Max Dieckmann and Gustav Glage, of Strasbourg, applied on October 10, 1906, for a patent on another type of cathode-ray relay which they claimed was capable of giving an output absolutely proportional to the input.[10] In their patent application reference was made to the von Lieben arrangement.

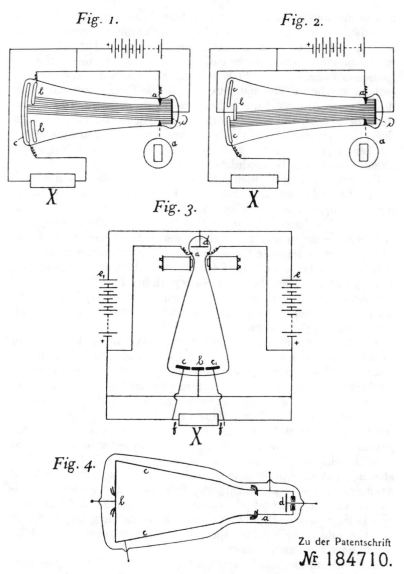

Fig. 5-4. Dieckmann and Glage cathode-ray relay of 1906, using magnetic deflection of cathode rays. (Reproduced from D.R.P. Nr. 184,710.)

Several possible structures were shown in the diagrams forming a part of the Dieckmann and Glage patent. These are reproduced in Fig. 5-4. The cathode was a plane and said to be "conveniently treated in order to facilitate the emission of electrons," and the aperture in the diaphragm *a* was used to obtain "a sharply defined bundle of cathode rays of comparatively large, preferably rectangular cross-section."[11] The axes of the deflecting coils were placed at right angles to the direction of flow of the cathode rays. This was unlike the von Lieben arrangement, in which the magnetic field was parallel to the cathode-ray beam. The magnetic field in the Dieckmann and Glage device acted to deflect the cathode-ray beam from side to side, instead of altering the focus, as did von Lieben's. By means of this deflection more or less of the beam could be caused to impinge on the center or side plates, and the current in the individual anode circuits could thus be modulated.

This relay had all the elements of the modern "electron gun," and the configuration marked "Fig. 3" in Fig. 5-4 was even capable of push-pull operation, providing the proper auxiliary apparatus was used at *x*. The patent also states that "the path of the cathode rays between the diaphragm 'a' and the screen 'b' must be as long as possible in order to increase the sensitivity."[12] The structure denoted as "Fig. 4" at the bottom of Fig. 5-4 shows how the electrodes might be arranged so as to keep the cathode-ray path free from the influence of extraneous forces. Hence the device may also be said to be self-shielded. Whether or not the electron emission was obtained by heating the cathode is not stated.

About the same time (1908), Otto von Baeyer of the University of Berlin described a three-electrode tube consisting of a central filamentary cathode rendered incandescent by a battery, surrounded by a cylinder of wire gauze, which in turn was surrounded by a cylinder of sheet metal.[13] The whole was contained in a cylindrical glass tube, evacuated to about 0.01 torr. This structure resembled some of the triodes that were still years in the future. Von Baeyer used this apparatus to measure the ionization produced by cathode rays emitted from the filament. For this work the inner gauze cylinder was operated at a potential positive to the cathode and the outer cylinder at a potential negative to the cathode. This enabled von Baeyer to collect on the outer electrode the positive ions produced by the cathode rays in their passage through the space between the gauze electrode and the outer cylinder. Had the potentials been reversed, the tube would have been an amplifier.

In the meantime, von Lieben continued to strive for a better telephone relay, working with Reisz and Strauss. Because of von Lieben's poor physical condition, Reisz did most of the later development work on the cathode-ray relay. According to Reisz, important details of later designs were due to von Lieben, who was still very active despite his severe pain.[14] All subsequent German patents on the cathode-ray relay were issued to all three jointly.

The next development of von Lieben, Reisz, and Strauss is covered

Zu der Patentschrift **236716**

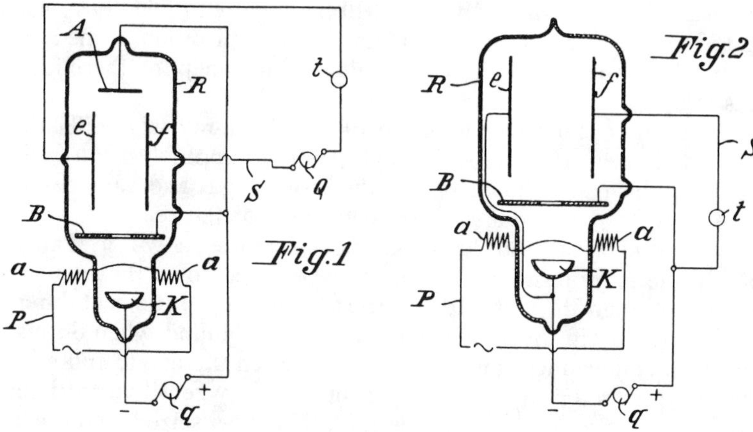

Fig. 5-5. Von Lieben gaseous cathode-ray relay of 1910, using magnetic deflection of the cathode-ray beam acting as "ionizer." (Reproduced from D.R.P. Nr. 236,716.)

by German Patent 236,716, which bears the application date September, 4, 1910.[15] The drawings which appear in this patent are shown in Fig. 5-5. It will be seen that the structure bears some resemblance to that disclosed by Dieckmann and Glage, but the action is very different: the current to be amplified flows through the coils a, and the magnetic field thus set up acts on the cathode-ray beam. This is described as causing changes in the ionization of the attenuated gas in the open space between the plates e and f. The diaphragm cuts off a portion of the cathode beam as the beam is deflected from side to side by the current in the coils a. This causes variation in the ionization of the attenuated gas between plates e and f. The load device is shown as a telephone in the circuit composed of the generator Q, telephone t, plates e and f, and the ionized space between the plates. Note that the concave-mirror-type cathode has been retained. No method of heating the cathode is shown, but the patent specification states: "The material used and the temperature of the cathode K as well as the gas in the discharge tube are so chosen that, with comparatively small potential difference, emission of the cathode stream results."[16]

It should also be noted that the inventors have abandoned the "high vacuum" referred to in the previous patent and now speak of ionization of the attenuated gas. "The difficulty of producing the hollow mirror cathode, the nonuniform emission of the cathode rays from the glowing oxide, and particularly the difficulty of maintaining a constant vacuum in the discharge tube were the main reasons" which motivated further development of the 1906 device.[17] From Patent 236,716, described above, it will be seen that difficulties relating to the high vacuum were overcome by the utilization of the ionization of a rarefied gas instead of depending on pure thermionic emission.

During the experiments with the 1906 cathode-ray relay difficulty was experienced because of the high potential applied to the outer cylinder. This caused ionization of the residual gas and gave rise to "blue glow," which reduced the effectiveness of the relay.

In their experimental work on the structure shown in Patent 236,716, Reisz proposed that a wire grid be placed over the aperture in the diaphragm B. This grid was tried in various positions at different distances from the anode. The solution was found when Strauss suggested connecting a high resistance between the anode and grid. Then it appeared that the arrangement was very sensitive to slight variations of the potential of this grid. This was seized upon as a method of control, and the magnetic-field method of deviating the cathode-ray beam was replaced by the electrostatic control of the grid.[18]

The next patent issued to these inventors was German Patent 249,142,[19] which bears the application date December 20, 1910, and is described as a supplement to 236,716. In this specification reference is made to the work of de Forest and his use of an "auxiliary electrode" in the form of a sieve, or grid. Concerning de Forest's device, the statement is made that "the currents to be magnified were led through the cathode and said electrode."[20] This indicates that von Lieben and his associates were cognizant of de Forest's work on the Audion and recognized the Audion structure to be an amplifier, even though de Forest himself had been unable to make it function as such. This is also the first use of electrostatic control by the von Lieben team.

One of the diagrams included in this patent is shown in Fig. 5-6. The modification consisted of the use of electrostatic control by means of an auxiliary electrode to produce variations in the amplified current, instead of using the variable ionization previously obtained by electromagnetically bending the cathode-ray beam. This auxiliary electrode is described as a "grid, grating or mesh" so constructed that it "perfectly divides the cathode space from that of the anode."[21] The effect of this auxiliary electrode is said to be that of modifying the resistance of the space between the cathode and the anode, which results in variations of the anode current corresponding to changes in the resistance of the space. It will be observed that there is provided in the potentiometer c a means of adjusting the

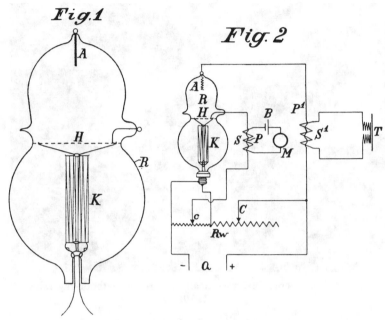

Fig. 5-6. Von Lieben gaseous cathode-ray relay of 1910, using electro-static control of cathode-ray beam. (Reproduced from D.R.P. Nr. 249,142.)

steady-state potential of the grid. Concerning this adjustment the patent reads:

> The adjustable potential thus brought to bear on H has been found to be of the greatest importance in the successful operation of the relay, because a proportional variation of the resistance of the gas discharge tube happens only at a certain definite value of potential difference, and this depends on the gas pressure and temperature of the cathode, etc.[22]

A von Lieben relay of the type covered by this patent is shown in Fig. 5-7. Further developments in this work will be covered in a subsequent chapter.

In the research field of the cathode-ray tube in this decade, in addition to the achievement of Wehnelt, we have the work of two other scientists. W. J. Milham, in 1901, using a tube made by Müller-Uri, attempted to measure electric fields.[23] He experienced trouble in obtaining a steady electrostatic deflection of the jet because of ionization of the residual gas. E. Madelung in 1905 used magnetic deflection on a Braun-type cathode-ray tube to determine the method of action of the Rutherford-Marconi magnetic detector.[24] Madelung did further work on magnetic hysteresis in 1907 using a tube with

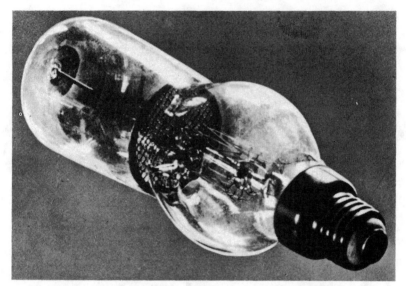

Fig. 5-7. Von Lieben electrostatically controlled cathode-ray relay
of 1910.

electrostatic deflection plates.[25] F. Giesel and J. Zenneck in 1908
suggested the use of zinc sulfide as a coating for the fluorescent
screen to give greater brightness and improved definition to the picture produced on the screen of the tube.[26]

REFERENCES

1. A. Wehnelt, "Über den Austritt negativer Ionen aus glühenden Metallverbindungen und damit zusammenhägende Erscheinungen," *Sitzungsber.
   Phys. Med. Soz. Erlangen*, 1903, pp. 150–158.
2. A. Wehnelt, "Über Kathodenstrahlen au glühenden Kathoden," *Verhandl.
   Deut. Phys. Ges.*, 1903, 5(No. 14):150–158, 423–426. A. Wehnelt, "Über
   den Austritt negativer Ionen aus glühenden Metallverbindungen und damit
   Zusammenhängende Erscheinungen," *Ann. Phys.*, 1904, *14*:425–468. See
   also *Phys. Z.*, 1904, 5(No. 21):680–681.
3. A. Wehnelt, D.R.P. Nr. 157,945, Klasse 21g, application date Jan. 15, 1904,
   issued Jan. 13, 1905.
4. A. Wehnelt, "Ein elektrische Ventilröhr," *Sitzungsber. Phys. Med. Soz.
   Erlangen*, 1905, 37:264–269. This is an abstract of the paper referred to in
   n. 6 below.
5. A. Wehnelt, "Emfindlichkeitsteigerung der Braunschen Röhre durch Benutzung von Kathodenstrahlen geringer Geschwindigkeit," *Phys. Z.*, 1905,
   6(No. 22): 732–733.
6. A. Wehnelt, "Ein elektrische Ventilröhr," *Ann. Phys.*, 1906, *19*:138–156.
7. W. Nernst, "Zur Errinung an Robert v. Lieben," *Telefunkenztg*, 1923,
   6(No. 32–33):6.

8. R. von Lieben, "Kathodenstrahlrelais," D.R.P. Nr. 179,807, Klasse 21g, Gruppe 4, application date Mar. 4, 1906, issued Nov. 19, 1906.
9. *Ibid.*, lines 15–19.
10. M. Dieckmann and G. Glage, "Stetig quantitativ wirkendes Relais unter Benutzung der elektrischen Ablenbarkeit von Kathodenstrahlen," D.R.P. Nr. 184,710, application date Oct. 10, 1906, published Apr. 2, 1907.
11. *Ibid.*, p. 1, lines 23–25, 26–29.
12. *Ibid.*, p. 2, lines 21–25.
13. O. von Baeyer, "Über Langsame Kathodenstrahlen," *Verhandl. Deut. Phys. Ges.* 1908, 5:96-114. An abstract of this paper appeared in *Phys. Z.*, 1909, 10(No. 5):168–176.
14. E. Reisz, "Neues Verfahren zur Verstärkung elektrischer Ströme," *Elektrotech. Z.*, Nov. 1913, 34:1359.
15. R. von Lieben, E. Reisz, and S. Strauss, "Relais für undulierende Ströme, bei welchem durch die zu verstärkenden Strömschwankungen ein Ionisator beeinflusst wird," D.R.P. Nr. 236,716, application date Sept. 4, 1910, published Jul. 11, 1911.
16. *Ibid.*, p. 2, lines 15–20.
17. Reisz, "Neues Verfahren," p. 1359.
18. K. Skowronnek, "Zur Entwicklung der Elektronenverstärker-Röhre (Lieben-Röhre)," *Arch. Gesch. Math. Naturwiss. Tech.*, 1930–1931, 13:225–276; see p. 240.
19. R. von Lieben, E. Reisz, and S. Strauss, "Relais für undulierende Ströme," D.R.P. Nr. 249,142, Klasse 21, Gruppe 4, application date Dec. 20, 1910, published Jul. 12, 1912.
20. *Ibid.*, p. 1, lines 25–33.
21. *Ibid.*, p. 2, lines 1–3.
22. *Ibid.*, lines 102–110.
23. W. J. Milham, "Über die Verwendbarkeit der Braunschen Röhre zur Messung elektrischer Felder," *Phys. Z.*, 1901, 2:637.
24. E. Madelung, "Über Magnetisierung durch schnellcervarlaufende Ströme und die Wirkungsweise des Rutherford-Marconischen Magnetdetektor," *Ann. Phys.*, 1905, 17:861–890.
25. E. Madelung, "Neue Verwendungsarten der Braunschen Röhre zur Untersuchung der magnetischen und dielectrischen Hysteresis," *Phys. Z.*, 1907, 8:72–75.
26. F. Giesel, and J. Zenneck, "Die Verwendung des Zinksulfids für die Braunsche Röhre," *Phys. Z.*, 1909, 10:377–379.

Chapter 6

The Entrance of Industrial
Laboratories and Military Demands,
1910-1920: *United States (Western Electric)*

To assist the reader in segregating the lines of development being
carried on concurrently in the United States, the period between
1910 and 1920 is subdivided as follows: Chapter 6, Western Electric;
Chapter 7, De Forest; Chapter 8, General Electric; and Chapter 9,
Independents. The early years of broadcasting in the United States,
1920–1930, are subdivided the same way in Chapters 14 through 17.

By the middle of 1912 Lee de Forest had succeeded in getting
audio-frequency amplification from the Audion. How he did it will
be covered in the next chapter.

In a letter dated August 3, 1912, to John Stone Stone, a former em-
ployee of the American Telephone & Telegraph Company, de Forest
asked Stone to act as go-between in an effort to sell the telephone
rights to the Audion to the telephone company for use as a telephone repeater. In order to do this de Forest gave Stone a six-
months option to buy exclusive rights to the use of the Audion for
wire telephone and wire telegraph purposes. Stone then entered
into a contract with de Forest to present the Audion to the officials
of the A.T.&T. Co. in an effort to sell this option to them for an
amount of not less than $50,000, of which Stone would retain
10 percent.

Stone arranged for de Forest to demonstrate the action of the
Audion as a telephone repeater to the members of the Engineering
Department of the Western Electric Company, the manufacturing
subsidiary of A.T.&T., at 463 West Street in New York. On Octo-

ber 30, 1912, Stone and de Forest made their demonstration. This showed that under the operating conditions chosen by de Forest—that is, operating with the grid condenser of its radio detector days—the Audion would function as an audio-frequency amplifier, but only at levels low enough to avoid the buildup of a blocking voltage on the grid. The demonstration was repeated the following day with the same results, and de Forest left the apparatus for further tests and experiments by the telephone engineers. The Audions used in these demonstrations were of the two types shown in Fig. 6-1.

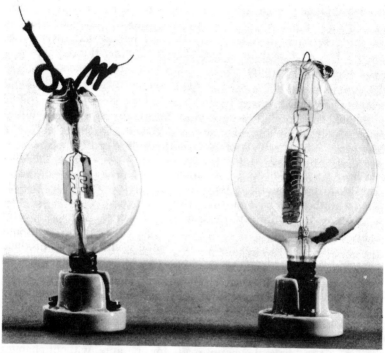

Fig. 6-1. Types of Audions used in de Forest's demonstration of its use as a telephone repeater on October 30–31, 1912.

This was not the first time an Audion had been submitted to A.T.&T. for consideration as a telephone repeater.[1] On January 27, 1912, Fritz Loewenstein submitted a sealed box, which he called an "Ion Controller," to F. B. Jewett and O. B. Blackwell of A.T.&T. for their consideration as a telephone amplifier. Loewenstein at that time refused to tell what the box contained. The action of this piece of apparatus was erratic and uncertain. A year passed, with correspondence back and forth, before Loewenstein disclosed the contents of the box. It proved to contain a de Forest Audion used in a circuit in which no grid condenser was used, but in which the grid was biased negatively with respect to the cathode of the tube. United States Patent No. 1,231,764, applied for on April 24, 1912, was issued on July 3, 1917, to Loewenstein on this arrangement. This patent became known as the "C-bias patent" and was eventually acquired by A.T.&T.

Dr. Harold D. Arnold, of the research branch of the Western Electric Engineering Department, had studied the infant science of electronics under Dr. R. A. Millikan at the University of Chicago. On November 1, 1912, Arnold saw the Audion and recognized its possibilities. Even though the device and its operating circuit as disclosed by de Forest were incapable of fulfilling the requirements for a telephone repeater, Arnold recognized the defects and how they might be remedied. The accomplishment of the remedies and the development of the comparatively crude Audion into a reliable telephone repeater was a long and arduous process. The manifold problems encountered were almost incapable of solution in any reasonable time by any one individual. It was only in the industrial laboratory where each problem could be attacked by a specialist that the desired result could be attained.

A satisfactory telephone repeater must meet many requirements other than the primary one—that of producing amplification. It must be capable of handling the energy levels which exist at repeater points on telephone lines. It must amplify all frequencies present without discrimination. It must have a long useful life and produce the same results throughout its life. It must be manufactured in quantities, and the individual devices so manufactured must be commercially interchangeable. In general, once the device is installed it must function satisfactorily without any attention other than routine inspection. At the end of its useful life, it must be possible to remove the unit and replace it with another commercially similar unit and have the circuit ready for operation without changes in the auxiliary apparatus and with only minor readjustments.

The Audion, as demonstrated by de Forest, fell far short of these requirements. It amplified very weak speech currents and amplified them accurately. When the input level was raised to that normally encountered at a repeater point in telephone practice, the quality was greatly impaired and the amplification considerably reduced. Under these conditions "blue haze" sometimes occurred. If the anode battery voltage was increased, a condition of permanent blue haze ensued. When the blue haze was present, not only was the amplification lowered and distortion high but the device introduced noise.[2] The life of the filament was very short, and frequent readjustment of filament and plate potentials was required. The structure was flimsy and the bulbs were fragile. Individual bulbs differed greatly in their characteristics.

Yet it would amplify, was remarkably simple in operation, and to one trained in the early science of electronics it gave immediate evidence of real promise. Arnold has testified that when he first saw the Audion he was amazed and realized that he "had overlooked the wonderful possibilities of that third electrode operation, the grid operation in the Audion."[3] He recognized that the presence of gas in the bulb, which de Forest considered esssential to its operation, was a liability rather than an asset. He knew that to make the operation uniform and reliable the gas should be removed, which would convert the Audion from a semi-gaseous thermionic tube into a pure electron-discharge device. He also felt that the difficulties presented by the metallic filament could be overcome by the use of a cathode of the Wehnelt, or oxide-coated, type—a more copious generator of electrons, which would operate at a comparatively low temperature. This would give an energy-carrying capacity, a stability, and a useful operating life more in keeping with practical requirements. The mechanical disadvantages could be overcome by a suitable redesign of the element structure.

Arnold and those in the Engineering Department who soon joined him in this work were familiar with the technique of high evacuation. Since joining Western Electric Arnold had been working on the mercury-arc repeater, which required careful evacuation even though it operated in the presence of positive ions. Previous to that he had been engaged in research work on high-vacuum devices at the Ryerson Laboratory of the University of Chicago under Professor Millikan. These scientists were also familiar with the literature on the Fleming valve and the Wehnelt cathode.

The first improvement effected was not in the Audion itself but in the circuit in which it was used by de Forest. The improvement consisted of removing the series condenser in the grid circuit. This condenser, although necessary for operation of the Audion as a wireless detector, caused blocking when the Audion was used at telephone operating levels.[4] The next step was to improve the mechanical construction of the Audion, which was done by adding a glass "arbor" to the element assembly to increase its rigidity. Fig. 6-2 shows an Audion so reinforced. The third improvement was to increase the anode area, which was accomplished by the addition of a second grid and anode assembly, thus producing the tube shown in Fig. 6-3. Up to this point the changes were comparatively easy to accomplish. The next steps were more difficult.

Meantime, work had begun on a theoretical and experimental investigation of the Audion to determine its mode of operation and operating characteristics. At the same time, the problems involved

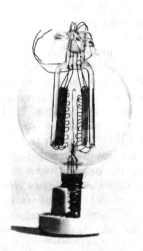

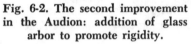

Fig. 6-2. The second improvement in the Audion: addition of glass arbor to promote rigidity.

Fig. 6-3. The third improvement in the Audion: addition of second grid-plate assembly to increase the plate area.

in obtaining the higher vacuum that was required, as well as developing a suitable commercial oxide-coated filament, or cathode, were attacked by Dr. Arnold and his associates.

Within a month of the time Arnold first saw the Audion, which was November 1, 1912, one of his assistants, working in accordance with his instructions, succeeded in "cleaning up" or increasing the vacuum in one of the Audions by electrical means. This increase was great enough that the tube could be operated as a pure electron-discharge device up to an anode potential in excess of 80 volts.[5]

The technique of obtaining high vacuums by the use of liquid air and charcoal had been developed in the late nineteenth century by James Dewar. However, this method could not be used at Western Electric, because there were no facilities available in the vicinity for obtaining the requisite quantities of liquid air, and the problems of its transportation had not yet been solved. In 1912 the Gaede Molecular Pump was put on the market by a foreign manufacturer. This was a pump capable of producing vacuums of the order of 10^{-5} torr and of removing vapors as well as gases from the space to be evacuated. One of these pumps was secured by the Engineering Department as soon as possible, and by its use tubes were made which could be operated at anode voltages in excess of 200 volts without harmful ionization. That is, they were pure electron-discharge devices.

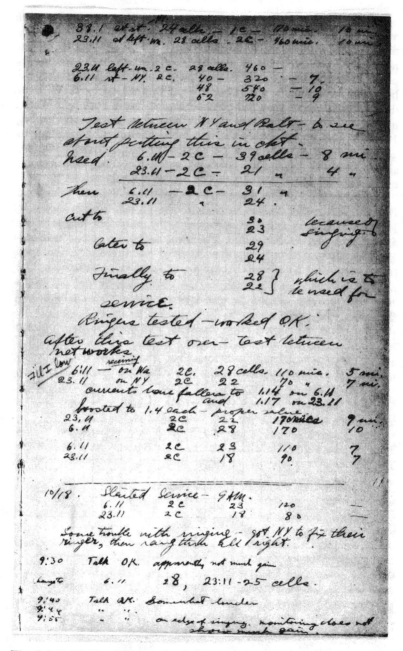

Fig. 6-4. B. W. Kendall's notebook entry of the first use of a vacuum tube repeater in commercial service.

Development of the oxide-coated filament had progressed at such a rate that by the middle of 1913 a preliminary form of such a filament had been obtained with a laboratory life of 1000 hours. By the fall of 1913 the problems of making a satisfactory high-vacuum repeater tube had been solved to such an extent that a field trial could be made. Accordingly, a trial installation was set up by B. W. Kendall at Philadelphia on a toll circuit between New York and Washington, and the repeater was actually placed in service on October 18, 1913. This was probably the first high-vacuum tube amplifier to go into commercial service in the annals of communication. Fig. 6-4 shows Kendall's laboratory notebook entry recording this historic event. Fig. 6-5 shows the remains of one of the tubes used.

The tubes used in this repeater were known as Type A Telephone Repeater Elements, and an unbroken tube of this type is shown in Fig. 6-6. It was an unbased spherical bulb about 2⅜ inches in diameter and was double ended. The stem and press at one end carried the filament which was the shape of an inverted V, the apex being supported by a wire extending upward from the press. The filament was of strip platinum, coated in the case of this particular tube with barium nitrate. It was approximately ⅞ inch high and the lower ends were about ⅜ inch apart. The anode and grid assembled were supported from the stem and press at the opposite end of the tube and were fixed rigidly in place by the use of glass arbors, one for each anode-grid assembly. The anodes were approximately 1⅛ inches high and made of nickel. The grids were made by welding narrow hairpin-shaped loops onto a supporting strip. The grid was about ⅝ inch wide by 1¼ inches high. Nine hairpin loops were used; hence the grid had eighteen laterals.

After a short period of use the Type A was superseded by the Type B (see Fig. 6-7), which was an improvement in several ways. The filament was somewhat larger and was of twisted platinum

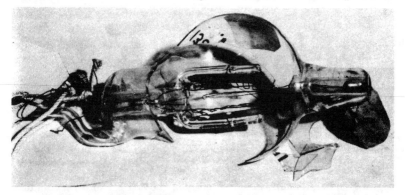

Fig. 6-5. The remains of Audion 6.11, used by Kendall at Philadelphia.

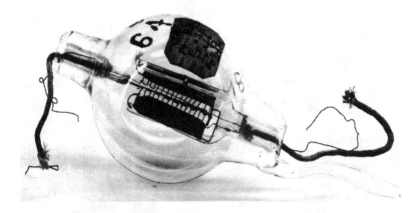

Fig. 6-6. Type A telephone repeater element.

ribbon. The most noticeable difference was in the grid structure: each grid was made up of eight horizontal wires evenly spaced in the vertical direction and welded to two upright supports. This construction became known as the ladder-type grid and was characteristic of Western Electric tubes for many years.

Early in 1914 it became apparent that the use of unbased tubes was unsatisfactory, and steps were taken to provide a suitable base and mounting socket for these tubes. The first based tubes were known as the Type M (M = mounted), and the socket was a heavy cast-brass affair similar to that used for a mechanical repeater. Fig. 6-8 shows the tube and Fig. 6-9 the socket. The base was a heavy machined-brass part, equipped with four studs mounted on an insulating insert on the bottom and a bayonet locking pin on the side. The four studs pressed against corresponding springs in the socket when the tube was inserted, thus completing the electrical connections required. This arrangement was made for facility and ease of replacement. The dimensions and locking arrangement of this base were eventually universally adopted for radio tubes, and it became known as the "UV-type" base (U = unit, V = vacuum tube).

Vacuum-tube repeaters were utilized over very long distances for the first time when the transcontinental telephone line from New York to San Francisco was opened on January 15, 1915. Type M tubes were used in the repeaters on that line. Fig. 6-10 shows the apparatus installed at the repeater station at Brushton, Pennsylvania. The Type M Telephone Repeater Element, later designated as the 101A Repeater Bulb, operated with a filament current of 1.45 ±0.1 amperes at a voltage of approximately 4 volts. The normal plate voltage was 100 volts, plate current was 10–15 milliamperes, the

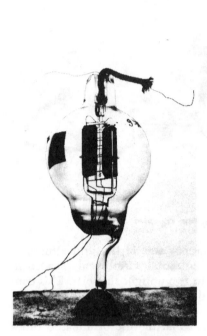

Fig. 6-7. Type B telephone
repeater element.

Fig. 6-8. Type M telephone repeater element, later coded the
101A repeater bulb.

amplification factor was 5, and the internal plate impedance about 5000 ohms. The useful life of about 400 hours was well in excess of that of the de Forest Audion.

Theoretical studies, especially by Dr. H. J. van der Bijl, indicated that this life could be improved considerably by increasing the electron-emitting area of the filament. This would permit operation at a lower filament temperature while still giving the requisite therm-

Fig. 6-9. Socket for the Type M
telephone repeater element.

Fig. 6-10. The repeater at Brushton, Pennsylvania on the transcontinental line in 1915.

ionic emission. Hence a new tube, which came to be known as the Type L (L = line amplifier) was designed and was first produced on a commercial scale in 1915. The Type M was still made, but only for replacement in existing equipment. Fig. 6-11 is a photograph of one of the early Type L tubes. It will be seen that the filament length has been approximately doubled, resulting in doubled emitting area. Other design changes have also been made. The grid has been increased from eight to nine laterals, and the bracing of the plates is different. The filament took 1.3 amperes at 5 volts. The normal plate voltage was 150 volts, with a normal plate current of 15 milliamperes. The amplification factor was 5 and the internal plate impedance 4000–5000 ohms. This tube had a life of about 4500 hours, which was eleven times that of the Type M and fifty to one hundred times that of the de Forest Audions. This tube was officially designated the 101B Repeater Bulb (later to become the 101B Vacuum Tube).

The terms Telephone Repeater Element and Repeater Bulb were used to distinguish the tubes made for telephone use from those for

Fig. 6-11. Type L or 101B telephone repeater element. Note the increased filament length as compared with the Type M.

nontelephone and U.S. Government use, which were officially known as Vacuum Tubes. This distinction continued till 1922, when the term vacuum tube was applied to all such devices, regardless of their purpose.

Late in 1917 the type of base used on repeater bulbs and vacuum tubes was changed. As has been described, up to this time it was a heavy machined-brass seamless shell. The new base was a formed casing of sheet nickel silver (at that time known as German silver). Into the bottom of this formed casing was fitted a cruciform insulating member on which the contact studs were mounted (see Fig. 6-12). The space around this insulating member was filled with red wax, commercially available as Zinssner's Regular Insulating Wax, a mixture of red iron oxide and shellac gums. The wax was poured in to fill the base flush with the bottom of the formed shell, and a die was applied to form the letters and numerals of the code marking in the center in raised characters. The color of the wax was always

Fig. 6-12. An early type of fabricated sheet-metal base (before wax filling), showing the cruciform insert to hold contact pins.

reddish, although the shade varied from lot to lot, sometimes almost to brown. Later a black compound was used.

When the new type of shell was put into use the patent marking, steel stamped on the shell, was as follows:

PAT. IN USA
1–15–07 TWO PATENTS
2–18–08   4–27–15
12–19–16
PAT. APPLIED FOR

and the code marking appeared only in the wax filling of the shell (Fig. 6-13). Late in 1918 the markings on the base shell of the 101B and other telephone tubes were changed to include the property marking of the A.T.&T. Co. The marking of the 101B then became that shown in Fig. 6-14. Late in 1919 the patent date 12-17-18 was added.

The element assembly of the 101B as constructed up to the end of 1918 is shown in Fig. 6-15. The assembly was supported by a glass arbor which was sealed to the edge of the press, and the plane of the element assembly was at right angles to the plane of the press, both being vertical. Difficulties were experienced with this form of assembly, the most common source of trouble being breakage of the

Fig. 6-13. An early-type of 101B repeater bulb with the patent markings steel-stamped on base shell. The code marking appears only in the wax on the bottom of the tube.

Fig. 6-14. A 101B repeater bulb with A.T.&T. Co. property markings.

Fig. 6-15. An early 101B repeater bulb with the arbor welded to the edge of the press.

arbor at the point where it joined the press. Many of the tubes still in existence show such breakage.

To eliminate this difficulty the element assembly was redesigned, and, beginning early in 1919, the arrangement shown in Fig. 6-16 was used. The arbor was made heavier and was welded to the stem somewhat below the press, positioned so that the element assembly was parallel to the press instead of at right angles to it. The grid structure was changed from nine to eleven laterals. The plates were made rectangular with the edges turned up at right angles to provide stiffening. The tie wires were welded to the turned-up edges instead of to the flat surface of the plate.

The development of the 101 type, up to 1920, has been followed in some detail because it is typical of early Western Electric prac-

Fig. 6-16. A 101B repeater bulb with the arbor welded to the stem below the press.

tice as far as telephone tubes are concerned. During this period other tubes were being developed for specialized telephone applications, one of the best known being the Type V. This was intended for use as a "voltage" amplifier and was originally known as the Type VM (V = voltage, M = mounted), but the M was soon dropped.

The earliest vacuum tube repeaters were single-stage affairs using the 101A tube. When the need arose for higher amplification a two-stage repeater was developed, and the V tube was used in the first stage to provide higher "voltage" amplification. Its plate-to-filament impedance was too high to permit it to be worked successfully (in that state of the art) as an output tube, and the second stage was thus an L tube because of its lower output impedance. The first experimental V tubes were made about the middle of 1914, and the first commercial product appeared early in 1915. The code designation 102A Telephone Repeater Element was assigned to this tube in 1916.

The ladder-type grid used in the 102A was characteristic of all the early Western Electric repeater tubes. With thirty-one laterals on each side, the grids were considerably larger in area than the plates, and the filament was the shape of an inverted V. The spacing between the grids was about ⅛ inch and between the plates about ½ inch. The base used was the same as that used on the L-type tubes. Like the L tubes, the first production carried no patent markings, but beginning late in 1915 markings were applied in a manner similar to those of the L tube of that time.

The need for close engineering supervision in the manufacture of these tubes was of paramount importance. All the V tubes and some of the other types produced by Western Electric were manufactured in the shops of the Engineering Department in New York up to the end of 1918. At that time progress was considered sufficient to permit their manufacture in the regular factory, and so the production of some tubes, including the 102A, was begun in the Hawthorne plant of the company in Chicago.

All the early telephone repeater tubes had a serial number etched or sand blasted on the bulb. These numbers were used by the staffs of repeater stations to keep records on the life and performance of each tube in the repeaters. In order to distinguish between tubes made in New York and those made in Hawthorne, the Hawthorne tubes had the letter H appended to the serial number. When production became great enough to require more than five digits in the serial number, the appended letter was changed to A and the numbering repeated. (The tubes made in New York had no letter attached to the serial number.)

The Hawthorne and New York tubes differed in some minor construction details, one of which was the positioning of the laterals of the grid structure. In tubes made in New York the laterals were welded to the verticals on the outside of the support wires, that is, the side away from the filament. In Hawthorne-made tubes the laterals were on the inside of the support wires, the side near the filament.

Another tube which was used in telephone equipment, but to a lesser extent than the 101 and 102 types, was the 104, which started life under the appellation of Type O. It was probably so designated because of its original use as an output tube. It had a lower plate impedance than either the L or V tubes. The first of this series, the 104A, was put into production in the shops of the New York Engineering Department late in 1917. As then made, it consisted of two plates ¾ inch wide by 1¼ inches high, spaced ⁵⁄₁₆ inch apart with two ladder type grids of the same size as the plates, each having nine laterals, the spacing between the grids being ⅛ inch. The filament was M shaped. The difference between the L and O tubes was chiefly in the spacing of the elements. The Type O originally had two glass arbors, one for each plate-grid assembly. Late in 1918 the use of the second arbor was abandoned, and the stem thus became similar to that of the Type L. Fig. 6-17 shows an early version of the single-arbor 104A.

All the Western Electric tubes so far considered were engineered for use under the carefully controlled conditions existing in the telephone plant. At the time of World War I, the engineering skill and manufacturing experience which produced these tubes were invaluable in providing background for the production of tubes for sorely needed military equipment. Vacuum tubes for military and naval equipment are a different breed from telephone repeater tubes. They must be capable of giving a reasonable service life under conditions

Fig. 6-17. A Type O or 104A repeater bulb; early construction, 1918.

which may vary widely at different times and in different places. In much equipment considerations of weight and space are paramount. Ambient temperatures vary from the cold of the radio cabin in the Arctic to the broiling heat of a destroyer engine room in the tropics. Filament and plate voltages may vary widely and rapidly. Mechanical shocks are inevitable.

Nevertheless, the Western Electric engineers, at the urgent request of the armed services, undertook the development of vacuum tubes of stable and rugged construction to meet these new but no less exacting requirements. From their labors emerged a number of reliable tubes, probably the best known being the VT-1 and VT-2.

VT-1 was the U.S. Signal Corps designation for the tube which in its inception was known to the Western Electric engineers as the Type J. This same tube was used by the U.S. Navy under the designation CW-933. The Western Electric code numbers assigned to this type were in the 203 series, the first being 203A.

The J tube was a general-purpose tube, used as detector, amplifier, and low-powered oscillator. Fig. 6-18 shows one of the early J tubes, the 203A. A cylindrical bulb was substituted for the spherical bulb common to Western Electric tubes. The element assembly used the same glass arbor construction as the telephone repeater tubes, and the earliest models had machined brass bases. The grids were of the ladder type, and the plates were flat sheets.

The glass arbor construction proved to be too fragile to withstand the vibration conditions imposed on the equipment in which the tubes were used. In order to insure permanent alignment of the elements, a type of element assembly which became known as the

Fig. 6-18. The earliest version of the 203A vacuum tube (Type J). This tube has a machined brass base and glass arbor construction (1916).

Fig. 6-19. Successive steps in the transformation of the early Type J tube into a rugged unit, suitable for military applications.

"iron-clad" construction was eventually adopted. In this form the plate supplied the support for the grid and filament. This structure was the result of an evolutionary process, the steps of which are shown in Fig. 6-19. The first change was in the base: the machined brass base was replaced by a lighter sheet-metal base, such as the one used for telephone repeater tubes. Next the glass arbor was eliminated and a new plate structure was introduced. The plates were supported from the stem and a stiffening rib was provided. Ladder-type grids with wire laterals were still used.

Fig. 6-20 shows the final product. A corrugated plate was substituted for the flat plate of the preceding version, and grids of punched sheet metal replaced those of the wire type. This completed the development of the VT-1, which was manufactured in large numbers. After World War I many of these tubes found their way into the general market via sales of surplus Signal Corps equipment and were used by amateur radio enthusiasts.[6]

The other widely known and used Western Electric tube was the VT-2. It was developed as the result of a Signal Corps request in 1917 for a small transmitting tube to operate at a plate voltage of 300 volts. The VT-2, which was also used by the U.S. Navy under the designation CW-931, was originally designated by Western Electric as Type E, and later code numbers in the 205 series were assigned. Fig. 6-21 shows one of the earlier E tubes. The construction was somewhat similar to the Type L, except that the plates had turned-up edges and different bracing wires. This difference in

Fig. 6-20. The final form of the VT-1 vacuum tube.

construction was necessitated by the higher plate dissipation of the E tube, which tended to warp flat sheet plates. The wax-filled base (which was standard in telephone repeater tubes) was used at first; later it was found to be unsatisfactory because of the higher temperature at which the E tubes operated. The base finally adopted used a phenolic insert, and the tube bore the Western Electric code number 205B (Figs. 6-22 and 6-23).

In addition to the VT-1 and VT-2 there were several other types supplied to the U.S. Government during World War I. One of these (Fig. 6-24) bore the Western Electric code number 201A and was known to the U.S. Navy as the CW-186. The grid construction was similar to the 102 except that it had thirty-seven laterals on each side instead of thirty-one. This tube had a three-contact base, specified by the Navy, the fourth connection (one side of the filament) being made to the bayonet pin. In the standard telephone repeater base this tube was known to the Western Electric engineers as the Type D and was assigned the code number 201B.

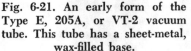

Fig. 6-21. An early form of the Type E, 205A, or VT-2 vacuum tube. This tube has a sheet-metal, wax-filled base.

Fig. 6-22. The final form of the VT-2, Navy CW-931 vacuum tube. Note the phenolic insert in base.

Up to now the tubes discussed have been telephone repeater tubes and a few types made for the Government during World War I. There were a number of other early tubes, and some of these may come into the possession of tube collectors. Some will bear few marks of identification but may be recognized from the descriptions and photographs which follow. Consider first the power tubes.

The low-power output tube for telephone applications (Type O) and the 5-watt tube (Type E) have already been discussed. The predecessor of the Type E was the Type K, shown in Fig. 6-25. This was originally intended for application in military equipment as a transmitter tube for aircraft use. It required 500-volts plate potential, a voltage considered by the Signal Corps to be too hazardous to the aircraft operator, and the Type K was abandoned in favor of the Type E, which operated at 300-volts plate. The Type K at first had a machined brass base similar to but larger than the early telephone repeater tubes. This tube was later assigned the code number 202A and was made with a wax-filled sheet-metal base, the code marking being applied in raised letters in the wax filling in the usual manner.

Before this time, the only extensive use of power tubes by the Western Electric Company had been in the famous transatlantic telephone tests in 1915, the so-called Arlington to Paris tests. These

Fig. 6-23. The 205B vacuum tube. The same as the VT-2 except for markings.

were one-way transmissions from Arlington, Virginia. A bank of 550 tubes, operating in parallel, was used in the final amplifier. To fully appreciate such a feat as this and to realize the difficulties which had to be overcome by the engineers, one should hear the stories told by the men who did the job. There were problems of division of load, intertube wiring, parasitic oscillations, cooling, and a host of others which can be imagined only by those who have tried to operate more than two tubes in parallel.

Fig. 6-24. The CW-186 (Western Electric 201A) vacuum tube.

Fig. 6-25. The Type K, or 202A vacuum tube. This is an early version with a machined brass base.

Fig. 6-26. One of the banks of power tubes comprising the final amplifier at Arlington, Virginia, during the Arlington-Paris radiotelephone tests conducted in 1915.

Fig. 6-27. The Type W, or 204B vacuum tube.

Fig. 6-26 is a view of one of the banks of racks in which these tubes were mounted. The oscillator was a 101A, which fed through an intermediate amplifier into the final linear amplifier. The tubes used in this amplifier were known as Type W, and the official designation was 204B Vacuum Tube. It operated with a filament current of 4–4.5 amperes at approximately 9 volts. The plate voltage was 600 volts maximum with plate current of 150–200 milliamperes. Most of the tubes used at Arlington were unbased, although some based tubes similar to that shown in Fig. 6-27 were used.

Fig. 6-28. The modulator panel at Arlington, Virginia, using a Type S or 204A vacuum tube as modulator.

Fig. 6-29. The Type S or 204A vacuum tube.

The most noticeable feature of the Type W tube was the anode. A solid sheet-metal plate of the required size would have contained much occluded gas difficult to remove with the evacuation technique of the day. Accordingly, the anode consisted of a piece of Climax ribbon bent back and forth as can be seen in Fig. 6-27. The two anodes were connected at the top, and the bottom connections were brought out separately. The tape was then heated by the passage of current from an external source during the evacuation process and the occluded gases thus expelled. Another similarly constructed tube, used in the modulator panel during these tests, was known as the Type S and had the code designation 204A. The modulator panel is shown in Fig. 6-28 and the Type S tube in Fig. 6-29.

It was the experience and knowledge gained in the development of these tubes which enabled the Western Electric Company to produce the power tubes urgently needed for radiocommunication by the armed services during World War I.

REFERENCES

1. F. B. Llewellyn, "The Birth of the Electron Tube Amplifier," *Radio Telev. News*, Mar. 1957, 57:43–45.
2. *Transcript of Record, General Electric Company vs. DeForest Radio Company*, U.S. Circuit Court of Appeals, 3rd District, Nos. 3799, 3800, 3801, March term, 1928. Testimony of E. H. Colpitts, pp. 497–500.
3. *Ibid.*, testimony of H. D. Arnold, p. 556.
4. B. Gherardi and F. B. Jewett, "Telephone Repeaters," *Proc. A.I.E.E.*, Nov. 1919, pp. 1280–1281.
5. *Transcript* (No. 2 above), testimony of Arnold, pp. 601–604.
6. K. B. Warner, "The Famous VT-1," *QST*, Jun. 1919, 2:11–12. Dr. Radio, "New Developments," *QST*, Jul. 1919, 2:3–7. A. E. Harper, "Amplifying Bulbs," *QST*, Feb. 1921, 4:27–28.

Chapter 7

The Entrance of Industrial
Laboratories and Military Demands,
1910-1920: *United States (De Forest)*

The Radio Telephone Company and other de Forest companies
mentioned in Chapter 4 were forced into bankruptcy and their
assets sold at auction by the sheriff of New York County on March
11, 1911. Lee de Forest, penniless, went to San Francisco and entered the employ of the Federal Telegraph Company. But he was
not free f.om financial and legal worries; he had an uncanny ability
to become involved with exploiters as business associates.

One year later, March 15, 1912, de Forest and some of his associates, James Dunlop Smith, Elmer E. Burlingame, Samuel E. Darby,
and the Ellsworth Company were indicted on a charge of using the
mails to defraud. (The Ellsworth Company were the brokers who
handled the stock of the Radio Telephone Company.) On November 24, 1913, a jury was impaneled and sworn in. The trial ran
until December 29, 1913; the verdict was rendered at 1 am, January 1, 1914. Smith and Burlingame were found guilty and drew
heavy fines and jail sentences. The Ellsworth Company was found
guilty on two counts and was heavily fined. Darby (de Forest's
patent attorney) and de Forest were declared not guilty on three
counts, and the jury disagreed on the fourth.[1] This was dropped
(*nolle prosequi*) on October 27, 1914.

When de Forest went to work for the Federal Telegraph Company in 1911, he found they were using continuous-wave arc transmitters in an attempt to transmit telegraph messages at high speed.
This posed the problem of getting energy enough to make a record
of the high-speed signals for later reproduction and transcription

Table 7-1. Data on Audion Sales by McCandless: Breakdown of Sales to Various Purchasers, 1909–1913

Customer Year and Month	de Forest and De Forest Companies	Federal Telegraph Company	Marconi W.T. Co. of America	Wallace and Company	J. H. Bunnell and Company	Manhattan Elec. Supply Company	F. B. Chambers Company	J. F. Arnold	Dr. Goldhorn	Dr. Walter G. Hudson	I. W. Henry	Aylsworth Agencies, Inc.	Western Electric Company	Electro Importing Company	Hammond and Hammond Laboratories	Miscellaneous	Cash	Total
1909																		
January	75																	75
February	101																	101
March	84																	84
April	27		1															28
May	16																	16
June	12																1	13
July	29																	29
August	38																	38
September	0																	0
October	34																	34
November	0																	0
December	24																	24
Total	440		1														1	442

1910						
January	0					0
February	28					28
March	40					40
April	0					0
May	36					36
June	42					42
July	0					0
August	22					22
September	0					0
October	22					22
November	0					0
December	24					24
Total	214					214
1911						
January	6				1	7
February	0					0
March	20				5	25
April	0				3	3
May	0				2	2
June	0			27*	5	32
July	12		1	4	1	18
August	0		35	2	4	41
September	2	1	24	6	6	39
October	3	3	25	2	8	41
November	2	2			18	22
December	0		8	1	32	41
Total	45	6	93	42	85	271

* 25 of these sold to Charles de Grave Sells.

Table 7-1 (Cont). Data on Audion Sales by McCandless

Customer Year and Month	de Forest and De Forest Companies	Federal Telegraph Company	Marconi W.T. Co. of America	Wallace and Company	J. H. Bunnell and Company	Manhattan Elec. Supply Company	F. B. Chambers Company	J. F. Arnold	Dr. Goldhorn	Dr. Walter G. Hudson	I. W. Henry	Aylsworth Agencies, Inc.	Western Electric Company	Electro Importing Company	Hammond and Hammond Laboratories	Miscellaneous	Cash	Total
1912																		
January	12		2	12	1	2		4						23		5	28	73
February	37		70	8	3	1			7					29		7	14	104
March	0	24	1		21				3		12	6				1	20	135
April	0			6	12	1								25		2	12	65
May	0			15	12									11		2	20	78
June	0	3			4				1		12	6		14		3	9	45
July	0	4			12							6				4	7	33
August	0			10				5								2	9	28
September	0			22	18				2			6		25	7		6	77
October	4				6				1								9	43
November	6				12					8			20	28		2	7	70
December	0			35	4				3		40					1	4	107
Total	59	31	73	108	105	4		9	17	8	64	24	20	155	7	29	145	858

1913																	Total
January	0		32	26							6		38	6	9	9	126
February	6	6	24	29							2	20			8	7	100
March	12		26	44							2		45	5	2	8	142
April	0	24	30	34			26				3		50		4	8	178
May	0		10	31		12	10					20	50	10		4	137
June	0						8				5	6				5	38
July	6	12	9	8			12	3	1						11	3	65
August	0		10	18		24	12	2	2		2		6	6	59†	12	153
September	33		17	64		12	9	1					12		19	17	183
October	20		14	25		12	25						10		5	4	117
November	105														4		109
December	360						7								1		368
Total	542	42	172	279		60	109	6	3	—	20	46	211	27	122	77	1716

† 50 of these sold to Wireless Specialty Apparatus Company.

at lower speed. They were attempting to use the Poulsen Telegraphone as a recorder, but the energy of the received signals was insufficient for satisfactory recording and reproduction.

Realizing that it was necessary to "boost" the energy of the received signal, de Forest took up the Audion anew and attempted to get it to amplify at audio frequencies. This work may have been inspired by a letter written by John Hays Hammond, Jr., to Beach Thompson, president of the Federal Telegraph Company, on January 25, 1912. In this letter Hammond told Thompson of the results which Fritz Loewenstein had obtained with his "ion controller" both as an amplifier and as an oscillator. The Audions which de Forest used were obtained by the Federal Telegraph Company from McCandless, whose sales records show shipments to Federal Telegraph beginning in May 1912. See Table 7-1.

Some of these Audions were equipped with a new type of filament, known as the Hudson filament. The older tantalum filament had a tendency in use to warp out of its original plane, in some cases to the point where it touched the grid, thus making the tube useless. McCandless then used tungsten for filaments, which was more satisfactory from a mechanical standpoint but not as good an emitter as tantalum. One of McCandless' over-the-counter customers, Walter G. Hudson, suggested that McCandless wrap fine tantalum wire around the tungsten filament to form a cathode in which the heating current would be carried by the tungsten while the emission would come from the indirectly heated tantalum. This was done and the results were very satisfactory. Fig. 7-1 shows an Audion with a Hudson filament, and Fig. 7-2 is an enlarged view of such a cathode. Hudson, who had filed an application for a patent on

Fig. 7-1. Spherical Audion with the Hudson filament.

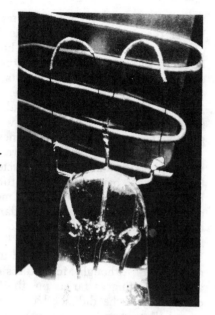

Fig. 7-2. Enlarged view of the Hudson filament as it was first made by McCandless.

this compound cathode on February 19, 1914, sold his patent application to de Forest. The patent, U.S. Patent No. 1,190,412, was issued on July 11, 1916, to the Radio Telephone and Telegraph Company.[2] (Many thousands of Hudson-filament Audions were sold to the U.S. armed services in 1914 and 1915, all made by McCandless.)

According to McCandless, the fabrication of such a cathode was tedious and expensive, and Hudson finally supplied McCandless with a quantity of finely ground tantalum mixed with an organic binder. A small dab of this on the arch of the tungsten filament substituted for the tantalum wire wrapping. How permanent the bond was is not known, but there are reports that some Audions have small particles of black material loose inside the bulb. Possibly in time the binder failed and the combination broke loose from the filament, resulting in these black particles.

In the spring of 1912 de Forest was assigned an assistant, Herbert B. Van Etten, who was familiar with audio-frequency circuits and apparatus, having previously worked for the Pacific Telephone and Telegraph Company. In May and June of 1912 Van Etten, under de Forest's supervision, started experimenting with audio-frequency transformers to provide coupling between the radio receiver output and the Audion, later between successive Audions in tandem, and finally between the Audion and the headphones. In July and August they succeeded in getting real amplification from their apparatus. Under the date July 26, 1912, de Forest wrote McCandless complaining that the vacuum in all but four of the tubes shipped to Federal was too low and the tubes lacked "sensitiveness"—they could not be used with anode voltages over 20 volts.[3] It is apparent that de Forest confused sensitiveness with output. On August 14, 1912, de Forest wrote that he had taken some of these bulbs to a glass blower in San Francisco, who had re-exhausted them and greatly increased their "sensitiveness" (i.e., output).[4]

The glass blower referred to was G. E. Lamont, whose business was the making and repairing of scientific apparatus made of glass— thermometers, barometers, X-ray tubes, incandescent lamps, Audion bulbs, and so forth. He used a mechanical pump followed by a mercury pump and heated the filament and the glass bulb during the evacuation process. This was done to free the filament and bulb structure from occluded gas. The filament was lighted to "over brilliance"[5] and the glass bulb heated to a temperature between 500 °F and 700 °F. Although McCandless used a Sprengel mercury pump, after exhausting as far as possible with a force pump of the mechanical type, he did not bake the Audions he made while they were being exhausted. Lamont's process produced a higher vacuum. However, de Forest got improved "sensitiveness" (output) because he could use a higher plate voltage without bringing on the "blue haze" which indicated ionization.

Later, while still trying to improve the arrangement as an amplifier, de Forest and Van Etten got a "howling" feedback circuit. Thus was born the Audion oscillator. At that time de Forest considered the "howling" a nuisance and tried to eliminate it because he did not understand it. Yet he used the records of these experiments in claiming priority in the development of the regenerative circuit and Audion oscillator.

In August 1912 de Forest started making arrangements to demonstrate the Audion as a voice-frequency amplifier to the A.T.&T. Co. with a view to selling them the rights to use it as a telephone repeater. The story of these demonstrations has been told in the previous chapter. After the Western Electric engineers had satisfied themselves that the Audion as submitted to them could be developed into a successful telephone repeater, A.T.&T. entered into negotiations with de Forest for the purchase of the patent rights to its use as a telephone repeater. It was found that the Audion patents had been assigned to the moribund Radio Telephone Company, which necessitated a long series of legal investigations for which A.T.&T. procured the services of an outside attorney, S. S. Meyers. The investigation took several months, but on July 26, 1913, Meyers obtained for A.T.&T. a valid exclusive license covering in general

Fig. 7-3. The Type S Oscillion. (Reproduced from *Elect. Exper.*, Apr., 1917.)

the use of the Audion in all fields except wireless telegraphy and telephony. For this de Forest received $50,000.

On August 7, 1914, A.T.&T. paid de Forest $90,000 for a non-exclusive license in the field of wireless telegraphy. On March 16, 1917, de Forest sold to A.T.&T. for $250,000 all the remaining rights, retaining to himself, under all his patents, a personal, nontransferable, nonassignable right

1. To make and sell direct to users for their use only,
2. To make and sell direct to the U.S. Government for its use,
3. To make and use for the radio distribution of news and music,
4. To make and sell radio apparatus for the radio reception of news and music,
5. To grant a license for use to the Marconi Company.

Fig. 7-4. Early version of the singer-type Audion, as used in the Type S Oscillion.

Fig. 7-5. Final construction of the singer-type Audion.

Fig. 7-6. Rectifier version of the singer-type Audion.

With the first payment from A.T.&T. de Forest went back to his work on the Audion itself. He rented a factory at High Bridge in the Bronx and equipped it with the necessary machinery, including pumping equipment. Here he began the development of Oscillions, the name given by him to Audions intended for use as power oscillators. He also began the production of radio equipment using Audions, although he did not manufacture the Audions, which were obtained from McCandless. In 1914 McCandless had sold his business to Westinghouse but continued to operate his plant for them until early 1916, when Westinghouse decided to close down that operation. This forced de Forest into the manufacture of Audions at High Bridge, and by the end of March 1916 the production rate was about fifty per day.

One of the smaller Oscillions developed was the singer-type Audion, which got its name from one of its intended uses—producing audio-frequency oscillations, or "singing." The earliest models of this type had candelabra bases, and the grid structure was wound on and supported by glass rods. One of the oscillators, known as the Type S Oscillion, incorporating this early model is shown in

Fig. 7-7. Early type of aircraft radiophone transmitter, held by Lee de Forest.

Fig. 7-3, and the tube itself is shown in Fig. 7-4. These Oscillions were used by de Forest in a musical instrument, the predecessor of the modern electronic organ. In December 1915 de Forest demonstrated this instrument before the New York Electrical Society. While the proceedings of this society contain no record of the demonstration, there appeared in one of the popular electrical magazines of that day an article by de Forest on this application of the Audion.[6] A later variant of the singer-type Audion, equipped with the Shaw-standard base and with radically different internal construction, is shown in Fig. 7-5. A rectifier version of this same tube, later used in some of the low-power de Forest transmitters, appears in Fig. 7-6.

Other sizes of Oscillions were subsequently made. The aircraft was growing in importance in the modern way of life and de Forest felt that the necessity of plane-to-ground communication would soon become imperative. Accordingly, he set about developing an Oscillion aircraft transmitter. One of the earlier steps in that direction was the transmitter unit held by de Forest in Fig. 7-7, known as Type A Aeroplane Transmitter. A somewhat similar unit, using the same type of tube and known as the Type OJ3 Oscillion Telephone (Fig. 7-8) was offered for sale to amateurs in 1917.[7] Higher-powered Oscillions followed. The tube shown in Fig. 7-9, used in a de Forest

Fig. 7-8. The Type OJ3 Oscillion Telephone. (Reproduced from *Elect. Exper.*, Jan., 1917.)

transmitter installed at the High Bridge laboratory, was also used to broadcast returns of the presidential election of November 1916.

Late in 1915 de Forest engaged Robert F. Gowen as chief engineer. Gowen was not only a trained scientist but an enthusiastic amateur wireless operator of long standing. As a student at Harvard he had aided in organizing a wireless network for intramural com-

Fig. 7-9. A high-power Oscillion, vintage of 1915, 50 watts input.

Fig. 7-10. Improved form of the spherical Audion. One of the glass arbors is broken off at the press.

munications. Under Gowen's supervision High Bridge turned out a variety of tubes in addition to the types formerly made by McCandless. One of these, a detector tube, was an improved spherical Audion (Fig. 7-10). This, like the earliest Western Electric tubes, had two glass arbors for supporting and stiffening the plate and grid assemblies, but unlike the Western Electric tubes, it had two tantalum filaments.

Meantime, competition for the business of the radio amateur began to appear. A cylindrical three-electrode detector tube called the Audio Tron (later AudioTron) was put on the market by E. T. Cunningham, a West Coast manufacturer, in October 1915. These tubes were good detectors and were sold to amateurs without strings requiring the purchase of auxiliary equipment. This was important to amateurs, and Cunningham prospered. At this time de Forest Audions could be obtained legitimately only by first buying a complete detector, after which renewal bulbs could be bought only upon the return of a burnt-out bulb or the grid and plate of a broken one. The AudioTron and other "independent" tubes which were being manufactured on the West Coast will be covered in Chapter 9.

To meet the West Coast competition, de Forest brought out a tubular Audion (Fig. 7-11). It was designated as the Type T and first offered for sale in April 1916.[8] The Type T was a single-filament tube and sold for about the same price as the double-filament Audio-Tron. Two Type-T Audions are shown in Fig. 7-12. A tubular Audion called an "Ultraudion" is pictured in Fig. 7-13. This name simply meant that the tube could be made to produce oscillations when used in a circuit which de Forest called the "Ultraudion cir-

ANNOUNCEMENT

For the benefit of the amateurs, and particularly the ones who cannot afford to purchase a complete Audion Detector, we now offer for the first time, the genuine DeForest Type T Tubular Audion SEPARATELY. As many may be purchased, without the instrument or accessories, as may be desired, without returning old tubes.

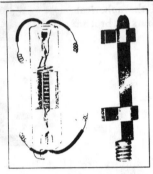

The Type T Tubular Audion has a single, straight-line filament of tungsten. It gives very loud response to signals. It passes our usual careful test against a standard which is fully 50 percent, more sensitive than any other known form of detector.

This type of Audion is not interchangeable with our round Audion Bulbs, which will be sold, as heretofore, for renewals only for our instruments, on return of the old bulb.

The adapter illustrated fits the tube to a regular screw socket. Price, 40 cents extra.

The Type T Tubular Audion will be furnished at $5.50 each with the guarantee that it has passed our test and that it will be delivered safely to our agents or users, but no further guarantee can or will be made covering accidental breakage or burning out thereafter by the operator.

NEW BULLETIN R16 WILL BE SENT IF STAMP IS ENCLOSED

DeForest Radio
Telephone & Telegraph Company
101 PARK AVENUE
New York, N. Y.

ALWAYS MENTION "QST" WHEN WRITING TO ADVERTISERS

Fig. 7-11. Advertisement announcing the Type T Audion.
(Reproduced from *QST*, Apr., 1916.)

cuit." The label states that this particular tube has a Hudson filament. It does not, for there is no tantalum wrapping on the filament and no trace of anything resembling tantalum paste in the tube.

With the entry of the United States into World War I in 1917, all amateur radio activity was prohibited, so de Forest began to manufacture tubes for the Government in addition to the various types of spherical candelabra-based Audions. One tube used by the Signal Corps was designated the VT-21. Two variations on the bulb shape of this tube are shown in Fig. 7-14. The VT-21 operated at a filament current of 1.1 amperes, had an amplification factor of 10–12, and an internal resistance of 6000 ohms when operated with 20 volts on the anode. Tubes for the U.S. Navy were also made by de Forest;

Fig. 7-12. Type T Audions. The one at the left shows the DF stamping on the plate.

one of these designated CF-185. This tube was at first supplied to fit the Navy standard three-contact socket and had a machined fiber base. The metal locking pin provided the fourth terminal. A sample of this early construction is shown in Fig. 7-15. The grid was of fine

Fig. 7-13. The tubular Ultraudion.

Fig. 7-14. Variants of the de Forest VT-21.

tungsten wire wound on a glass frame, and the plates were of sheet tungsten. Subsequently these tubes were provided with the standard four-pin base. One of this variety with a sheet-metal base shell is shown in Fig. 7-16. There was also an adaptor available to provide for the use of the CF-185 in the candelabra socket, characteristic of earlier Audion equipment. The CF-185 was the first tube made

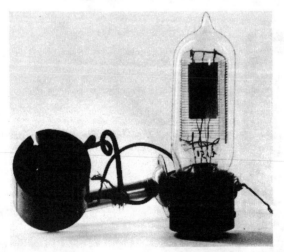

Fig. 7-15. An early CF-185 with three-point base and socket.

Fig. 7-16. Later type of CF-185 with four-point base and socket.

Fig. 7-17. De Forest Radio Telephone and Telegraph Company exhibit
at the Panama-Pacific Exposition at San Francisco in 1915.

Fig. 7-18. Radiotelephone equipment for use on railroad trains, displayed in the booth shown in Fig. 7-17.

by de Forest which used an oxide-coated filament. This was claimed to have a life of 5000 hours at a filament current of 0.85 ampere,[9] but there is no information available to corroborate this claim.

At the Panama-Pacific Exposition in San Francisco in 1915 the De Forest Telephone and Telegraph Company had a booth in which de Forest exhibited radiotelephone equipment (Fig. 7-17). On display was a radiotelephone designed for use on a railway train (Fig. 7-18). It consisted of a quenched-arc transmitter and an Audion receiver. At this booth either de Forest himself or Elman B. Myers (one of his employees) sold Audion bulbs. Myers left de Forest in the fall of 1915 and went into the vacuum tube business on his own.

About this time Otis B. Moorhead went into the tube manufacturing business and brought the West Coast infringers to a total of three—Cunningham, Myers, and Moorhead. The work of these entrepreneurs is covered in detail in Chapter 9. Some reference to the activities of Moorhead is included here to preserve the continuity of the de Forest story.

It will be remembered that when de Forest sold the rights to the Audion to A.T.&T., he retained a personal, nontransferable right to make and sell Audions direct to the user for radio applications. This he continued to do. In 1914 the Marconi Wireless Telegraph Company of America, owners of the patent on the Fleming valve,

Fig. 7-19. American Marconi Type D valves.

instituted suit against the De Forest Radio Telephone and Telegraph
Company and Lee de Forest, claiming that the Audion was an infringement on the Fleming valve. A countersuit was promptly filed by
de Forest, claiming infringement of his patents by Marconi. Samples
of the infringing Marconi Type D tubes are shown in Fig. 7-19, and

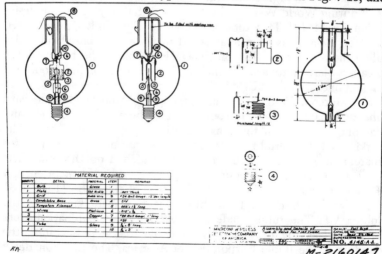

Fig. 7-20. American Marconi manufacturing drawing for Type D valve.

the Marconi manufacturing drawing is shown in Fig. 7-20. Before the case came to trial the Marconi Company confessed judgment as to the infringement and was enjoined from further infringement. The case against de Forest, which will be discussed in a later chapter, was tried and the decision of the District Court was rendered on September 20, 1916.[10] This decision was later upheld by the Circuit Court of Appeals.[11] The decision held that the Fleming patent had been infringed, and an injunction was issued restraining de Forest from further manufacture and sale for radio use. This produced a stalemate. Audions could not be made by de Forest because they infringed the Fleming patent; the Marconi Company could not make Audions because they infringed the de Forest patents. They could make Fleming valves, but nobody wanted them.

During World War I de Forest made Audions for the Government under guarantee of immunity, but after the war the injunctions again became operative and the stalemate was restored. It was broken early in 1919 when representatives of the Marconi Company met with O. B. Moorhead.[12] The conference resulted in de Forest joining forces with Moorhead to make use of de Forest's personal license, and the Marconi Company extended its patent rights to de Forest and Moorhead for the manufacture and sale of radio receiving tubes; the Marconi Company was made the distributing agent for the de Forest-Moorhead coalition. (For a detailed account of this alliance see Chapter 9.)

The first tubes put out by this combination were the unbased Moorhead Electron Relay and the Moorhead VT Amplifier.[13] The latter tube was a high-vacuum tube which had been made by Moorhead during World War I and sold to the U.S. Navy under the designation SE-1444.[14] This tube is shown in Fig. 7-21. The unbased Electron Relay was soon abandoned in favor of a based tube also called the Moorhead Electron Relay (Fig. 7-22). The base was the so-called Shaw standard,[15] which had been used on the Moorhead VT amplifier and the SE-1444.

The Marconi Company in advertising the Moorhead-made hard tube designated it the Marconi VT. This bore the De Forest and Marconi markings on the brass base in depressed characters. The marking VT, the serial number, and the license notice "Licensed for amateur or experimental use only" were etched on the bulb. The life was claimed as 1500 hours.[16] It operated with a filament current of 0.7 ampere at about 4 volts.[17] The glass of this tube (Fig. 7-23) had a golden tinge, and the tube was familiarly known as the Golden VT. The tubes made and sold by this combination were the only receiving tubes legally available to the public until the founding of the Radio Corporation of America. The Electron Relay was soon replaced by the De Forest Type 20 Detector, which was

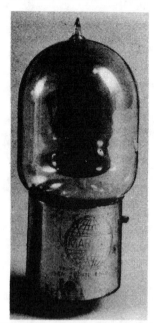

Fig. 7-21. Moorhead-Marconi-
de Forest VT amplifier.

Fig. 7-22. Moorhead-Marconi-
de Forest Electron Relay.

Fig. 7-23. Marconi VT tube.

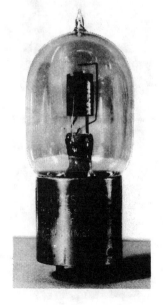

Fig. 7-24. The de Forest Type 20 detector. Left: early type of soft tube. Right: later type with getter.

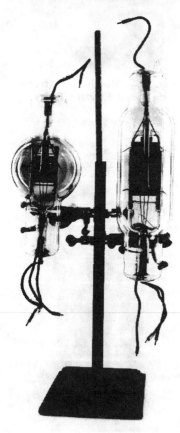

Fig. 7-25. Early 250-watt and 500-watt (input) Oscillions.

Fig. 7-26. Oscillion transmitter Type OT200, using two 500-watt-
input tubes.

at first advertised as a "soft" tube[18] and is shown at the left of
Fig. 7-24. Later is was apparently made as a "hard" tube, since
the variant at the right in Fig. 7-24 has a getter.

After World War I de Forest began to develop higher-power
Oscillions. These he could sell because the injunction applied only
to receiving tubes. Fig. 7-25 shows two of the early postwar Oscillions, the one at the left with an input rating of 250 watts and the
one at the right rated at 500 watts input. Fig. 7-26 shows a transmitter, made by the De Forest Company, which uses two of these
500-watt-input tubes. Later models of these Oscillions, designated
1D and 1G, are shown in Fig. 7-27. There were also 1J and 1K
Oscillions rated at 750 and 1000 watts input respectively.[19] These

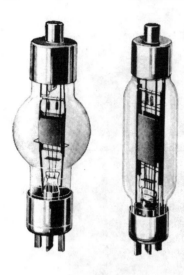

Fig. 7-27. The 250-watt-input Type 1D and 500-watt-input Type 1G Oscillions, vintage 1920, equipped with end fittings.

Oscillions were provided with end fittings to facilitate mounting and circuit connections. They appeared on the market in 1920.

After World War I the idea prevailed that Audions had not been widely used prior to the war. An analysis of the records of McCandless in the period 1909–1915 refutes this. Table 7-1, 1909–1913 inclusive, shows the names of purchasers, except for two columns labeled "Misc" and "Cash." "Misc" includes sales to purchasers who did not warrant a separate column. "Cash" represents sales to unrecorded purchasers.

For the years 1914 and 1915 no breakdown by customers is given, but the actual sales for each month are divided into three headings in Table 7-2. There is some indication that all these sales were made to the De Forest Radio Telephone and Telegraph Company. The distinction between "Audions" and "Amplifiers" is unknown. The price of Audions was $1.50 and of Amplifiers was $2.50; hence the term Audion in this tabulation probably refers to the single-grid and plate type, and Amplifiers to the double-grid and plate type. "Oscillators" were low-powered transmission tubes, sold at $7.50 each.

In addition to the Audions made by McCandless for the De Forest Company, the De Forest Radio Telephone and Telegraph Company, beginning sometime in 1914, manufactured Audions in their own factory, in the High Bridge section of New York City.

An accounting was rendered to George C. Holt, Special Master of the U.S. Circuit Court of Appeals, as a result of the Fleming-de Forest patent litigation, of all Audions sold by the De Forest

Table 7-2. Data on Audion Sales by McCandless, 1914–1915

Year and Month	Audions	Amplifiers	Oscillators	Total
1914				
January	340	184	0	524
February	113	505	0	616
March	226	383	0	609
April	504	45	0	549
May	340	19	0	359
June	0	232	0	232
July	175	173	1	349
August	0	889	0	889
September	371	200	1	572
October	470	75	10	555
November	425	15	0	440
December	175	63	0	238
Total	3139	2781	12	5932
1915				
January	60	110	0	170
February	94	364	0	458
March	251	216	0	467
April	457	212	0	669
May	0	419	3	422
June	76	647	5	728
July	295	669	0	964
August	488	388	2	878
September	112	377	0	489
Total	1833	3402	10	5245

Company to the U.S. Government up to February 27, 1919. The author has an abstract of this accounting, from which the following information was extracted.

1. Between March 4, 1914, and August 28, 1918, the De Forest Company supplied to the U.S. Government 1,393 single-grid and plate tubes designated as Audions.
2. Between June 11, 1914, and November 26, 1918, the De Forest Company supplied to the U.S. Government 12,437 double-grid and plate tubes designated as Amplifiers.
3. Between October 5, 1916, and October 5, 1917, the De Forest Company supplied to the U.S. Government 2,156 tubes designated as "oxide-coated filament tubes." These were of the type designated as CF-185.
4. Between March 8, 1918, and September 18, 1918, the De Forest Company supplied to the U.S. Government 15,057 tubes designated VT-21.

Comparison of these figures with the McCandless output figures for 1914 and 1915 (Table 7-2) indicates that Government orders could account for most of the double-grid and plate tubes made by McCandless in those years. However, this is not the case with the single-grid and plate Audions. The balance of these sales, over and above those sold to the Government, can be assumed to be largely sales to radio amateurs. This market disappeared about the middle of 1917, when all U.S. amateur licenses were cancelled and all U.S. amateur stations ordered dismantled.

McCandless sold his business to the Westinghouse Lamp Company late in 1914 but continued to operate for them at least until the end of 1915.

REFERENCES

1. "Two Guilty in Radio Case—Jury Disagrees on Charges against Darby and De Forest," *N.Y. Times*, Jan. 1, 1914, p. 1.
2. Walter G. Hudson, "Electrode for Devices for Varying Electrical Resistance," U.S. Patent No. 1,190,412, application date Feb. 19, 1914, issued Jul. 11, 1916.
3. Gerald F. J. Tyne, "The Story of McCandless and the Audion," bound manuscript in Clark Collection, Smithsonian Institution, Washington, D.C.
4. *Ibid.*, letter from de Forest to McCandless dated Aug. 14, 1912.
5. *Transcript of Record, General Electric Company vs. DeForest Radio Company*, U.S. Circuit Court of Appeals, 3rd District, Nos. 3799, 3800, 3801, March term 1928. Testimony of G. E. Lamont, Vol. 2, p. 1029.
6. Lee de Forest, "Audion Bulbs as Producers of Musical Tones," *Elect. Exper.*, Dec. 1915, 3:394.
7. Advertisement of De Forest Radio Telephone and Telegraph Co., *Elect. Exper.*, Apr. 1917, 4:920.
8. Advertisement announcing Type T Audion, *QST*, Apr. 1916, *1*, advertisers' section.
9. Bernard Kahn, "Navy Type Audion Detector," *QST*, Nov. 1916, 1:335.
10. 236 Federal Reporter 942.
11. 243 Federal Reporter 960.
12. *Radio Amat. News*, Aug. 1919, 1:77.
13. Moorhead advertisement in *Pacif. Radio News*, May 1920, *1*, inside back cover.
14. O. B. Moorhead and E. C. Lange, "The Specifications and Characteristics of Moorhead Vacuum Valves," *Proc. I.R.E.*, Apr. 1921, 9:95–129. Paper presented at the San Francisco section on Nov. 19, 1919.
15. U.S. Patent No. 1,458,153.
16. Marconi Wireless Telegraph Co. of America advertisement in *Radio Amat. News*, Aug. 1919, 1:52.
17. "The Marconi VT," *Wireless Age*, Aug. 1919, pp. 33–34.
18. Pacific Radio Supplies advertisement in *Radio Amat. News*, May 1920, 1:606.
19. Catalogue No. 101, Lee De Forest, Inc., 451 Third St., San Francisco.

Chapter 8

The Entrance of Industrial
Laboratories and Military Demands,
1910-1920: *United States (General Electric)*

The General Electric Company became interested in the Audion because they needed a high-power device, one with the characteristics exhibited by the Audion at low power levels. Although the name of General Electric was associated primarily with power equipment in the early 1900s, the engineers of this company had been trying for some years to develop a radio-frequency alternator for long-distance wireless communication. This work was begun at the request of Reginald A. Fessenden, of the National Electric Signalling Company. Fessenden was working at Brant Rock, Massachusetts, trying to develop a method of obtaining a continuous flow of high-frequency energy. He was using an arc transmitter, the only satisfactory generator of continuous waves of that day. He experienced many difficulties. The arc was unstable and not entirely free from self-modulation. He then turned to the alternator as a power source. Fessenden designed an alternator which he claimed would operate at 100,000 cycles and appealed to the General Electric Company to build it according to his specifications. The GE engineers, being experts in the design and manufacture of power machinery, were convinced that an alternator constructed according to Fessenden's specifications would not operate above 10,000 cycles, but they finally consented to accept the order. The alternator was delivered in 1906, and with it came the statement that in the company's opinion it was not possible to operate it above 10,000 cycles.[1]

The General Electric Company, foreseeing the need for such a machine, determined to develop a high-power alternator to operate at high frequencies. E. F. W. Alexanderson was assigned the job of this development. The result of the ensuing years of work on his part became known as the Alexanderson Alternator. The true significance of this development was realized in 1919 when General Electric, although having spent millions of dollars to make such a machine practicable, refused to sell it to their only potential customer, the British-controlled Marconi Wireless Telegraph Company of America. By so doing, General Electric was instrumental in returning control of transatlantic radiocommunication to the United States.[2]

In 1913 Alexanderson was building alternators of several kilowatts output at frequencies up to 200,000 cycles per second.[3] They could be used for continuous-wave telegraphy but not for radiotelephone communication, because no method of adequate modulation of their output was available. Alexanderson tried to accomplish modulation in several ways and finally developed a so-called magnetic amplifier, or magnetic modulator.[4] This was not completely successful; it required much more audio power than could be generated by known sources to drive it to the required level. Alexanderson continued his search for a better modulator.

In 1912 the General Electric Company sold to John Hays Hammond, Jr., two high-frequency alternators for use in experimental work on radio-controlled devices. In October of that year Alexanderson discussed with Hammond at the latter's laboratory at Gloucester, Massachusetts, the problem of obtaining the necessary modulation. While there, Alexanderson was told of some receiving apparatus, designed and constructed by Benjamin F. Miessner, one of Hammond's assistants, in which Audions were used. Miessner had worked during the winter of 1911–1912 with Fritz Loewenstein on the development of the ion controller previously discussed. This work had made Miessner cognizant of the possibilities of using the Audion as an amplifier.

Alexanderson, who had never seen an Audion, thought from the information given him that it might be promising as a high-frequency relay. He was made aware of its limitations but thought that these might be overcome. He therefore arranged to obtain an Audion from Hammond to see if it might be developed into a suitable instrument for his own purpose. The Audion was sent to him at Schenectady, and Alexanderson showed it to W. D. Coolidge and Irving Langmuir, with whom he frequently discussed problems. Langmuir had been in the employ of General Electric since 1909. He was graduated from Columbia University in 1903 and had done postgraduate work under Nernst at the University of Göttingen, receiving his Ph.D. in 1906. When he went to work for General Electric he attacked some of the problems still to be solved in connection with tungsten-filament incandescent lamps. The Coolidge process of making drawn tungsten wire had recently been introduced into commercial manufacture and, like any new process, had given rise to a number of problems.

One of the problems which Langmuir studied in connection with tungsten-filament lamps was the blackening of the bulbs in service. This same problem in connection with carbon-filament lamps, the reader will recall, led to the discovery by Edison of the "Edison effect." It was the common idea in the General Electric laboratory that this blackening, in the case of the tungsten-filament lamp, was due to secondary causes, among them electrical discharges. It was known that the presence of water vapor in the lamp bulb accelerated the blackening, and from this it seemed that better vacuums were desirable. But while others had attempted to solve the problem by increasing the vacuum, Langmuir adopted a different approach. He attempted to determine the cause of blackening by increasing the amount of the impurities in the bulb. In particular, he studied the effect on the filament of gases introduced. Some of these gases would disappear if introduced in limited quantities; others, such as nitrogen, would react with the tungsten vapor given off by the filament.

In this work Langmuir had to differentiate between the effects due to evaporation of the filament—because of its high operating temperature—and the effects due to electrical discharges within the bulb. To accomplish this he used low-voltage lamps to study the evaporation phenomena and high-voltage ones (50–250 volts) to study the effect of discharges. From all this he began to get a picture of what would happen in a perfect vacuum. He concluded that the blackening of the bulb was due to normal evaporation of the filament. He found the reason why the presence of water vapor accelerated the blackening. He found that even if the vacuum was perfect, the blackening would still occur. From his studies he concluded that the presence of pure gases was not harmful, and from this work came the high-efficiency gas-filled incandescent lamp.

During the period, shortly before Alexanderson brought the Audion to his attention, Langmuir had been studying the properties of filaments as a function of their length. It was thought at that time that, in lamps with long filaments requiring a comparatively high voltage for operation, there might be a considerable amount of current flowing through the vacuous space. If this were so, for a given total current the actual current through the filament would be less and the lamp less efficient. Langmuir looked for this effect but could not find it. He found that in a well-exhausted lamp there was a negligible space current regardless of the length of the filament. Others had worked along the same line and were of the opinion that in a perfect vacuum there would be no space current.

Dr. Coolidge was one of this group. He was working on X-ray

tubes. In the early X-ray tube of high power most of the electrical energy supplied to the tube appeared at the anode, which would sometimes operate at white heat. Coolidge used tungsten for the anode and sometimes for the cathode as well. In the case of the tungsten cathodes he found that after the tube had been in operation for some time the cathode became white hot, and shortly thereafter the tube ceased to pass current and became inoperative. Coolidge was aware of the "clean-up" effect of white-hot tungsten, and he believed that the stoppage of the tube was caused by its becoming "too hard"—the vacuum had become too high to permit the passage of current. This was in agreement with Langmuir's own experimental work, which indicated that these currents would become very small when the highest vacuums were attained.

Langmuir was familiar with the work of O. W. Richardson on thermionic emission, which showed that the emission increased with temperature.[5] Calculations based on Richardson's equations indicated that at the temperature at which Langmuir was operating his tungsten filaments, the thermionic currents should have been hundreds of amperes per square centimeter of filament surface. Langmuir checked the discharge from a hot filament to a cold anode in the presence of mercury vapor and found that the space currents followed Richardson's law up to very high filament temperatures. Hence he concluded that there was nothing abnormal about tungsten and that the filaments were actually emitting electrons in accordance with Richardson's law. He found that at first the space current followed this law, but as the temperature increased, the space current tended toward a constant value. This always occurred, although the limiting value was different for different voltages between the hot and cold electrodes. He found that this limiting current was approximately proportional to the voltage difference between the hot and cold electrodes, and to the area of the anode.

Langmuir discovered also that a potential applied to the bulb externally affected the space current. If, for example, he placed one hand on the bulb and with the other hand touched a terminal of the direct-current power circuit in the laboratory, the space current increased or decreased, depending on whether he touched the positive or negative terminal.

By November 22, 1912, Langmuir had accumulated enough data to enable him to formulate a qualitative theory concerning the space current. This theory, as entered in his laboratory notebook under that date, was as follows:

New Theory of Edison Current.
The velocity of electrons in a conductor corresponds to that produced by a fall through a potential diff. of only a few tenths of a volt. Electrons

leaving a filament will leave irrespective of the presence of a field, but they will only travel a very short distance if there is an electric field of only 0.1 volt per centimeter against them. Hence around filament there is an atmosphere of electrons in equilibrium with the filament. Below a certain temperature the potential is by the wires (i.e. electrodes) only.

Above a certain temperature the concentration of electrons becomes so great that they determine the field. Hence, two laws: Richardson's at low and some other at high temperature. Cooling bulb has no effect when no gas molecules present, but if gas is there the molecules collide with electrons (which have the same velocities as those of the filament) and slow them up and make them more readily absorbed by the anode wires.[6]

This last paragraph was an attempt to explain the fact that the presence of gas caused an increase in the space current. This we know now was not the correct theory. The increase in current when gas is present is due to the positive ions formed which neutralize the space charge—thus allowing the space current to rise toward the temperature saturation value. These experiments threw an entirely new light on the theory of discharges from hot electrodes in very high vacuums. They showed why, in the past, such small space currents were indicated by Richardson's equations.

Langmuir attached great importance to his explanation and theory and proceeded to make a detailed study of the laws governing the phenomena under high-vacuum conditions. His first step was to have constructed another lamp in which were placed two independent filaments, both of which could be heated during the exhaust process. The lamp was baked at high temperature and a liquid-air trap was used to remove traces of water vapor and carbon dioxide. Thus Langmuir removed as much of the occluded gases as possible and pushed the vacuum to the limits attainable with the available equipment. Tests were run on this new bulb using anode voltages up to 250 volts dc and about 500 volts ac. When the test data were plotted, the shape of the curve indicated that the space current varied as the 1.5 power of the anode voltage.

This was the background of knowledge born of experience which enabled Langmuir to tell Alexanderson in 1913 that he could improve the gadget which Alexanderson had obtained from Hammond. He could make of it an instrument which would solve Alexanderson's problem. But in order to accomplish this he needed another assistant, and William C. White was assigned to this work.

White studied the characteristics of the sample Audion and discussed the results of his tests with Langmuir. While White was making the tests Langmuir had made up a tube similar to the Audion but with leads widely separated. This was done in order to enable him to apply high voltages during the exhausting process, thus heating the electrodes by bombardment to free them from

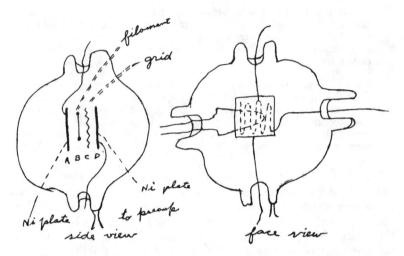

Fig. 8-1. Sketch of Langmuir's first attempt to build a high-vacuum Audion. (Reproduced from Langmuir's laboratory notebook No. 413, p. 228.)

occluded gases. Fig. 8-1 shows Langmuir's sketch of this tube, which he designated Audion #1. The results obtained were unsatisfactory, and Langmuir decided to drastically alter the construction of the tube in order to facilitate evacuation as high as possible.

To accomplish this he abandoned the conventional Audion construction and made a three-electrode tube in which all three—filament, grid, and anode—were made of tungsten wire. The filament was of 2.7-mil tungsten wire and was about 5½ inches in length. The grid was 1.5-mil wire, hand wound on a glass frame. The anode was a zigzag tungsten wire 5 mils in diameter. The filament when operated at about 1.05 amperes at about 4.1 volts had a temperature of about 2480 K. To exhaust this tube White assembled a pumping system which included a Gaede mercury pump and a liquid-air trap. This tube was designated Tungsten Wire Audion #2, shown in Fig. 8-2. This tube was designed so that the electrodes could be heated by current from an external source during exhaust in order to free them from occluded gases.

White exhausted this tube on the new pumping system on March 15, 1913.[7] He sealed the tube off the pump at a pressure of 0.05 micron and subjected it to a number of tests. In one test the anode voltage was held constant at 235 volts and the anode current was measured as a function of the grid voltage. Curves plotted of total space current (Fig. 8-3) showed that the current obeyed the 3/2 power law.[8] This tube when tested functioned satisfactorily as a

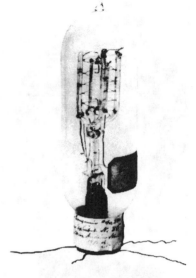

Fig. 8-2. Tungsten-wire Audion #2.

detector of radio signals. Other tubes made up in a similar fashion were tested by Alexanderson in May 1913 and were found to function satisfactorily as radio-frequency amplifiers.

The practice of using wire electrodes to facilitate degassing was

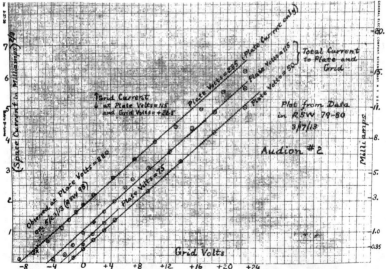

Fig. 8-3. Characteristic curves of tungsten-wire Audion #2 at various plate voltages. (Reproduced from transcript of record, General Electric Company vs. De Forest Radio Company, U.S. Circuit Court of Appeals, 3rd District, Nos. 3799, 3800, March Term, 1928, Vol. 4, p. 46.)

Fig. 8-4. An early type of wire-element Pliotron, now in the Science Museum, London.

followed from March 1913 until well into 1914 for all small "Pliotrons" intended for operation up to 250 volts on the anode. This tube design was discontinued at that time. Manufacture of those in production continued through 1917. Figs. 8-4 through 8-8 show

Fig. 8-5. An early Pliotron before exhaust (Pliotron 225). The exact date is unknown, but probably late 1915. The grid is tungsten wire 0.4 mil in diameter, wound on a metal frame with pitch of 120 turns per inch. The anode is 7-mil tungsten wire. Note the five leads: two filament, one grid, and both ends of the anode.

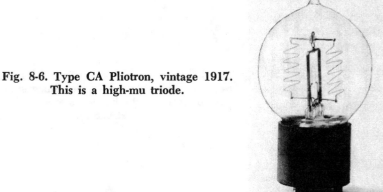

Fig. 8-6. Type CA Pliotron, vintage 1917.
This is a high-mu triode.

variants of the Type CA Pliotron particularly designed for resistance-coupled amplifier use, voltage amplification factor 50–150, internal resistance 0.5 to 5.0 megohms, maximum anode voltage 250 volts, filament current 1.1 amperes at about 4.0 volts.

It was in November 1913 that a need was felt for characteristic names for these new electron tubes. The term Kenotron was chosen for the pure electron-discharge two-element tube. The word Kenotron is derived from the Greek *kenos*, signifying "empty space" (vac-

Fig. 8-7. Type CA Pliotron, vintage 1918. Left: completed tube. Right: element assembly on stem.

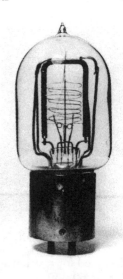

Fig. 8-8. Later sample of the Type CA Plio-tron with cylindrical bulb and Shaw standard base. This tube has an improved electrode structure.

uum), and *tron,* used by the Greeks to denote an instrument. Pliotron is derived from the Greek *pleion,* meaning "more"; a Pliotron (three element) is thus an instrument for giving more, or an amplifier.

While Langmuir and White were engaged in this development, Coolidge continued his work on the X-ray tube. In December 1912 Langmuir suggested to Coolidge that he try a tungsten cathode which could be heated by electric current from an external source for the purpose of getting electrons in his X-ray tube. Coolidge found it necessary to add a focusing shield around the cathode. With this modification the tube was steady in operation and had none of the crankiness of the cold-cathode tube; it gave reproducible results. By December 1913 Coolidge had developed this tube to the point of commercial use and described it in a paper before the American Physical Society.[9]

In April 1913 Langmuir and Dr. Saul Dushman of the General Electric Laboratory attended a series of lectures delivered by Professor Wilhelm Wien at Columbia University. During their return trip to Schenectady, Langmuir and Dushman discussed the work which Langmuir and White had been doing. It was agreed that Dushman would take over that portion of the work on the new device which had to do with its application as a high-voltage hot-cathode rectifier and relay, and that White would continue to work on tubes for wireless and other low-voltage applications.

By June 1913 Dushman had a three-electrode tube which was capable of operation—while still on the pump—at 20,000 to 40,000 volts on the anode, the space current of 100 milliamperes. This tube had been exhausted to a high vacuum by the use of a Gaede molecular pump and liquid-air trap. It was a bulb of about 7 inches in diameter with side arms which contained the leads to the electrode terminals. The anodes were plates of tungsten sheet, and the grid a spiral of 1.5-mil tungsten wire wound on glass supports. It was at first operated while still on the pump but was then sealed off and became in effect a large power tube. After it was sealed off it could be operated without blue glow at 10,000 volts on the anode and space current of 100 milliamperes. This tube is shown in Fig. 8-9. On May 14, 1913, it was used to successfully accomplish what Alexanderson had in mind when he first brought the Audion to the laboratory—to control the output of one of his high-frequency alternators. Still later it was used as a modulator in actual wireless tests between Schenectady and Pittsfield, Massachusetts.

This single tube was later replaced by a bank of tubes, and in 1919 the 200-kilowatt Alexanderson alternator was modulated through a magnetic amplifier by a bank of thirty Type P Pliotrons operated in parallel. Fig. 8-10 shows the bank of tubes, while Fig. 8-11 shows one of the tubes. The anode voltage used was about 2300 volts, and the anode current varied over the range 0–4 amperes, which represented a variation in modulating energy of about 4 kilowatts.

Fig. 8-9. The tube used by Alexanderson to modulate a small high-frequency alternator in wireless tests between Schenectady, New York, and Pittsfield, Massachusetts, in 1914.

Fig. 8-10. Bank of thirty Type P Pliotrons used to modulate a 200-kilo-watt Alexanderson alternator in 1918.

The first publication dealing with Langmuir's work came in 1913 when Langmuir read a paper in which he disclosed the method which had been used to prepare the electrodes and exhaust the tubes in order to obtain a pure electron discharge. The paper was read at Columbia University and subsequently published.[10] During the discussion, Dr. H. D. Arnold brought out the fact that the 3/2 power law had been published by C. D. Child in 1911[11] and J. E. Lilienfeld had deduced the 3/2 power law from experimental observations and published his results in 1910.[12] Lilienfeld himself commented on Langmuir's paper rather caustically by correspondence.[13] Later Langmuir published, in a German journal, two other

Fig. 8-11. Type P Pliotron used in modulator panel shown in Fig. 8-10.

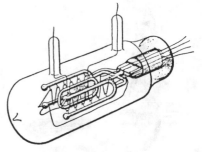

Fig. 8-12. Langmuir's drawing of small Pliotron. (Reproduced from *Proc. I.R.E.*, 1915, 3.)

papers which covered the same ground as his Columbia paper but went into somewhat greater detail.[14] Lilienfeld commented on these papers also.[15]

The next publication was by Dushman, in the *General Electric Review*, and dealt with high-power rectifiers.[16] The tubes described were high-voltage rectifiers (Kenotrons) exhausted to a pressure of 5×10^{-7} millimeters of mercury (0.0005 micron). Tubes which operated at voltages up to 100,000 volts with space currents up to 100 milliamperes were described.

On April 7, 1915, Langmuir presented to the Institute of Radio Engineers his famous paper on "The Pure Electron Discharge and Its Applications in Radio Telegraphy and Telephony."[17] In this he gave the theoretical equations for the maximum space current between parallel plates and for cylindrical structures. These equations became known, albeit somewhat incorrectly, as "Langmuir's 3/2 power law." He gave diagrams of the structures used in two of the types discussed, both of which had wire elements. He also disclosed that Dushman had succeeded in making Kenotrons for operation at 180,000 volts with a current of 250 milliamperes (Figs. 8-12 and 8-13).

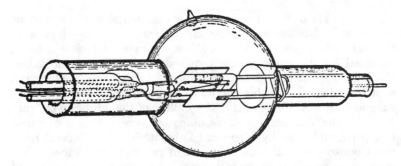

Fig. 8-13. Langmuir's drawing of large Pliotron. (Reproduced from *Proc. I.R.E.*, 1915, 3.)

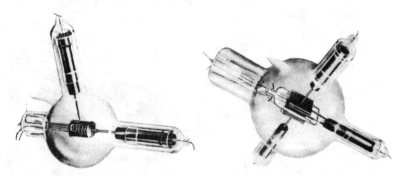

Fig. 8-14. Hull's Dynatron. (Reproduced from Proc. I.R.E., 1918, 6.)

Fig. 8-15. Hull's Pliodynatron.
(Reproduced from Proc. I.R.E.,
1918, 6.)

Meantime Dr. Albert W. Hull of the General Electric Research
Laboratory had also been working on a pure electron discharge
device. This first came to light when he presented a paper on October 30, 1915, before the American Physical Society in New York.[18]
His work was somewhat unorthodox. The title of his paper was
"Negative Resistance." He had succeeded in getting a negative-
resistance characteristic in the anode circuit of a three-electrode
discharge tube by operating it with a positive voltage on the grid
higher than the anode voltage; that is, he found a region of operation where increasing the anode voltage caused a decrease rather
than an increase in the anode current. Hull continued to work on
this device, a triode, which he called the Dynatron. He described it
in a paper sent to the I.R.E. in January 1917.[19] In the same paper
he also described his Pliodynatron, a four-electrode tube. Figs. 8-14
and 8-15 reproduced from Hull's paper show the Dynatron and Pliodynatron, respectively. This paper is probably the first to describe
a four-electrode tube.

During World War I extensive developmental work was done
in the field of radiocommunication. Apparatus developed prior to
the war rapidly became obsolete. New equipment which was being
designed for the armed forces required the use of vacuum tubes.
For such applications large quantities of tubes were needed, and
a uniform interchangeable product was an absolute necessity. We
have already noted that over half a million of these tubes were supplied by the Western Electric Company, some by the De Forest
Company, and some by Moorhead Laboratories. The General Electric Company was also called upon to produce such tubes. They
were in an excellent position to do this because of the research of
Langmuir and his associates and the company's long experience in
incandescent lamp manufacture. They supplied over 200,000 tubes

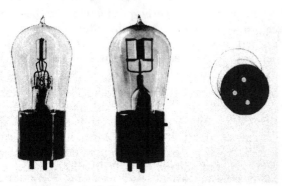

Fig. 8-16. Kenotron TB1 tube.

to the armed services, most of them in 1918. The majority were
manufactured at the Nela Park plant of the National Lamp Works
of the company at Cleveland, Ohio.

The bulk of the GE tubes supplied to the armed forces can be
divided into five classifications: (1) Kenotron TB1, (2) Type G
Pliotron, (3) Type T low-power oscillator, (4) Type U—the 50
watter, (5) Type P—250-watt tube.

The Kenotron was designated by the Signal Corps as the TB1.
Approximately 4500 of these were delivered to the Signal Corps.
This Kenotron was utilized to regulate the output voltage of the
wind-driven generators used to furnish power to aircraft radio
equipment. Because of the vibration encountered in service, they
had to be of extremely rugged construction. Fig. 8-16 shows three
views of one of these tubes which had a three-contact base; Fig.
8-17 shows a generator with the tube in place. The bulb was about
1¾ inches maximum diameter and extended upward from the base

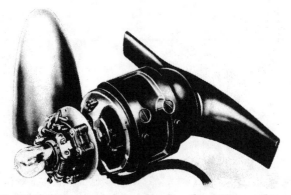

Fig. 8-17. Wind-driven generator, showing the TB1 regulator tube
in mounting.

about 2½ inches. In the early production the base was of the Shaw-standard type, but later a fabricated sheet-metal shell with a ceramic insert was used. The filament was tungsten wire 3.15 mils in diameter, with a total length of about 2½ inches and was helical in form. The inside diameter of the helix was 0.145 inch and the pitch of the winding was 14 turns per inch. The anode was a molybdenum cylinder 5 mils thick, $\%_{32}$ inch in diameter, and $\%$ inch long. The anode voltage varied under operating conditions but had a maximum value of about 250 volts. Maximum anode current was about 125 milliamperes. The filament operated at 1.45 amperes and the maximum filament voltage was 10.75 volts.

The Type G Pliotron was used by both the Navy and the Signal Corps as detector, amplifier, and local oscillator for heterodyne reception. It was originally made for the Navy under the designation CG-886. It had a Navy standard three-pin base of composition material and is shown in Fig. 8-18. Somewhat later, at the request of the Signal Corps, this same tube was equipped with a four-pin base and designated as the Signal Corps VT-11. The Navy soon adopted the four-pin base tube and assigned to it the number CG-890. This tube (Fig. 8-19) had a tungsten filament 3.25 mils in diameter and approximately 1 inch long, wound as a helix with an inside diameter of 0.065 inch and pitch of 22 turns per inch. The grid is also helical, of 3.9-mil tungsten wire, 0.120-inch inside diameter, and a pitch of 20 turns per inch. The anode is cup-shaped of 5-mil nickel, about ¼ inch in diameter and $\%_{16}$ inch high. The normal filament current was 1.1 amperes at a voltage of 3.3–3.9 volts. The anode voltage ranged from 18 to 44 volts and the anode current from a few tenths to 1 milliampere. The filament voltage was chosen so that it could be operated from a two-cell lead storage battery without a rheostat.

Fig. 8-18. Type G Pliotron with three-point composition base, designated CG-886 by U.S. Navy.

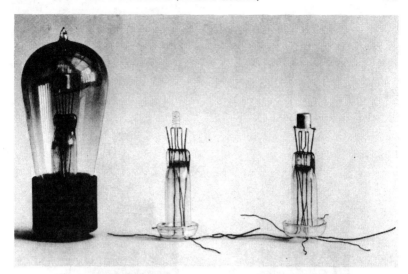

Fig. 8-19. Type G Pliotron (VT-11, early CG-890). Left: completed tube. Center: with bulb removed. Right: with bulb and anode removed.

About 110,000 of these tubes were delivered to the Signal Corps early in 1918.

The construction of this tube was later changed to use a cylindrical anode instead of the cup-shaped one; this also resulted in an improvement in the operating characteristics of the tube. The improved tube (Fig. 8-20) was designated VT-13 by the Signal Corps, while the Navy continued to use the former designation CG-890. The VT-13 had a 3.25-mil tungsten filament about 1 inch long, mounted in the form of an inverted V. The grid was of 7-mil tungsten wire wound in a helix, about 0.55 inch long on a mandrel 0.155 inch in diameter, with a pitch of 20 turns per inch. The anode was of 5-mil sheet nickel about ¼ inch in diameter and ½ inch long. About 3800 CG-890 tubes of both types were supplied to the Navy. A total of about 1100 of the VT-13 type were delivered to the armed forces.

The Type T Pliotron was used as a low-power oscillator for small radiotelegraph and telephone sets chiefly by the Navy on submarine chasers and in aircraft transmitters. The Type T was first designated VT-12 by the Signal Corps (Fig. 8-21). This designation was used only a short time before changes were made in the filament design to increase the life of the tube. The revised design was designated VT-14 by the Signal Corps and CG-1162 by the Navy. The VT-14 is shown in Fig. 8-22. The bulb was similar to that of the TB1. The filament was a helix of 4.05-mil tungsten wire wound with an

Fig. 8-20. The VT-13, or later Type CG-890 tube.

Fig. 8-21. Type T Pliotron; Signal Corps VT-12.

outside diameter of 0.130 inch and a pitch of 10 turns per inch. The length of the grid wire was about 3⅜ inches, making a helix about ¹¹⁄₃₂ inch long. The anode was a cylinder of molybdenum 5 mils thick with an inside diameter of ⁹⁄₃₂ inch and was ⅝ inch long. The filament normally took 1.75 amperes at 7.5 volts. The normal anode voltage was about 350 volts with a space current of 40 milliamperes. The power output as an oscillator was about 5 watts. It is interesting to note that many of these tubes were used as Barkhausen oscillators in the early days of amateur activity at ultrahigh frequencies after the tubes appeared on the salvage market.

The Type U Pliotron was the first of the General Electric "50 watters" and the prototype of the RCA UV203. It was designated CG-1144 by the Navy and VT-18 by the Signal Corps and is shown in Fig. 8-23. The bulb was cylindrical, about 2 inches in diameter and 6 inches long. The filament was of 10.1-mil tungsten wire and about 3⅞ inches long. It was helical in shape, ⅛-inch inside diameter with a pitch of 20 turns per inch. The filament was inside a helical grid and supported by a molybdenum rod passing up the axis of the helix. The helical grid was of 5-mil molybdenum wire, with an inside diameter of ²⁄₁₀ inch; pitch was 20 turns per inch,

Fig. 8-22. Type T Pliotron (VT-14 or CG-1162). Left: complete tube. Center: with bulb removed. Right: with bulb and anode removed.

the length of the helix being ⅞ inch. The grid was supported by two molybdenum wires electrically welded along the sides of the helix. The anode was of 5-mil sheet molybdenum bent so as to form a cylinder ½ inch in diameter and 1⅛ inches long, having four fins extending radially outward ⅜ inch. These fins were intended to increase the radiating surface of the anode thereby increasing anode dissipation. The tube operated with a filament current of 6.5 amperes at 10 volts. The normal anode voltage was 750–1000 volts and anode current 150–200 milliamperes. As a high-frequency oscillator this tube had an output of about 50 watts. Although developed later than the other Pliotrons, this tube was used to a considerable extent by the Navy in seaplane transmitters. About 1200 were supplied to the Navy and 200 to the Signal Corps.

Type P was the largest of these Pliotrons. An early sample was shown in Fig. 8-11. Structural modifications were made, end fittings were added, and it became known to the Navy as the CG-916 and to the Signal Corps as the VT-10. Fig. 8-24 is an early version of the modified tube, and a later model with an improved plate structure is shown in Fig. 8-25. The bulb of this tube was about 5 inches

Fig. 8-23. Type U Pliotron
(CG-1144, VT-18).

Fig. 8-24. Early version of CG-916, or VT-10, with end fittings.

in diameter; the filament was W shaped of 7.0-mil tungsten wire with a total length of 6¼ inches. It operated with a current of 3.6 amperes at 13–19 volts. Surrounding the filament was a grid of 3-mil tungsten wire wound on a rectangular form of tungsten or molybdenum. The pitch of the grid was 30 turns per inch, and it was spaced 0.090 inch from the filament. The anode in the earlier tubes consisted of two rectangular plates of 25-mil tungsten, $2 \times 2\frac{3}{8}$ inches, set parallel and ½ inch apart. The anode voltage was normally 1500–2000 volts and the anode current 150–200 milliamperes. As an oscillator it delivered about 250 watts and was used by the Navy in seaplanes and flying boats.

Fig. 8-25. Later version of CG-916, or VT-10, with different anode structure.

Fig. 8-26. Small Kenotron with medium screw base and conical anode. Used about 1919.

There were other tubes made in limited quantities during this period. One of these was the VT-16, which was being worked on at the time of the Armistice in 1918. This differed only in minor details from the VT-14. Two other interesting tubes made by General Electric are shown in Figs. 8-26 and 8-27. The one in Fig. 8-26 is a small Kenotron made in the Research Laboratory in 1916 or 1917. The cone-shaped molybdenum anode fits closely around the filament in order to minimize the voltage drop in the tube. It was used to provide high-voltage direct current for some of the early experiments which led to broadcast transmitters. The Pliotron shown in Fig. 8-27 might almost be considered the first "variable-mu" tube. The filament and grid were coaxial helices. The anode was conical; hence the ratio of grid-filament distance to anode-filament distance varied along the axis of the tube. This tube was made about 1919, but only on an experimental basis.

To tube collectors who wish to identify the place of manufacture of specimens of these tubes, the following may be of interest. Many of these earlier GE tubes have handwritten markings on the press, such as H6, G25, or the like. Those with the letter H were made at the Harrison Lamp Works, and those marked G were made at Nela Park. The numbers following the letter designation are lot numbers. Also tubes made during 1917 and 1918 at Harrison were, in general, characterized by lead wires through the glass press that were made of one-piece Dumet, while the Nela Park tubes had leads welded in three sections with only the part actually embedded in the glass being Dumet. The Harrison tubes often had a getter which discolored the glass to some extent.

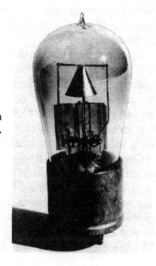

Fig. 8-27. Small receiving-type Pliotron with helical grid and filament and conical anode. Made about 1919.

Fig. 8-28. The Western Electric VT-1 (left) and General Electric VT-11 (right). These tubes were interchangeable in use.

A comparison of the tubes made by General Electric and Western Electric for the U.S. armed forces during World War I is rather startling. Tubes made by these two companies for identical purposes were totally different in appearance, materials, and structure, yet were interchangeable in use. The General Electric VT-11 and Western Electric VT-1 are shown in Fig. 8-28. No more forcible illustration could be made to bring out the point that each company brought to the field of development of the vacuum tube its own particular background of experience gained through trying to solve its own problems in other fields. The scientists and engineers of these two companies who sought answers to the same questions had, because of experience, taken different paths to arrive at a common destination.

At the time this work was done, the General Electric Company was primarily interested in the production of electrical apparatus and equipment for industrial applications. The work which they did on vacuum tubes for radiocommunication was undertaken at the urgent request of the U.S. Government. In later years General Electric developed high-vacuum tubes for industrial applications, but such tubes are not within the scope of this volume.

General Electric developed one type of gas-filled tube during the period 1910–1920 which later found application in conjunction with high-vacuum tubes used in radio receivers. This was the hot-cathode argon-filled tube known as the Tungar rectifier. The development of the Tungar rectifier tube was a byproduct of the work being done in the early part of this decade on gas-filled incandescent lamps. This project engaged the attention of Langmuir early in 1912, when

Fig. 8-29. Group of Tungar bulbs.

he had two assistants on this work, G. S. Meikle and G. M. J. Mackay. In June 1913 Meikle was assigned to work on mercury vapor lamps. These lamps used heavy coiled tungsten-wire filaments which operated at low voltages. The bulb volume was relatively small, so that it would operate at a high temperature, and a small quantity of mercury was placed in the bulb. These experimental bulbs were operated from a 110-volt dc circuit through a series resistance. The operating temperature of the filament was very high, so there were frequent filament burnouts. Sometimes an arc was formed at the break. In June 1913 Meikle recorded the fact that in one case the arc current was 30 amperes. Meikle also obtained such arcs even with an ac source of power. In July 1913 he sketched a tube with a hot filament and separate anode plus liquid mercury for use as a power rectifier. Other work interfered, and not until November 1913 did he get back to working part time on his rectifier tube. During March 1914 he first mentioned the use of argon gas in place of mercury vapor. The argon-filled tube proved to be a very satisfactory rectifier and was finally adopted for commercial use.

A market survey showed that there would be a demand for rectifier equipment using such tubes with ratings of 5–10 amperes. With the advent of the self-starter in automobiles and the increased use of storage batteries, garages were finding it necessary to install charging equipment. This equipment could be produced at a moderate cost by using this simple rectifier, fed from the usual 110-volt ac line. In January 1915 battery-charging equipment was installed

Fig. 8-30. Tungar rectifiers for home use. Left: for automobile batteries. Right: for radio A batteries.

in a garage in Schenectady by the General Electric Company for a field test. It was found to be quite satisfactory.

Meikle described this work in a paper published in the *General Electric Review*.[20] The word Tungar is not used in this article but must have been adopted soon after, for an article appeared in the *Electrical Review* (Chicago) under the title "The Tungar Rectifier" in December 1916.[21] In July 1917 6-ampere and 2-ampere rectifier units were put into production. Tungar bulbs were usually half-wave rectifiers, but some of the full-wave type were also made.

With the widespread use of 6-volt storage batteries for supplying filament power for broadcast receivers of the early 1920s there arose a demand for low-powered rectifiers which could be connected to the battery whenever the set was not in use to keep it charged. These rectifiers were known as "trickle chargers" and used Tungar bulbs with a rating of 0.5–0.6 ampere. Fig. 8-29 shows a group of Tungar bulbs, and Fig. 8-30 shows Tungar rectifiers for charging automobile batteries and radio A batteries.

REFERENCES

1. Helen A. Fessenden, *Fessenden—Builder of Tomorrows* (New York: Coward-McCann, 1940), p. 149.
2. *Report of the Federal Trade Commission on the Radio Industry* (Washington, D.C.: GPO, 1924), pp. 14–16.
3. E. F. W. Alexanderson, "Alternator for 100,000 Cycles," *Trans. A.I.E.E.*, 1909, *28*(2):399–415. E. F. W. Alexanderson, "Magnetic Properties of Iron at Frequencies up to 200,000 Cycles," *Trans. A.I.E.E.*, 1911, *30*(3):2433–2454.

4. E. F. W. Alexanderson, "A Magnetic Amplifier for Radio Telephone," *Proc. I.R.E.*, 1916, *4*:101–129.

5. For a preliminary note on this work, see O. W. Richardson, *Proc. Cambridge Phil. Soc.*, 1902, *11*:296. O. W. Richardson, "The Electrical Conductivity Imparted to a Vacuum by Hot Conductors," *Phil. Trans.*, 1903, *201*A: 497–549; an abstract of this paper will be found in *Proc. Roy. Soc.*, 1903, *71*:415–418. O. W. Richardson and F. C. Brown, "The Kinetic Energy of the Negative Electrons Emitted by Hot Bodies," *Phil. Mag.*, 1908, 6th Ser. *16*:353–376. O. W. Richardson, "Thermionics," *Phil. Mag.*, 1909, 6th Ser. *17*:813–833.

6. Langmuir's Laboratory Notebook No. 451, pp. 144–145.

7. White's Laboratory Notebook No. 452, p. 32.

8. *Transcript of Record, General Electric Company vs. De Forest Radio Company*, U.S. Circuit Court of Appeals, 3rd District, Nos. 3799, 3800, 3801, March term, 1928. Testimony of Irving Langmuir, Vol. 2, p. 1195.

9. W. D. Coolidge, "A Powerful Roentgen-Ray Tube with a Pure Electron Discharge," *Phys. Rev.*, Dec. 1913, 2nd Ser. *2*:403–439.

10. Irving Langmuir, "The Effect of Space Charge and Residual Gases on Thermionic Currents in High Vacuum," *Phys. Rev.*, 1913, 2nd Ser. *2*:450–486. See also *Sci. Abstr.*, A, 1914, No. 725.

11. C. D. Child, "Discharge from Hot CaO," *Phys. Rev.*, May 1911, *32*:492–511.

12. J. E. Lilienfeld, "Die Elektrizitätsleitung im extremen Vacuum," *Ann. Phys.*, 1910, 4th Ser. *32*:673–738.

13. J. E. Lilienfeld, "A Reply to Mr. Irving Langmuir's Paper 'The Effect of Space Charge and Residual Gases on Thermionic Currents in High Vacuum,'" *Phys. Rev.*, May 1914, 2nd Ser. *3*:364–365.

14. Irving Langmuir, "Thermionenströme im hohen Vakuum. I. Wirkung der Raumladung," *Phys. Z.*, Apr. 1914, *15*:348–353. Irving Langmuir, "Thermionenströme im hohen Vakuum. II. Die Elektronenemission seitens des Wolfram und die Wirkung von Gasresten," *Phys. Z.*, May 1914, *15*:516–526.

15. J. E. Lilienfeld, "Thermionenströme im hohen Vakuum. Entegegnung auf die Arbeit von I. Langmuir," *Phys. Z.*, Aug. 1914, *15*:744–746.

16. Saul Dushman, "A New Device for Rectifying High Tension Alternating Currents—The Kenotron," *G.E. Rev.*, Mar. 1915, *18*:156–167. See also *Phys. Rev.* Apr. 1915, 2nd Ser. *5*:339.

17. Irving Langmuir, "The Pure Electron Discharge and Its Applications in Radio Telegraphy and Telephony," *Proc. I.R.E.*, Sept. 1915, *3*:261–293. See also *G.E. Rev.*, May 1915, *18*:327–339; *Electrician*, May 21, 1915, *75*: 240–245; *Lumière Élect.*, 1915, *29*:241–245, 272–279; *Sci. Abstr.*, B, 1915, No. 614.

18. Albert W. Hull, "Negative Resistance," *Phys. Rev.*, Jan. 1916, 2nd Ser. *7*:141–143. Abstract of paper presented at a meeting of the American Physical Society in New York, Oct. 30, 1915.

19. Albert W. Hull, "The Dynatron—A Vacuum Tube Possessing Negative Resistance," *Proc. I.R.E.*, Feb. 1918, *6*:5–35. See also *Sci. Abstr.*, B, 1916, No. 300; *Ann. Post. Télégr. Téléph.*, 1918, *7*:269–280: *Wireless Age*, May 1918, p. 634.

20. G. S. Meikle, "The Hot-Cathode Argon-Filled Rectifier," *G.E. Rev.*, Apr. 1916, *19*:297–304. Abstracts appeared in *J. Franklin Inst.*, 1916, *181*:704–705; *Elect. Rev. Lond.*, Apr. 28, 1916, *78*:472–473; *Lumière Élect.*, May 27, 1916, *33*:209–211.

21. "The Tungar Rectifier," *Elect. Rev. Chicago*, Dec. 23, 1916, *69*:1109–1110. See also *Sci. Abstr.*, B, 1917, No. 110.

Chapter 9

The Entrance of Industrial
Laboratories and Military Demands,
1910-1920: *United States (Independents)*

Between 1910 and 1920 a number of factors tended to promote the use of the Audion. The ranks of the amateur fraternity of radio operators were swelled by hundreds of teenage boys (and older ones as well) whose interest in this fascinating avocation had been aroused by newspaper tales of rescues at sea. The dramatic significance of the part played by wireless in the rescue of survivors of the ill-fated S.S. *Republic*, 1909 (Jack Binns with his C.Q.D.), and the S.S. *Titanic*, 1912, excited widespread interest in this newest branch of the communications art.

Once the desire was stimulated, the ingenuity of young America was called upon to provide the necessary equipment for the home station. The family rolling pin disappeared from the kitchen. Bereft of its handles and disguised by the application of a layer of wire, it reappeared as a tuning coil. Bits of wire, scraps of metal, odd chunks of wood—all provided grist for the mill which turned out the wireless set of the eager constructor. Practically all the components except the headset could be made in the cellar workshop. They usually were. It was the era of "haywire" and home-brewed apparatus even for elaborate stations.

By 1915 the Audion was much better known than it had been a few years earlier, particularly on the West Coast. It was also promoted by the opening of the transcontinental telephone service with its attendant publicity, and the Panama-Pacific Exposition in San Francisco with its displays of wireless equipment. It became the ambition of every embryonic Marconi to possess an Audion. Now that the problem of obtaining and maintaining the requisite storage battery had been diminished by the advent of electric starting and lighting systems for automotive use (Chapter 8), the chief problem confronting the amateur was simply acquiring the Audion.

The only legitimate source of supply was the Radio Telephone Company, a de Forest company which was in deep financial trouble. The company policy was to sell not Audions but Audion Detectors. The detector consisted of an Audion, a filament rheostat, a plate battery, a condenser which was used in series with the grid, a tap switch for varying the plate potential, and an off-on switch for the filament. This assembly was all contained in a beautiful little mahogany box, no doubt a good buy for $18, but disaster for the amateur who had all the accessory parts and needed only the Audion. Replacement Audions could be purchased for the detectors, but the initial cost was too much. Amateurs who lived in or near New York City could buy Audions over the counter from H. W. McCandless Company, but such sales were in the minority (see Table 7-1). When the Radio Telephone Company was finally forced into bankruptcy (Chapter 7), the legitimate source for the mail-order buyer dried up completely.

But other sources of supply began to appear. The sale of vacuum detectors by "independent" manufacturers came into being. The term "independent" in this chapter is a euphemism for predator. Some of these manufacturers made an attempt to circumvent the de Forest triode patent by using an external control electrode; others frankly infringed. As may be appreciated, authoritative information on these early independent products is difficult to obtain. Manufacture and sale in some cases were sub rosa, and the only method of tracing the evolution of this equipment is through the study of advertisements offering these products for sale. The ads frequently made extravagant claims. Very little reliable information on their characteristics is available.

The earliest of the independents was Wallace & Company, 59 Fifth Avenue, New York City. This firm consisted of two men, Paul E. Wallace and Merrit D. Mosher. Wallace, who lived near Rochester, New York, was an amateur radio enthusiast accustomed to using an Audion. In January 1910 he made a trip to New York and visited the de Forest station in the Metropolitan Tower. While in New York he met O. T. Louis of the O. T. Louis Company, 59 Fifth Avenue. In February 1911 Wallace rented space from Louis and went into business, at first known as the O. T. Louis Wireless Department. In the summer of 1911 Mosher began working for Wallace, and in January 1912 he joined Wallace as a partner, this

Fig. 9-1. The Wallace valve receiver, 1912.

new combination becoming Wallace & Company, at the same address. Mosher left in July 1912, and Wallace continued in business until December 1913.

The Wallace Valve Detector, which had a tubular Audion, was first made and marketed in the summer of 1911. It was advertised on page 843 of *Modern Electrics* in November 1912. Wallace used the spherical Audion in the Wallace Valve Receiver shown in Fig. 9-1. A crystal detector was also installed in this set for emergency use. All Audions were purchased from McCandless. Apparently business was good, because McCandless' records show sales of 280 Audions to Wallace in 1912 and 1913. Prior to 1912 no records were made of the names of individual customers. It is worthy of note that the peak of the Wallace sales was 1912–1913, at a time when the only legitimate source—the Radio Telephone Company—was moribund. E. H. Armstrong dubbed Wallace "the original tube bootlegger."

The next independent tube to appear was also the last to disappear. This was the AudioTron and was the most widely sold and used of all the independent tubes. The name was registered as a trademark by Elmer T. Cunningham on March 30, 1916, and he claimed its use since October 22, 1915.[1] (The terms Audio Tron, AudioTron, and Audiotron were used interchangeably without significance until after the war, when Audiotron was generally adopted.) The AudioTron was made in Oakland, California, and according to Cunningham was first sold in August 1915. It was first advertised in November 1915.[2] This advertisement is reproduced as Fig. 9-2. Note that the price quoted was $7.50. The AudioTron was a double-ended cylindrical unbased tube. In manufacture it

The Audio TRON Bulb

Price $7.50

The cost of a complete Audion" type receiving set has prevented many experimenters from enjoying the advantages of this improved detector.

This Is Your Opportunity

to purchase the latest and most sensitive type bulb only and thereby greatly increase your receiving radius.

Special Offer

All orders mailed prior to November 30, 1915, will be shipped postpaid and insured at the Special Introductory Price,

$6.50 each

including full set of wiring diagrams and directions.

You are protected by an unusually strong guaranty—such is our confidence in the efficiency and reliability of the Audio Tron Detector.

Guaranty:—All Audio Tron bulbs are alike and all extra sensitive. Every bulb is carefully tested and all non-sensitive bulbs discarded. This "one type" Audio Tron is used as a detector, amplifier or ultra-audibility detector. So great is its sensitiveness that a two-step Audio Tron amplifier has a greater efficiency than any other three-step amplifier. Every Audio Tron is guaranteed to have a life of 1,000 hours and to arrive in perfect condition.

DEALERS: A splendid opportunity to increase your sales. Write for trade propositions

Audio TRON Sales Co., **315 Lick Building, SAN FRANCISCO**

Fig. 9-2. First announcement of the AudioTron. (Reproduced from *Pop. Sci. Mon.*, Nov., 1915.)

varied in diameter from ⅝ to ¾ inch and in length from 3 to 3½ inches. It comprised a double tungsten filament, a coarse spiral grid of copper wire, and a cylindrical aluminum anode. The anode fitted rather closely the inside diameter of the tubular glass bulb. Fig. 9-3

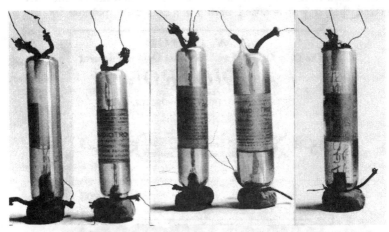

Fig. 9-3. AudioTrons. The second from the left has a label printed in black ink; the third and fourth from the left have labels in red ink. The one on the extreme right has markings etched on the glass bulb.

shows several of these tubes. A paper label was applied to the outside of the tube; sometimes it was printed in red and sometimes in black. The information also varied from time to time. The Audio-Tron sprang into instant popularity, especially among those who could not afford the luxury of "all de Forest" equipment.

Steps were soon taken by de Forest to prosecute the AudioTron Sales Company for infringement. In February 1916 the De Forest Company filed suit against them and others. The AudioTron Sales Company posted bond on August 14, 1916, and continued the manufacture and sale of their product.[3] The suit was later settled out of court. When de Forest attempted to meet this competition by bringing out the single-filament Type T Audion in April 1916 at a price of $5.50, Cunningham promptly cut the price of his double-filament AudioTron to $5.25.[4] (See Fig. 9-4.)

The advertisement of the AudioTron in at least one publication was discontinued,[5] but for a short time thereafter another tube of the two-element type with an external control element, called the Amplitron, was advertised in its place[6] (Fig. 9-5). This continued for only two or three months, and subsequent ads of the AudioTron Sales Company were confined to the suggestion that readers write for information.

With the war proclamation issued on April 6, 1917, the dismantling and sealing of amateur equipment was ordered, and the market for this apparatus disappeared. After the war, advertisements for the AudioTron reappeared, first in June 1919 in one magazine[7] and later in others.[8] These later ads describe the AudioTron as having a thoriated-tungsten filament with a life of 2000 hours, and further stated that it was licensed under the de Forest patents for use as

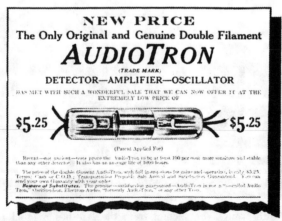

Fig. 9-4. Advertisement giving price reduction on the AudioTron to meet de Forest competition. (Reproduced from *Elect. Exper.*, Aug. 1916.)

Fig. 9-5. Advertisement for the Amplitron. (Reproduced from *Elect. Exper.*, Dec. 1916.)

an amplifier in radio communication. It was described as "The Original Vacuum Tube Amplifier" and was priced at $6. Almost simultaneously the Marconi VT, made by Moorhead Laboratories, appeared for sale, and the ads for these tubes carried a warning that the AudioTron was not licensed under the Fleming patents.[9] These advertisements continued to appear for some time.

The Radio Corporation of America was formed in October 1919. They promptly initiated litigation for patent infringements, instituting suit against Cunningham in the U.S. District Court for the Northern District of California, charging infringement of the Fleming and de Forest patents. Cunningham must have been in a unique bargaining situation. His position was set forth in an article entitled "The Vacuum Tube Situation" in the February 1920 issue of the *Pacific Radio News*.[10] The case was settled out of court by two extraordinary agreements signed the same day.

The first agreement, dated June 15, 1920, gave to Cunningham for a period of ninety days a personal, nontransferable license under the Fleming and de Forest patents to manufacture and sell tubes of not more than 5 watts output.[11] Total production and sale was limited to 5000 tubes. These tubes were to be permanently marked "For amateur and experimental use only" and were to be made by Cunningham "doing business under the name and style of Audio-Tron Manufacturing Company" (formerly AudioTron Sales Company). When Cunningham began to market the tubes made under this agreement he used paper labels, was then censured by RCA for breach of license conditions, and changed to etched markings on the glass tube. The tube is shown at the extreme right in Fig. 9-3.

The second noteworthy agreement between RCA and Cunningham, also dated June 15, 1920, provided that when the ninety-day license had expired the AudioTron Manufacturing Company would discontinue making vacuum tubes.[12] RCA agreed to supply Cunningham with tubes until the expiration of the de Forest Patent No. 879,532 on February 18, 1925. The tubes were to be of Cunningham's choice, selected from samples submitted by RCA, and supplied in cartons ready for delivery. Both tubes and cartons were to bear trade names and marks designated by Cunningham. There was to be no indication of the name of the manufacturer or of RCA. These tubes were to be sold to Cunningham at a discount 20 percent below the lowest net price quoted to any other customer and were to be marketed as AudioTrons.

According to the agreement, Cunningham was to receive not less than 25,000 tubes in each of the four periods of twelve consecutive months covered. He was to receive not more than 50,000 tubes in the first period, 60,000 during the second, 70,000 during the third, 80,000 during the fourth, and not less than 10,000 nor more than 20,000 during the remaining months of the contract. Deliveries were to begin September 15, 1920, or as soon thereafter as possible.

As a result of the first agreement, subsequent advertisements of the AudioTron Manufacturing Company stated that the AudioTron was now free from all restrictions.[13] The first agreement was modified on September 13, 1920, and the license period was extended to October 15, 1920. The ads continued until November 1920. With the December 1920 ads the effects of the second agreement began to appear.[14] A full-page ad in *Radio News* offered for sale the "Audiotron Detector Type C-300" with a four-pin base at $5 and a "Type C-301 High Vacuum Navy Type Amplifier" at $6.50. A similar ad in *QST* had one word changed: Audion was substituted for Audiotron. The rest of the copy was identical. The tubes were "Guaranteed by E. T. Cunningham, trading as the Audiotron Manufacturing Co."

The next advertisement, in January 1921, refers to Cunningham Audiotron Tubes in the heading, but Cunningham Tubes in the body of the ad.[15] The following month the outstanding feature was the Cunningham Detector Tube Type C-300, and the word Audiotron appears only in the name Audiotron Manufacturing Company.[16] The March issue emphasized Cunningham Power Tubes C-302 and C-303 and stated that these were the product of General Electric Company research.[17] From then on the prominence given to the name Audiotron Manufacturing Company lessened. In December 1922 the word Audiotron was dropped from the ads.[18] The business was renamed E. T. Cunningham, Inc. and continued to advertise as such for years, until one line was inserted under the name: "A Subsidiary of Radio Corporation of America." That was in April 1931.

The success of the original AudioTron in 1915 seems to have served as encouragement to other independents. Shortly after the

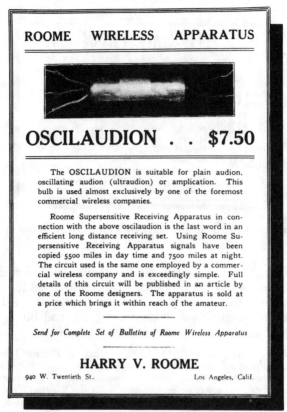

Fig. 9-6. Announcement of the Roome Oscilaudion. (Reproduced from
Wireless Age, Jan. 1916.)

introduction of the AudioTron another tube came on the market,
enough like the AudioTron to have been cast in the same mold.
This was the Roome Oscilaudion, first advertised in January 1916
(Fig. 9-6), by Harry V. Roome of Los Angeles.[19] Roome had been
advertising wireless apparatus for some time, but this was the first
mention of vacuum tubes. Two months later, in March 1916, the
ad appeared again, this time for the Oscilaudion Bulb and Cabinet.[20]
No further ads appeared until July 1916, when the Thermo Tron
was advertised by "The Thermo Tron Company" from the same
address as that of Harry V. Roome.[21] This advertisement, reproduced in Fig. 9-7, is very ambiguously worded, making no mention
of any restrictions as to use. Since the ad was printed in a wireless
magazine, the reader might be justified in assuming that the Thermo
Tron was intended for wireless use. However, when the purchaser
received the device, it was accompanied by a descriptive leaflet

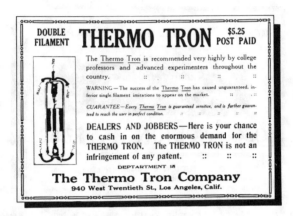

Fig. 9-7. Announcement of the Thermo Tron. (Reproduced from *Elect. Exper.*, July 1916.)

which contained no ambiguous statements whatever, but described it as an "experimental hot cathode apparatus designed for the study of the Edison effect, thermionic currents, pure electron discharge, passage of electricity through electrons [sic], and other scientific phenomena." It also carried the following warning:

> It is distinctly understood by the purchaser that the Thermo Tron is sold for the purpose of scientific study to be used for the circuits shown in this bulletin. If the Thermo Tron is used for commercial work in wireless telegraphy as a detector, amplifier or oscillator, or if the Thermo Tron is used for commercial work in an Armstrong Circuit, or if the Thermo Tron is used in any way as an infringement of any patent, the Thermo Tron Company assumes no liability whatever.

"Thermo Tron" proved to be a new name for the Oscilaudion which Roome had sold as a wireless detector.

Now about the time Roome began to advertise vacuum tubes, early 1916, de Forest first initiated legal action against Cunningham *et al.* Possibly this alarmed Roome and explains his change of tube names. Perhaps this also accounts for the interrupted sequence of his ads. Roome must have kept well posted on the legal developments, for the success of Cunningham's Audiotron Sales Company in staving off an injunction and continuing business as usual is reflected in Roome's next ads in August 1916.[22] He boldly advertised the Supersensitive Oscilaudion as a detector, amplifier, and oscillator. With the Supersensitive Oscilaudion the purchaser received a leaflet of the same size and typography as that supplied with the Thermo Tron, using the same cut for an illustration, but setting forth the virtues of the Supersensitive Oscilaudion as a wireless device.

No records are available to show how many tubes this independent sold, but I do have the record of one investigator who was trying to smoke out infringers. He interviewed Roome in March 1916 and was quite surprised to find that Harry V. was a high-school boy in Los Angeles. He was getting his tubes from a San Francisco manufacturer who would sell him only a limited number. It is probable that the manufacturer eventually cut off his supply, for there were no further ads by Roome after August 1916.

Otis B. Moorhead of San Francisco was the only independent other than Cunningham to achieve at least pseudo-legitimate status. The first of the Moorhead tubes was known as the Electron Relay, a name that was also applied to many of the later tubes which he made. It was the work of Moorhead and Ralph Hyde, and it first appeared in April 1915.[23] Moorhead, who had been for some time an ardent radio fan, had worked in the de Forest booth at the Panama-Pacific Exposition selling Audions. They sold so well that he was impressed with the possibility of reaping a financial harvest by manufacturing them. Hyde, an expert glass blower, had formerly been superintendent of the Oakland Mazda Lamp Works of the General Electric Company and had been repairing Audions as a sideline.[24] He left the employ of the General Electric Company on March 1, 1913, and worked for Cunningham for a while. Hyde joined forces with Moorhead in 1915, and they produced the original Electron Relay, but the combination later split. Hyde went back to work for Cunningham, who was bringing out the AudioTron.

The first advertisement for the Moorhead Electron Relay appeared in July 1916 and announced that "the former manufacturers of the AudioTron are now making a newer and better tube."[25] The Electron Relay was advertised for use as an amplifier, detector, or oscillator and could be obtained with either a single or double filament. The "guaranteed life" was 400 hours per filament and the price of the double filament was $5.50. The advertisement was signed "Pacific Laboratories—O. B. Moorhead, Manager."

The Electron Relay, so featured, was similar in appearance to the AudioTron, having a straight axial filament of tungsten, a coarse spiral grid of copper wire, and an anode of aluminum sheet bent into the form of an almost closed cylinder. It was claimed that these materials were chosen because of their relative position in the electrochemical series "and also because we could procure these materials with ease on the Pacific Coast."[26] It can scarcely be doubted that the latter of the two reasons was the controlling one. It was claimed that the Electron Relay was a "high vacuum" device, being exhausted to a vacuum better than 0.04 millimeters of mercury.

The avowed purpose of the production of this new tube was "to bring the sacred Audion to terms." What it first succeeded in doing was having the makers prosecuted for infringement of the Audion patents. Together with the AudioTron, however, it furnished a source of tubes for the lean-pursed amateur, and it was instrumental in de Forest's putting on the market a similar tube, sold without the necessity of purchasing the "little red box" for $18.

Although the author has found no ads prior to July 1916 offering the Electron Relay for sale, it apparently had been sold to a considerable extent in 1915, because on February 15, 1916, the De Forest Radio Telephone and Telegraph Company filed complaint against Moorhead and Hyde alleging infringement of seven de Forest patents. Several Pacific Coast radio "experts" submitted affidavits in reply to the complaint in support of Moorhead and Hyde. This action was brought at the same time as that of de Forest against Cunningham.

The action was begun by requesting an injunction against Moorhead, Cunningham, Hyde, and others. Justice Van Fleet heard the arguments in the premliminary injunction and ruled that since the validity of the de Forest patents had not yet been passed on, an injunction would not be granted, but an indemnity bond would be required from the defendants until the question of validity had been settled.[27] Apparently Moorhead posted the required bond, because in July 1916—when the advantage of operating sub rosa had been eliminated by the court proceedings—the first Electron Relay advertisement appeared.[28] The next ad, in August 1916, announced that there had been a "25% improvement" in the Electron Relay during the preceding month and claimed that the new tube was the "Most Sensitive Wave Responsive Device Known."[29] This was signed by the "Pacific Research Laboratories Sales Dept.," Moorhead's name not being mentioned.

Possibly Moorhead did not feel too secure in the matter of patent infringement, because his next ad was for a totally different tube.[30] This new Moorhead tube (Fig. 9-8) had a single filament, was guaranteed for 1200 hours, and claimed a much superior performance. The photograph of this tube shows a radical change in construction. The anode has been changed from an aluminum cylinder to an aluminum disk and the filament from straight to hairpin shaped. The grid has been removed from the tube and replaced by an external control electrode. This control electrode was a perforated band of brass clamped around the outside of the tube opposite the filament-anode space. The filament was intended for operation at 4 volts and the anode voltage was stated to be 10–35 volts.

The manufacturer of the tube was indicated by the marking "Moorhead—Patent Pending" in raised letters on the disk anode. It is noteworthy that this was the first of the independent tubes to bear the name of the manufacturer indelibly impressed thereon,

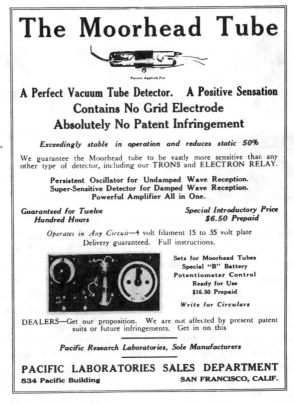
Fig. 9-8. Moorhead tube with external control element.
(Reproduced from *Elect. Exper.*, Sept., 1916.)

and to be supplied with definite information as to normal operating
parameters. This tube, with the external control electrode, continued to be advertised for the remainder of that year.

Apparently this new construction was not as great an advance
over the former one as was claimed. In the January 1917 advertisement, the Electron Relay came again to the fore, and the Moorhead tube received less attention.[31] The Electron Relay had again
undergone improvement "within the last thirty days," and the "improved tube" could be identified by the letters ER steel-stamped
on the cylindrical anode. This tube is shown in Fig. 9-9. It may
well be that the decision handed down in an Eastern District Court
holding the de Forest Audion patent to be subservient to the Fleming diode patent had something to do with the reappearance of
the Electron Relay.

Fig. 9-9. Electron Relay with ER stamping
on the plate.

In February 1917 the Pacific Research Laboratories were taken over by the Moorhead Laboratories, Inc.,[32] although advertisements for the Moorhead tubes continued to be signed by the Pacific Laboratories Sales Dept. In this month Moorhead sent to the Institute of Radio Engineers a paper entitled "The Manufacture of Vacuum Detectors," in which he described the processes used in the manufacture of the Electron Relay.[33] In the light of present-day knowledge of the factors affecting the electrical characteristics of vacuum tubes, one statement contained in that paper is of interest: "The spacing between the elements is not very critical in this type of device, but it is best to wind the grid to a large enough diameter so that it will strike the plate rather than the filament when the tube is jarred."[34]

During World War I Moorhead made tubes for the U.S. armed forces and for the British government.[35] Those made for Great Britain were high-vacuum tubes patterned after the British R-type valve. These tubes could be operated at 6-volts and 0.84-ampere filament. At 400 volts on the anode this tube was required to dissipate 15 watts for 3 minutes. When operated at 4-volts filament it had a life of 800 hours. In the earlier models, one of which is shown in Fig. 9-10, the axis of the element assembly was vertical and the tube had a spherical envelope. Later they were made with a cylindrical envelope and horizontal element assembly. When equipped with a European base, it was designated by the British as a VT-32 (Fig. 9-11). When equipped with the American four-pin base and vertical element assembly, it was used by the U.S. Navy under the designation SE-1444. Some of the SE-1444 tubes had clear glass, others were reddish in color, which may have been caused by the use of phosphorus as a getter. The SE-1444 was usually operated at 4.5-volts and 0.65-ampere filament. It had a mutual conductance

Fig. 9-10. Moorhead version of British Type R in spherical bulb and with Shaw standard base.

of 180 micromhos, an amplification factor of 9, and anode impedance of 50,000 ohms. It was generally operated at 40-volts anode and −1.3-volts grid.

After the war there was a stalemate in tube manufacture because of the decision in the de Forest suit. The first step toward breaking this deadlock was taken on November 30, 1918, when the Marconi Company granted to the Moorhead Laboratories a nonexclusive license to make and sell apparatus under the Fleming patent to amateurs and to any government. By the terms of this agreement the Moorhead Laboratories admitted past infringements, paid dam-

Fig. 9-11. Moorhead British VT-32 tube.

ages, and agreed to pay royalties to the Marconi Company on future tube production.

With this agreement in hand Moorhead approached de Forest with a view of obtaining a license under the de Forest Audion patents. The end results of these negotiations—carried on over a considerable period—were a series of agreements between Marconi Company, de Forest, Moorhead Laboratories, and Otis B. Moorhead as an individual.[36] These agreements were first signed on April 30, 1919, and later modified on June 6, 1919. They provided that Otis B. Moorhead and the Moorhead Laboratories were to enter the employ of de Forest, who engaged them to make tubes for him under his personal license. Then de Forest was to sell all such tubes to the Marconi Company, which agreed to act as distributing agent and sell tubes back to the De Forest Radio Telephone and Telegraph Company and to other purchasers. These tubes were to be sold to the public for amateur and experimental use in radio reception and amplification. These agreements were to run until February 18, 1925 —the date of expiration of the de Forest triode patent—but could be cancelled by any of the parties on six months notice.

The tubes to be made under this partnership were of several types described as follows:

Type A—The Type A tube was a hard amplifier tube, the same as that which had been supplied to the U.S. Navy under the designation SE-1444. It had a cylindrical bulb and a standard Navy four-pin base of the Shaw type. The filament was of drawn tungsten wire, approximately 2.4 mils in diameter and about $1\frac{3}{16}$ inch long. The grid was an eleven-turn spiral of nickel wire with an internal diameter of 0.167 inch. The plate was of sheet nickel about 9 mils thick, rolled into a cylinder about ¾ inch in diameter. The tube operated with a filament current of 0.4 ampere at 4 to 5 volts and with an anode voltage of 60–90 volts.

Type B—The Type B was similar to the Type A, but it had a low vacuum for operation as a detector with 18–40 volts on the anode.

Type C—The Type C tube was also similar to the Type A, except that the grid was constructed of 22 turns of molybdenum wire with a pitch of 0.30 inch, instead of nickel. It was to operate at anode voltages of 80–500 volts.

Type D—The Type D tube was the unbased Electron Relay previously made by Moorhead.

Type E—The Type E tube was the British standard Type R. It was similar to the Type A, but it had a spherical bulb and a British standard four-pin base.

Type F—The Type F tube was similar to Type E, but with a low vacuum like the Type B.

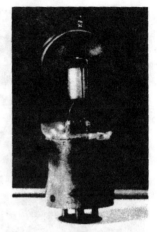

Fig. 9-12. Marconi VT with "Class II" rubber-stamped on base.

Type G—The type G was similar to the Type C but it had a spherical bulb and a British standard four-pin base. This tube was the same as the British standard Type B tube.

The tubes advertised and sold by the American Marconi Company in 1919 and early 1920 as the Marconi VT[37] were Type A and Type B tubes as described above. In the advertisements the Type A was designated as Marconi VT-Class II (Fig. 9-12), and the Type B as the Marconi VT-Class I. A life of 1500 hours was claimed for these tubes.

The first consignment of tubes (about 25,000) delivered to the Marconi Company bore no Marconi or de Forest markings. They were stamped on the glass bulb with the legend "Moorhead Audion —San Francisco," and the class was rubber-stamped on the base. The cartons in which they were packed were marked to restrict their use to amateur and experimental purposes. About 8000 of these tubes were sold. The remainder had the words "Patented Nov. 7, 1905. Sold only for amateur and experimental use" stamped on the bulb before being sold. Subsequently both the Marconi and de Forest patent numbers and the restrictive legend were steel-stamped on the brass base (Figs. 9-13 and 9-14).

The contracts between Moorhead Laboratories, De Forest Radio Telephone and Telegraph Company, and Marconi Company were cancelled on January 30, 1920, by the Marconi Company, the cancellation being effective, in accordance with the six-months clause, on July 30, 1920. This was probably done in anticipation of the necessary de Forest license being acquired by the Marconi Company's successor, the Radio Corporation of America. This actually occurred on July 1, 1920, a month before the cancellation of the Moorhead *et al.* agreement. A contributing factor to this cancella-

Fig. 9-13. Group of Electron Relays showing de Forest and Marconi
steel-stamped base markings.

tion was the Marconi Company's difficulty in getting from Moorhead Laboratories enough satisfactory tubes to meet their demand.
All shipments contained a large percentage of defective tubes, in
some cases as high as 75 percent. These rejects had to be weeded
out before deliveries could be made to customers.

While this complicated business union was being dissolved early
in 1920, the Moorhead Laboratories underwent a reorganization,
and de Forest became associated with them.[38] Henry B. Shaw of

Fig. 9-14. The Marconi VT with steel-
stamped base markings.

the Shaw Insulator Company became president and O. B. Moorhead became chief engineer. Two distributing companies were formed—the Pacific Radio Supplies Company to handle business in the West, and the Atlantic Radio Supplies Company to be the East Coast distributor. While all the bargaining was taking place, de Forest had established a new firm of his own—Lee de Forest, Inc.—with a factory at 451 Third Street in San Francisco.[39] The purpose of this new company was to manufacture radiotelephone transmitting equipment exclusively. It was also to carry for Pacific Coast dealers a full line of the radio receiving apparatus made at de Forest's High Bridge plant in New York.

Instant catalogues and ads flooded the market from all these enterprises. Articles appeared in wireless magazines describing each new business, naming the officers, and extolling the merits of the equipment being marketed. Some ads offered items "manufactured under the Fleming and de Forest patents." The formation, rise, and fall of all of these companies revolved about de Forest's personal license to make and sell Audions. His claims to rights under this license were stretched constantly to fit the machinations of each new endeavor. To get a comprehensive picture of the panorama of chaos in the wireless industry in 1920 it would be essential to explore the intricate, private maneuvers of Lee de Forest.

One of the Marconi Company–RCA lawyers tried to do this—to attempt to untangle the inextricable legal knots in the confusion of 1920. After systematically studying ads in the *Radio Amateur News*, April 1920, the *Pacific Radio News*, May 1920, an article in the same *Pacific Radio News* entitled "New De Forest Company to Manufacture Radio Telephones in San Francisco," another ad in the June 1920 *Pacific Radio News* which also carried an article "Big Radio Deal Closed" covering the reorganization of the Moorhead Laboratories, this lawyer analyzed the catalogues, tried to separate fact from fiction in the labyrinthine affair, and reported succinctly to his boss as follows (in part):

> The apparatus apparently infringes the Fleming and de Forest patents, and the receiving apparatus may infringe the Marconi tuning patent. Either Lee De Forest, Inc. is infringing both the Fleming and de Forest Audion patents, or De Forest Radio Telephone & Telegraph Co. is violating the injunction of the Fleming patent, or Lee De Forest, Inc. is infringing both the Fleming and de Forest Audion patents and the De Forest Radio Telephone & Telegraph Co. is violating the Fleming injunction.[40]

He recommended further study and preparation of suits against de Forest "on all patents owned by G.E. Co., Western Electric Co., Radio and A.T.&T. and proceed for contempt if possible."

While this was going on, back on the West Coast the first tubes offered for sale by the new Moorhead organization were the unbased Electron Relay shown in Fig. 9-9 and the Moorhead VT Amplifier-Oscillator.[41] The unbased Electron Relay was soon replaced by another soft tube, the Moorhead Electron Relay.[42] Early designs of this tube had a cylindrical anode and spiral grid. Both grid and anode were supported only from the press, the upper ends being left free. This construction was extremely sensitive to mechanical disturbances, since the grid and anode were free to vibrate under mechanical impulses. Tubes of this construction are shown in Fig. 9-13. They differ in the surfaces of the anodes: the one at the left has a glossy, almost polished, surface; the one at the right has a dull, possibly oxidized, finish. It will be noted also that the diameter of the anode was somewhat greater than that used in the amplifier tube.

A later version of the Moorhead Electron Relay, in which steps had been taken to reduce the sensitivity to mechanical disturbances, is shown in the center in Fig. 9-13. In this tube the anode structure has been extended at the top to permit the addition of a mica spacer through which an elongation of the upper end of the grid projects. This positions the grid more accurately with respect to the anode and provides it with mechanical restraint. The bottom of the anode has been extended in the form of two tabs bent to squeeze against the sides of the press, thus providing stiffening of the element assembly to some extent. The other tube which was offered for sale at this time, the Moorhead VT Amplifier-Oscillator, was the same as the Marconi VT-Class II (Fig. 9-14).

Beginning with the August 1920 advertisement, these tubes were designated the A-P Electron Relay and the A-P Amplifier-Oscillator, respectively, and were represented as being manufactured under the de Forest and Fleming patents.[43] This was misrepresentation, since the license under the Fleming patent had been cancelled as of July 30, 1920. The December advertisements announce the sale of the A-P Transmitting Tube (see Fig. 9-15),[44] which was the same tube as had been made for the Marconi Company under the designation Type C. This was also claimed to be licensed under the de Forest and Fleming patents, but it was sold for use only in apparatus manufactured by the De Forest Radio Telephone and Telegraph Company.

The A-P Rectifier (Fig. 9-16) was offered for sale in May and June 1921.[45] This tube was the same as the singer-type Audion then being offered for sale by de Forest (Fig. 9-17),[46] except that the grid was omitted. Fig. 9-18 shows a later version of the A-P Rectifier. No restrictions were placed on the use of this tube, because as a power-frequency rectifier it did not infringe either the Fleming or de Forest patents.

The Moorhead Series D Electron Relay (Fig. 9-19) was made

-and here it is!

Licensed for use only in apparatus manufactured by the De Forest Radio Tel. & Tel. Co.

You have hoped for it. You have looked for it. You have asked for it. And here it is—a transmitting tube for telephone and telegraph C-W transmission, built right up to British and to French Government specifications. Capacity about 12.5 watts, and any number may be used in parallel—four, make telephone conversation possible over 25 miles, telegraph signals over 50 miles.

The plate of this transmitting tube is nickel, a special molybdenum grid is provided and the high vacuum permits operation on plate potentials of five hundred volts without breakdown.

By connecting the grid and plate together, the tube may be used as a rectifier for obtaining from an alternating current supply the high plate potential necessary for the generator tube.

Adopted by the De Forest Radio Tel. & Tel. Co. as the standard transmitting tube in all De Forest sets of less than ¼ k.w. capacity. Licensed under the De Forest Audion and Fleming patents. Other patents applied for and pending.

Equipped with the SHAW standard four-prong base. PRICE $7.50. Order from your dealer.

Atlantic Radio Supplies Co.
8 Kirk Place, Newark, N. J.

Pacific Radio Supplies Co.
638 Mission St., San Francisco, Cal.

Distributors for Moorhead Laboratories, Inc., Manufacturers of

The A-P Transmitting Tube

Fig. 9-15. Announcement of A-P transmitting tube. (Reproduced from *Radio News*, Dec. 1920.)

-for experimental cw

NEW A-P RECTIFIER TUBE MAKES EXPENSIVE HIGH VOLTAGE D-C GENERATOR UNNECESSARY.

A wonder—this newest A-P tube—a Rectifier that can be used effectively with *any* transmitter tube of *any* voltage up to 750, and *without* a high voltage D-C generator. Step up your 110 V A-C lighting supply to 350, 500, or 750 volts, using a small transformer, and two of the new A-P tubes do everything else, rectifying both halves of the cycle so the plates of your transmitter tubes get all the high potential direct current necessary —*without the use of a high voltage D-C generator.*

The **A-P Rectifier** has a 75 milliampere carrying capacity, which is sufficient to operate five A-P Transmitting Tubes in parallel. For high power CW transmission, use additional **A-P Rectifier** Tubes in parallel.

A-P Rectifiers used in Type O A-C De Forest Radiophones, equipped with the SHAW standard condensite four-prong base, and licensed under SHAW patents. **Price $9.75.** Order from your dealer, or direct from either address below.

Diagram of Connections Furnished Free With Each Tube

And for the best book on Radio, ask your dealer for "Elements of Radiotelegraphy," by Lieut. Ellery W. Stone, U. S. N., or order direct from—

Price $9.75 each. Order from your dealer. or write direct to either address in this ad.

ATLANTIC RADIO SUPPLIES CO.
8 KIRK PLACE, NEWARK, NEW JERSEY

PACIFIC RADIO SUPPLIES CO.
638 MISSION ST., SAN FRANCISCO, CAL.

Distributors for Moorhead Laboratories, Inc.,

Fig. 9-16. Announcement of A-P rectifier tube. (Reproduced from *Radio News*, May, 1921.)

Fig. 9-17. The de Forest singer-
type tube, 1920.

Fig. 9-18. Later version of A-P
Rectifier tube.

about this time, and de Forest may have been responsible for it. Its design is reminiscent of the early de Forest CF-185 (see Chapter 8). As far as the author can determine, the Series D Electron Relay was never advertised.

Shortly after the Moorhead advertisements began to appear in August 1920, the Radio Corporation of America, successor to the Marconi Company, claimed that these tubes were not licensed under the de Forest and Fleming patents. The word *imbroglio* best describes the condition of the finances of the Moorhead Laboratories at this time. The business was being managed by a stockholders-creditors committee of which Henry S. Shaw was the chairman. Large quantities of raw materials were on hand, and the indebtedness was heavy. In order that the situation might be cleared up to the benefit of all concerned, negotiations were entered into and RCA granted to the Moorhead Laboratories a license, dated January 25, 1921, to manufacture and sell a limited number of tubes under the Fleming and de Forest patents. The license was delivered to the Moorhead Laboratories in July 1921. Subsequent ads stated correctly that the tubes were being made and sold under license from RCA. Moorhead Laboratories continued producing tubes until the middle of 1922, when the assigned number was completed, after which they consented to an injunction restraining them from further infringement.

Fig. 9-19. Moorhead Series D
Electron Relay.

This did not restrain Moorhead. He proceeded to organize another company, the Universal Radio Improvement Company, of Alameda, California. His associates in this venture were I. W. Hubbard, F. I. Hubbard, and George K. Ford, all of San Francisco, and R. Whitney of Seattle. An article in a newspaper dated January 22, 1923, announced that the Universal Radio Improvement Company had opened a giant plant in Alameda and was manufacturing an average of 1000 tubes per day, tubes which were patented by Moorhead and infringed no other patents.[47]

The death of Moorhead on January 31, 1923, as the result of an accident did not deter his associates from continuing the project. They were making the A-P Solenoid Tube (Fig. 9-20), which did not infringe either the Fleming patent (expired 1922) or the de Forest grid patent. The instruction sheet which accompanied this tube is shown in Fig. 9-21. It may be considered the final product of the Moorhead enterprise.

In Chapter 7 it was noted that at the beginning of the Marconi–de Forest litigation over the Fleming diode and the de Forest Audion patents in 1914, the American Marconi Company confessed judgment as to having infringed the triode patent and was enjoined from further infringement. The Marconi Company apparently was not too sure of its chances of winning the suit and was motivated to develop an alternative to the de Forest triode. This work was done under the guidance of Roy A. Weagant, who was at that time

Fig. 9-20. Moorhead A-P solenoid tube.

chief engineer of American Marconi. Weagant started with a tube of the Fleming valve type and endeavored to exert control over the electron stream by means of a third electrode which was placed on the outside surface of the glass tube and hence might not be considered to be within the scope of the de Forest triode patent. On April 2, 1915, he applied for a patent on such a tube. This was issued on December 31, 1918, as U.S. Patent No. 1,289,981 (see Fig. 9-22).

Development of the Weagant tube was carried on to the point where a commercial form of the receiving type had been developed and multistage amplifiers had been designed. Experimental work was being done on transmitting tubes also. However, the Weagant tubes never went into commercial production, probably because the decision in the Marconi–de Forest litigation was favorable to the Marconi Company. Fig. 9-23 shows a variety of experimental Weagant tubes, Fig. 9-24 is the proposed commercial form, and Fig. 9-25 is a photograph of a ten-stage amplifier equipped with this commercial form. Fig. 9-26 shows an experimental Weagant transmitting tube. The circuits to be used with the receiving tube were similar to those used with conventional triodes and were published in a magazine article about the time Weagant's patent was issued.[48]

There were a few other prewar independent tubes on which a little information is available. The Tigerman Detecto-Amplifier was

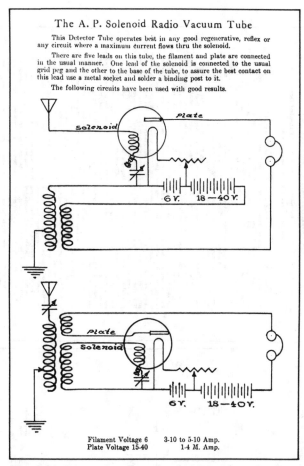

The A. P. Solenoid Radio Vacuum Tube

This Detector Tube operates best in any good regenerative, reflex or any circuit where a maximum current flows thru the solenoid.

There are five leads on this tube, the filament and plate are connected in the usual manner. One lead of the solenoid is connected to the usual grid peg and the other to the base of the tube, to assure the best contact on this lead use a metal socket and solder a binding post to it.

The following circuits have been used with good results.

| Filament Voltage 6 | 3-10 to 5-10 Amp. |
| Plate Voltage 15-40 | 1-4 M. Amp. |

Fig. 9-21. Instruction sheet for the A-P solenoid tube.

advertised in 1916 by the National Electrical Manufacturing Company of Chicago.[49] Fig. 9-27 is a reproduction of the ad which announced this tube. It was double ended with two sets of filament-anode electrodes, one at each end. The control electrodes were applied on the outside of the glass tube and were simple metallic bands clamped around the outside of the tube. The tube was about 5 inches long and had a candelabra base at each end. In effect it was two Weagant tubes in one bulb. Apparently it was not sold to any great extent. An advertisement in April 1917 offered the tubes for sale "while they last" at $5 each.[50]

The Electron Audio, similar in construction to the AudioTron, was first advertised in June 1916 by the Electron Manufacturing

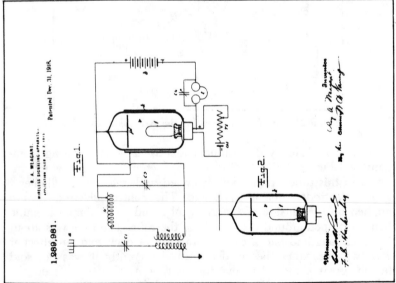

UNITED STATES PATENT OFFICE.

ROY A. WEAGANT OF ROSELLE, NEW JERSEY, ASSIGNOR TO MARCONI WIRELESS TELEGRAPH CO. OF AMERICA OF NEW YORK N. Y. A CORPORATION OF NEW JERSEY

WIRELESS SIGNALING APPARATUS

1,289,981.   Specification of Letters Patent.   Patented Dec. 31, 1918.

Application filed April 7, 1915.

Fig. 9-22. Weagant U.S. Patent No. 1,289,981.

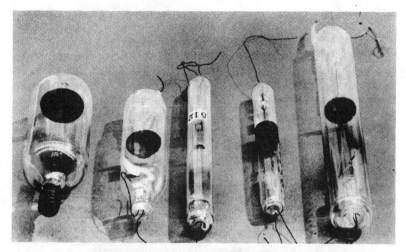

Fig. 9-23. Group of experimental Weagant valves.

Company with the claim that it was "Formerly the Audio Tron."
The next advertisement, reproduced in Fig. 9-28,[51] showed a tube
of the same construction as the AudioTron. The Electron Audio,
however, could be obtained with either a single or double filament.
This quickly lapsed into obscurity, although it was regularly supplied by at least one manufacturer as part of a radio receiver. In this
receiver the tube was inserted into an "auto-transformer" which
was claimed to be of "remarkable importance to our undamped wave
apparatus since the magnetic field oscillations are absolutely in
synchronism and consequently stimulate the periodical electron
discharge from the filament and the ionization of the gas within
the bulb by the heat of the filament."[52]

Two other tubes of the same type were advertised by the Radio
Apparatus Company of Pottstown, Pennsylvania, the Type 36 Electron Detector[53] and the Liberty Valve.[54] The Liberty Valve is shown
in Fig. 9-29. Since this company also advertised the AudioTron at

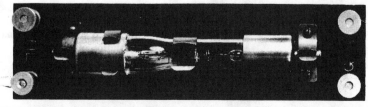

Fig. 9-24. Proposed commercial form of Weagant receiving valve in
mounting. Note that the external control electrode is part of the mounting, not of the tube.

Fig. 9-25. Ten-stage Weagant amplifier with the front open to
show the valves.

about the same time,[55] it may well be that the Liberty Valve was
the AudioTron with a different label.

The Oscillotron was advertised briefly by the G. & M. Specialty
Company of Cleveland, Ohio, just after amateur activity was resumed following the end of World War I.[56] Two other tubes were
made during these years, the Bartley, which was sold about 1919,[57]

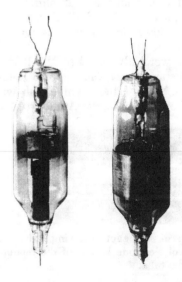

Fig. 9-26. Developmental Weagant
transmitting valve. The view at the
right has the external control electrode removed to show the internal
construction of the valve.

Fig. 9-27. Advertisement announcing Tigerman Detecto-Amplifier.
(Reproduced from *Elect. Exper.*, Dec., 1916.)

and the Corcoran, which is alleged to have been made at Lynn,
Massachusetts, about 1914 or 1915.

In August 1919 the Wireless Specialty Apparatus Company of
Boston began advertising "Triode (Trade Mark)" tubes and other
apparatus. These advertisements continued only a short time, while
protests were heard questioning the ethics of registering as a trademark a word which was becoming a generic term. The W.S.A. Co.
replied that they had used the word as a trademark beginning on
August 28, 1919, and had applied for its registration as a trademark
before it had come into use as a generic term in this country. The
first suggestion for the use of "triode" as a name for any three-
electrode vacuum tube was made by Dr. W. H. Eccles of England
in the London *Electrician* for April 18, 1919.[58] The W.S.A. Co. cancelled its registration as a trademark in April 1922.

This chapter would not be complete without mention of Hugo
Gernsback and his Electro Audion, which he sold through his Elec-

Fig. 9-28. Advertisement showing Electron Audio tube.
(Reproduced from *Wireless Age*, June, 1916.)

tro Importing Company. Founded in 1904, this company was one of the chief sources of wireless equipment. Gernsback introduced the Electro Audion in 1911, listing it in his Catalogue No. 10 which was sent to customers in May of that year. He advertised this tube

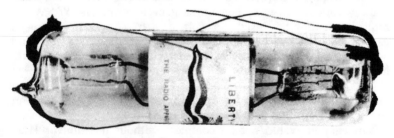

Fig. 9-29. The Liberty valve.

THE "ELECTRO" AUDION.

After long deliberation, we herewith present the best audion manufactured to-day in the United States. Of all the detectors in use, none present the accumulation of advantages offered by the Audion, the "Electro" model being designed from the result of long and extended experiments. While the crystal types of detector present many advantages, they have the one great defect of not holding their adjustment, especially on receiving from a nearby station. The Audion, not only ranks as the highest in sensitiveness, but possesses that much sought for characteristic, stability of adjustment. Loud signals do not affect the adjustment, and, on the

8200

contrary, seem to improve the sensitiveness. When receiving from loud or nearby stations, the light will be noticed to flicker in the bulb, and the signals can thus be read without the use of a telephone receiver, this feature being found in no other detector. Signals received by the Audion are extremely loud, and most stations in the vicinity of the receiving station may be heard with the phones three feet or more. from the operator's ears.

The "Electro" Audion, consists of a vacuum bulb containing two filaments of tantalum, connected in series with a lead taken off at the connecting point of both filaments. One filament is used at a time, and at the exhausting of one filament, the other may be resorted to. This gives double the life which is obtainable from other audions. The filaments are used on 4 volts, which may be obtained from storage battery or dry cells. The bulb also contains a wire which is bent in a zig-zag form, and called the "grid." A small sheet of nickel foil is also contained in the bulb. It is behind the grid and the metal foil. Under normal conditions, the current from a 30-35 volt battery connected with a telephone receiver has great difficulty in passing through the heated vacuum space. However, on reception of the wave trains, the current from the battery passes through the vacuum and produces an audible sound in the receiver. The audion is the most suited detector for wireless telephony. owing to its faithful reproduction of every wave. The 30-35 volts required for the telephone receiver circuit, may be obtained from 6 to 7 flash light batteries. Inasmuch as the current used is practically zero, a set of these cells will last for a long time. The apparatus is connected as shown in the diagram. In this instance a loose-coupler is shown, giving the set the maximum degree of selectivity. The rotary rheostat is also used, our No. 5000, which is very suitable for this purpose in regulating the filament current. The flash lamp dry cells are also shown connected in series with the telephone receiver.

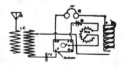

IMPORTANT: On account of the great manufacturing difficulties we do not guarantee the Audion. We carefully test each and every one but cannot take back Audions under any circumstances whatever.

Full instructions given with each instrument. Size of base, 5¼ in. x 3¼ in. Height, 3½ in.

No. 8200. The "Electro" Audion as described and illustrated .$5.00

Fig. 9-30. Electro Audion advertisement, from Gernsback's Electro Importing Company catalogue of 1913.

in his magazine *Modern Electrics* in July 1911 (p. 272). It was sold during the period 1911–1913.

Electro Importing Company never claimed to be the makers of the Electro Audion. The tubes were purchased from McCandless and were of the double-filament spherical type. Gernsback did not sell these tubes in their ordinary cartons. The tube was mounted in a socket which was molded in a neat little block of insulating material. There were five binding posts for the five leads, and this attractive assembly with the tube cost $5. The records of Gernsback's company were destroyed by fire in 1917, but the McCandless records are still extant. They show sales to the Electro Importing Company of 104 Audion bulbs in 1911, 156 in 1912, and 211 in 1913, a total of 481 bulbs in this three-year period. Fig. 9-30 shows one catalogue entry which offered the Electro Audion for sale. Those who have had experience with Audions of that vintage will be interested in the claims made.

REFERENCES

1. *U.S. Pat. Off. Gaz.*, Apr. 25, 1916, 225:1434.
2. *Pop. Sci. Mon.*, Nov. 1915, 87:120.
3. "The Vacuum Detector Patent Situation," *Pacif. Radio News*, May 1917, 1:203–206.
4. *Wireless Age*, Jul. 1916, 3:1; *Elect. Exper.*, Aug. 1916, 4:282.
5. Hugo M. Gernsback, "De Forest vs. Electrical Experimenter," *Elect. Exper.*, Mar. 1917, 4:808–809.
6. *Elect. Exper.*, Dec. 1916, 4:607.
7. *QST*, June 1919, 2:29.
8. *Radio Amat. News*, Feb. 1920, 1:441; *QST*, Apr. 1920, 3:81.
9. *Radio Amat. News*, Feb. 1920, 1:396; *Pacif. Radio News*, Feb. 1920, 1, inside back cover; *QST*, Mar. 1920, 3:78.
10. E. T. Cunningham, "The Vacuum Tube Situation," *Pacif. Radio News*, Feb. 1920, 1:267–269.
11. *Report of the Federal Trade Commission on the Radio Industry* (Washington, D.C.: GPO, 1924), Exhibit Z-1.
12. *Ibid.*, Exhibit Z-3.
13. *Radio News*, Jul. 1920, 2, inside front cover; *QST*, Sept. 1920, 4:61.
14. *Radio News*, Dec. 1920, 2, inside front cover; *QST*, Dec. 1920, 4:101.
15. *Radio News*, Jan. 1921, 2, inside front cover; *QST*, Jan. 1921, 4:93.
16. *Radio News*, Feb. 1921, 2, inside front cover.
17. *Radio News*, Mar. 1921, 2, inside front cover.
18. *Radio News*, Dec. 1922, 4, inside front cover.
19. *Wireless Age*, Jan. 1916, 3:1.
20. *Wireless Age*, Mar. 1916, 3:1.
21. *Wireless Age*, Jul. 1916, 3:111; *QST*, Jul. 1916, 1:188; *Elect. Exper.*, Jul. 1916, 4:193.
22. *QST*, Aug. 1916, 1, advertising section; *Elect. Exper.*, Aug. 1916, 4:283.
23. O. B. Moorhead, "The Electron Relay," *Pacif. Radio News*, Apr. 1917, 1:166–167,183.
24. *Transcript of Record, General Electric Co. vs. DeForest Radio Company*, U.S. Circuit Court of Appeals, 3rd District, Nos. 3799, 3800, 3801, March term, 1928. Deposition of Ralph Hyde, Vol. 2, pp. 993–1005.
25. Advertisement of Pacific Research Laboratories, *Elect. Exper.*, Jul. 1916, 4:193; *QST*, Jul. 1916, 1, advertising section.
26. See Moorhead, "The Electron Relay," p. 166.
27. O. B. Moorhead, "Dr. Lee de Forest vs. O. B. Moorhead," *Pacif. Radio News*, Jan. 1917, 1:10–13.
28. See No. 25 above.

29. Advertisement of Pacific Laboratories Sales Department, *Elect. Exper.*, Aug. 1916, *4*:273.
30. Advertisement of Pacific Laboratories Sales Department, *Elect. Exper.*, Sept. 1916, *4*:355; *QST*, Sept. 1916, *1*, advertising section.
31. Advertisement of Pacific Laboratories Sales Department, *Pacif. Radio News*, Jan. 1917, *1*, inside front cover for Electron Relay; *Elect. Exper.*, Mar. 1917, *4*:786, for Moorhead Tube.
32. Announcement in *Pacif. Radio News*, Feb. 1917, *1*, inside front cover.
33. O. B. Moorhead, "The Manufacture of Vacuum Detectors," *Proc. I.R.E.*, Dec. 1917, *5*:427–432.
34. *Ibid.*, p. 429.
35. O. B. Moorhead and R. C. Lange, "The Specifications and Characteristics of Moorhead Valves," *Proc. I.R.E.*, Apr. 1921, *9*:95–129.
36. "Radio Vacuum Tube Litigation Settled," *Radio Amat. News*, Aug. 1919, *1*:77.
37. "The Marconi VT—A Three-Electrode Oscillation Detector of Approved Operating Characteristics," *Wireless Age*, Aug. 1919, *6*:33–34.
38. "The Reorganization of the Moorhead Laboratories," *Pacif. Radio News*, June 1920, *1*:387–389. "Big Radio Deal Closed," *Pacif. Radio News*, June 1920, *1*:387, 389, 408.
39. "New De Forest Company to Manufacture Radio Telephones in San Francisco," *Pacif. Radio News*, May 1920, *1*:361, 362, 371.
40. From Marconi-RCA patent attorney's files now in the author's library.
41. Advertisement of Pacific Radio Supplies Company, *Pacif. Radio News*, May 1920, *1*, inside back cover.
42. Advertisement of Pacific Radio Supplies Company, *Pacif. Radio News*, June 1920, *1*, inside back cover; *Radio Amat. News*, 1920, *1*:711; *QST*, June 1920, *3*:73.
43. Advertisement of Pacific Radio Supplies Company, *Radio News*, Aug. 1920, *2*:119; *Pacif. Radio News*, Aug. 1920, *2*, front cover.
44. Advertisement of Pacific Radio Supplies Company, *Radio News*, Dec. 1920, *2*:389; *QST*, Dec. 1920, *4*:99; *Pacif. Radio News*, Dec. 1920, *2*, front cover.
45. Advertisement of Pacific Radio Supplies Company, *Radio News*, May 1921, *2*:833; *QST*, May 1921, *4*:99; *Pacif. Radio News*, May 1921, *2*, front cover.
46. See Catalogue No. 101, Lee De Forest, Inc., 451 Third St., San Francisco, p. 26.
47. "Grant [sic] Radio Plant Comes to Alameda," *San Francisco Examiner* (Alameda edition), Jan. 22, 1923. ("Grant" was a typographical error; it should have been "Giant.")
48. "The Weagant Oscillation Valve—A Striking Improvement on the Original Fleming Oscillation Valve," *Wireless Age*, Mar. 1919, *6*:24–25.
49. *Elect. Exper.*, Dec. 1916, *4*:602.
50. *Pacif. Radio News*, Apr. 1917, *1*:182.
51. *Wireless Age*, June 1916, *3*:III.
52. "Mignon Undamped Wave System," *Pacif. Radio News*, Feb. 1917, *1*:79.
53. *QST*, Apr. 1917, *2*:83.
54. *QST*, Jan. 1920, *3*:48.
55. *Wireless Age*, Jul. 1919, *6*:45.
56. *QST*, Dec. 1919, *3*:64.
57. "Fleming's Valve and Up," *Radio Craft*, Mar. 1938, *9*:582.
58. W. H. Eccles, "Nomenclature in Wireless Telegraphy," *Electrician*, Apr. 18, 1919, *82*:475; Apr. 25, 1919, *82*:500; May 2, 1919, *82*:521.

Chapter 10

The Entrance of Industrial
Laboratories and Military Demands,
1910-1920: *France*

The development of vacuum tubes in France during this period was due almost exclusively to the work done by, or under the direction and control of, the French Military Telegraphic Service. Colonel (later General) Gustav Ferrié was in charge of this work.

In 1908 de Forest went to France to make radiotelephone tests and demonstrations, and he brought with him an arc-type radiotelephone transmitter.[1] He met Colonel Ferrié, who allowed him to use the main antenna on the Eiffel Tower for some of the tests. It was at this time that Ferrié obtained his first knowledge of the Audion. Apparently it did not make a permanent impression, although in the 1909 edition of a book of which he was co-author he described the use of the triode type Audion.[2] In 1910 he published a well-documented technical study of all French and foreign accomplishments concerning transmission and reception of radioelectric waves, including the use of the Audion.[3] Fig. 10-1 is taken from that study.

Prior to this time very few vacuum tube devices had been made in France. In 1910 the Compagnie Générale des Lampes (which later became Compagnie des Lampes) made a few Fleming diodes for some laboratories, and in 1912 this same company made several triodes for the French Navy. This work was done under the direction of Auguste Petit. Fig. 10-2 is a later drawing of one of these triodes, based on the recollections of Petit.

The pressure for development of wireless communications at this

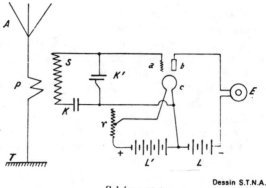

Schéma n° 1 :

Dessin S.T.N.A.

Récepteur de Forest avec lampe Audion

Fig. 10-1. Ferrié's "Schema No. 1" for the use of the Audion, from his 1910 report. (Reproduced from *Progr. Sci.*, 1968.)

time was engendered by political tension in Europe. Germany had built a tremendous navy and was openly preparing for war. Britain was matching the German navy two to one for self-defense. Wireless communication was imperative. Reports had reached Europe that American Engineers were accomplishing wonders with the Audion; A.T.&T. had put a high-vacuum, hot-cathode triode into commercial service as a telephone repeater in Philadelphia on October 18, 1913 (Chapter 6). Germany was struggling to achieve the same results by using a gaseous tube, the LRS Relay (Chapter 12). As the threat of war increased, the military powers tried

Fig. 10-2. Artist's rendition of the Audions made by the Compagnie des Lampes for the French navy in 1912.

191

desperately to acquire the most sophisticated wireless apparatus for military use. European eyes turned toward the United States. In the spring of 1914, Ferrié came to the U.S. He visited, among others, Reginald A. Fessenden, who was employed by the Submarine Signal Company. Fessenden was working on underwater sound-ranging and depth-finding projects. In this work he was using a three-stage low-frequency amplifier which utilized de Forest Audions. De Forest was manufacturing and selling such amplifiers at that time. Ferrié was so impressed with the possibilities of the equipment that his interest in the Audion was reawakened, and on his return to France he told Emile Girardeau, one of his associates, about his experience and instructed him to get one of these Audion amplifiers. Girardeau did so, and in June 1914 sent it to the Radiotélégraphie Militaire for a test[4] in accordance with Ferrié's instructions. Girardeau heard no more about it.

In 1914, when World War I broke out, there was in transit from the United States to Germany a Paul Pichon; in 1900 this same Pichon, a deserter from the French army, had emigrated to Germany. He earned his living as a professor of French and became a tutor to the children of Count von Arco, one of the founders of the Telefunken Company. Pichon became deeply interested in radiotelegraphy and began intensive study of physics and electricity. He was engaged by Telefunken as a technical representative. He advanced rapidly in the company, and in 1912, when he was chief of patent service for Telefunken, he was sent to France. He visited Ferrié and Girardeau to try to persuade the French to exchange information and cooperate with Telefunken in fighting patent infringement suits instituted by British Marconi.

In 1914 Pichon was in the United States. Having completed his assignment of gathering samples of the latest wireless equipment and information for Telefunken, he embarked on his return trip about July 25, and arrived in London on August 3, the day Germany declared war on France. Pichon went immediately to Godfrey Isaacs, the managing director of Marconi's Wireless Telegraph Company, to ask his advice. He declared he was still a Frenchman but explained that as a deserter he would inevitably be arrested if he went back to Calais now that war was declared. Isaacs advised him to go nevertheless and to enter the service of France.

Pichon went to Calais and was promptly arrested. He declared that he had brought back from America information and objects of the highest interest to Commandant Ferrié, whom he knew. The authorities telephoned Ferrié, who told them to send Pichon with all his baggage and papers to him at once. When brought before Ferrié, Pichon pulled out of his pocket a three-electrode tube (several cartons of which were in his luggage together with information on their uses and manufacture)[5] and explained in detail the triode's inherent characteristics and advantages. Ferrié quickly conscripted Pichon, assigned him to the military radio service, and took definitive action on the Audion. He sent the sample Audion to Lyon, where the prominent physicists Max Abraham, Marcel Brillouin, and L. Bloch were working. He instructed them to analyze the elements of the tube and prepare to reproduce it in quantities in the shops of the incandescent lamp makers E.C.&A. Grammont in Lyon. Grammont's trademark was FOTOS.

Another industry at Lyon was also converted to meet military needs. Établissements Bocuze had employees skilled at wire drawing of precious metals used in gauze known as *lamé* produced by the Lyonnaise silk-weaving industry. These employees were to make the wire and other metal parts for the tubes. Jacques Biguet, former chief of manufacture for Bocuze, had entered military service but was recalled and assigned to this project. Also assigned were Captain Michel Peri, electrical engineer, Marius Latour, M. René Jouaust, C. Gutton, Gabriel Pelletier, and others.

When Ferrié first told Girardeau about Pichon's return and the Audion he brought, Girardeau reminded him of the three-stage amplifier which he had obtained at Ferrié's request before the war broke out. He had sent it to the Radiotélégraphie Militaire for testing as directed, but had received no report. Ferrié exclaimed, "How could I have forgotten it!" A search was instituted: the amplifier was found in the basement of a storehouse.[6]

The first samples made by Grammont had cylindrical elements mounted vertically without insulating braces. They were not satisfactory. The loss due to displacement of electrodes and to breakage of bulbs was high. The lamp-making machinery available was not adapted to the production of double-ended bulbs. It was necessary to redesign the tube to make it stronger mechanically and to make it single ended. The idea of using a cylindrical coaxial construction mounted horizontally came perhaps from Abraham and Jouaust,[7] but it was also claimed by both Peri and Biguet. After conferences among these four, the idea was eventually reduced to practice by Peri and Biguet, who applied for a patent on this construction on October 23, 1915.[8] The base used on these tubes is shown in Fig. 10-3 and first appeared in the drawing of the Peri and Biguet patent, but no claim was made for its invention.

The demand for tubes rocketed over night. Grammont could not produce them fast enough, so another incandescent lamp manufacturer, the Compagnie Générale des Lampes, at Ivry, was pressed into service. The tubes they made were designated TM Métal (Fig. 10-4), whereas those produced by Grammont were designated TM Fotos (Fig. 10-5). There are slight differences in the structures,

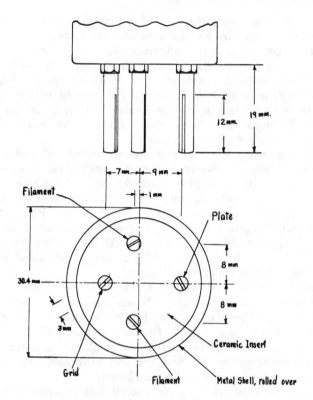

Fig. 10-3. Base used on TM tubes and subsequently on most European four-pin tubes.

sufficient to enable the tube collector to identify the manufacturer of any sample of the TM tube even if all the etched markings have been obliterated. The differences are shown in Table 10-1.[9]

In both tubes the filament is about 2.1 centimeters long and is of tungsten. The glass envelope is about 5.5 centimeters in diameter. When used as an amplifier the TM tube was operated at 4-volts filament, the current being 0.6 to 0.8 ampere, and 40 to 120 volts on the anode. When used as an oscillator in a transmitter, the filament was operated at 5–6 volts with the anode voltages as high as 500 volts.

To operate at high voltages it was necessary to have very high vacuums, and this required the removal of the gases occluded in the metal elements and the glass of the bulb. Georges Beauvais introduced the practice of bringing out both ends of the grid so that it might be heated to white heat for use as a cathode during the pumping process.[10] The application of a high positive voltage on

Table 10-1. Differences in TM Tubes

	Lampe Fotos	Lampe Métal
Plate		
length	1.5 cm	1.5 cm
diameter	1.0 cm	1.0 cm
material	nickel	nickel
Grid		
length	1.6 cm	1.9 cm
diameter	0.45 cm	0.40 cm
number of turns	12	11
pitch	0.13 cm	0.17 cm
material	molybdenum	nickel
Filament		
diameter	0.02 cm	0.03 cm

the anode at the same time resulted in heating the anode to red heat by electronic bombardment. This freed the gases occluded in the grid and plate. The bulb was heated to about 400 °C by external heaters, and the occluded gases were removed by the pumps prior to sealing off. The total production of TM tubes in World War I was in excess of 100,000, and at the time of the Armistice the production rate was 1000 tubes per day.

When attempts were made to utilize these tubes in a multistage radio-frequency amplifier, difficulties were encountered. The amplifiers used at that time were of the resistance-capacity coupled type, and the high input capacitance of the TM tube (15 picofarads)

Fig. 10-4. TM Métal tube.

Fig. 10-5. TM Fotos tube.

Fig. 10-6. TMC tube.

limited its use to frequencies below about 600 kilohertz. To overcome this limitation a version of the TM tube known as the TMC was developed. Fig. 10-6 is the TMC, which was also called irreverently the horned tube or the Kamerad type. In this modification the grid and anode are mechanically supported by wires which are embedded in the press, but the electrical connections are brought out to caps on the top of the bulb which are separated by a considerable distance. This construction reduced the input capacitance of the tube.

During this period transmitting tubes of higher power were also under development. This work was started in March 1915 by Hector Pilon, whose company made the first prototypes of the TM tube. Établissements H. Pilon had made X-ray tubes for some time before the war and had the equipment and know-how necessary to obtain the needed high vacuums. By 1916 Pilon had succeeded in producing a tube with 40 watts output (Fig. 10-7), and his subsequent work resulted in the production at Ivry of the TMB and the 50-watt E4M shown in Fig. 10-8. By 1920 Lampe Métal had developed a transmitting tube, designated Neuvron, which produced 500 watts output with 4000 volts on the anode. The filament of this tube took 6 amperes at 18 volts.

Apropos of postwar patent claims, one tragicomic incident may be noted. Peri and Biguet did not fully appreciate the possibilities of exploiting their patent on the concentric cylindrical element structure and, needing money, sold it to Marius Latour. Latour had amassed quite a fortune from the royalties on his high-frequency alternator patents. The royalties he received from the Peri-Biguet patent made him very wealthy. This so outraged Peri that he spent years of torment trying to design tubes which would not infringe

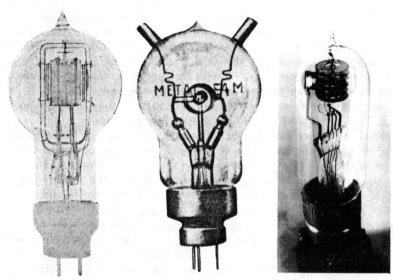

Fig. 10-7. Pilon's experimental 40-watt tube.

Fig. 10-8. E4M tube.

Fig. 10-9. One Peri design.

the Peri-Biguet patent but would accomplish the same purpose. He never succeeded. One such design is shown in Fig. 10-9.

After the war the surplus of TM-type tubes was sufficient to take care of the demands of radio amateurs, the only buyers until broadcasting started in the early 1920s. Little further development work was done in France until broadcasting began.

The need for telephone repeaters did not arise in France as early as in other countries. This was partly due to the limited use of the telephone. In 1915 a French news reporter expressed his opinion of the telephone: when American engineers tried to explain to him the American telephone system and its slogan "universal service," his reaction was startling. He said that he could not see any sense in telephones anyhow—all the people he wanted to talk to in a hurry lived with him, others did not matter, and a letter was quick enough in any case. He spoke for many a Frenchman, because the service was poor.

There was little standardization of equipment. A subscriber bought any phone he fancied, regardless of electrical characteristics, and then contracted for service. No two central offices were alike in construction or operation.[11] Long-distance telephony was practically nonexistent until late in World War I. In 1921 distances of the order of 500 miles were spanned only with difficulty, even when conditions were most favorable.[12]

The first telephone repeater used in France was installed and operated on an experimental basis at Lyon on a Paris-Marseilles circuit in 1917. It was a two-stage affair using TM-type tubes.[13] Following the success of this trial installation, an increase in the use of repeaters was proposed with the suggestion that the first step be the installation of cord-circuit repeaters in Paris.[14]

By 1920 there were only thirty repeaters in use in all France. Of these, three were of the French type using TM tubes. Eight were British repeaters installed at Abbeville and Lyon by the British Army during the war. The other nineteen (of which seven were the cord-circuit type) were American repeaters of Western Electric manufacture. These last had been obtained from the stocks of the U.S. Army in France.[15] Further increase in the number of repeaters was slow. In 1923 there was a total of thirty-eight in use; of these, twenty-six were cut in on specific circuits, and twelve were of the cord-circuit type. Up to this time the French had designed no tubes specifically to meet the requirements of telephone repeater service.[16]

Pichon's timely arrival in Paris with the Audion was of vital importance to the French but not a significant loss to the Germans. Von Bronk was familiar with the Audion and had patented its use as a high-frequency amplifier in 1911 in Germany (see Chapter 12). After the war Pichon returned to Germany and represented Telefunken on the Commercial Radio International Committee. He died in 1929.[17]

REFERENCES

1. Lee de Forest, *Father of Radio* (Chicago: Wilcox & Follett, 1950), pp. 237–238.
2. J. Boulanger and G. Ferrié, *La Télégraphie sans fil and les ondes électriques* (7th ed., Paris: Berger-Levrault, 1909), pp. 325–326.
3. Georges Petitjean, "Le Général Ferrié," *Progr. Sci.*, 1968, 4(18):49.
4. Émile Girardeau, "Hommage à Gustave Ferrié," *Progr. Sci.*, 1968, 4(18): 16. Émile Girardeau, *Souvenirs de longue vie* (Paris: Berger-Levrault, 1968), p. 81.
5. Petitjean, "Le Général Ferrié," p. 49.
6. Girardeau, *Souvenirs*, p. 83.
7. *Ibid.*
8. M. Peri and J. Biguet, République Française, Brevet d'Invention, No. 492,-657, application date Oct. 23, 1915, published Jul. 16, 1919.
9. C. Gutton, *La lampe à trois électrodes* (Paris: Librairie Scientifique Albert Blanchard, 1925), pp. 23–24.
10. Girardeau, "Hommage à Gustave Ferrié," p. 50; also Pierre Dejussieu-Pontcarral, *L'épopée du tube électronique* (Paris: L'Imprimerie Joly, 1961), p. 43.
11. G. Valensi, "Le téléphone en France et à l'étranger," *Ann. Post. Télégr. Téléph.*, 1923, 12:565–599.
12. G. Martin, "La téléphonie à grande distance en Europe," *Ann. Post. Télégr. Téléph.*, 1921, 10:263–270.

13. "Les relais téléphoniques employés par l'Administration Française," *Ann. Post. Télégr. Téléph.*, 1918, *7*:403-410.

14. G. Valensi, "Application des amplificateurs à l'exploitation téléphonique," *Ann. Post. Télégr. Téléph.*, 1917, *6*:595-613.

15. Ruat, "Les relais téléphoniques en France," *Ann. Post Télégr. Téléph.*, 1920, *9*:429-431.

16. "Utilisation des relais amplificateurs dans le reseau téléphonique français," *Ann. Post. Télégr. Téléph.*, 1923, *12*:768-769.

17. Obituary of Paul Pichon, *Telefunkenztg*, Dec. 1929, p. 80.

Chapter 11

The Entrance of Industrial
Laboratories and Military Demands,
1910-1920: *Great Britain*

The problem of telephonic transmission over long distances was
not as acute in Great Britain or on the European continent as it
was in the United States. This was chiefly because of the shorter
distances involved: such distances as lay within the boundaries of
any one country, presumably all that would be required at that
time to be serviced by any one telephone system, could be spanned
by the use of heavy-gauge conductors and loading. Nevertheless,
from the economic standpoint, the advantages of a satisfactory repeater were realized, and efforts were being made to develop such
devices in Great Britain and Germany.

A study of repeater and repeater-tube developments in Europe
brings out the contrast between European and American telephone
systems. In the United States the local and long-distance telephone
systems are, for the most part, under a single central control which
is a public service corporation subject to government regulation in
the public interest. This corporation, the American Telephone and
Telegraph Company, has numerous subsidiaries—operating, developmental, and manufacturing. Such an arrangement is a powerful
stimulus to systematic development and standardization. Such a
connected development procedure is well exemplified in Chapter 6,
in which the evolution of the U.S. telephone repeater in the period
1910–1920 has been covered.

In contrast, telephone and telegraph systems in Great Britain and
on the European continent are in general controlled and operated

directly by the Post Office departments of these countries. While the earlier steps in new developments may come either from the government research laboratories or from those of industry, the actual equipment for use is obtained from competitive manufacturing companies.

When a new project, such as the installation of a long-distance cable, is proposed, the Post Office engineers make preliminary experiments and determine what kinds of apparatus should be used and the requirements they should meet. Based on these studies, specifications are written and bids for the equipment and installation are invited from contractors. The equipment supplied by the successful bidder can differ drastically from that used in previously installed systems meeting similar requirements but purchased from some other manufacturer. This hinders standardization of equipment in the early stages of system development and results in the installation and use of different patterns of repeaters equipped with different types of tubes in various parts of any one country.

Prior to the invention of the vacuum tube, the British Post Office engineers attacked the problem of making a repeater along lines parallel to development in the United States. All were concentrating on producing a satisfactory receiver-microphone unit. In America the so-called Shreeve Repeater came in for attention.[1] In Great Britain a "telephone relay" was devised by S. G. Brown. There were several varieties of Brown's relay, one of which—designated Type G —is shown in Fig. 11-1. In this relay the received currents flowed through an electromagnet, which actuated a steel reed. The vibration of this reed was applied to the carbon granules of a microphone unit and caused telephonic variations in the microphone current. In the carbon microphone the electrical output is usually greater than the acoustical or mechanical input, and therefore such a mechanism can be made to function as an amplifier or telephone repeater. It was claimed that the Brown Type G relay gave a gain of about 20.

Under favorable conditions as many as three of these relays could be used in tandem on a one-way circuit, but not without some distortion. The inherent disadvantage of this relay was that the frequency range which could be repeated was limited both by the mechanical characteristics of the moving element and by the difficulties in getting and maintaining optimum mechanical adjustments.

The first installation using this relay was made in Leeds in 1914 on a London-Glasgow circuit.[2] This was a one-way repeater and was utilized in connection with a so-called jumping switch, a voice-operated relay which automatically made the necessary changes in connections to permit two-way operation. Its use caused undesirable "clipping" of the conversation.

The engineers of the British Post Office had been well aware of the limitations of the mechanical repeater. In 1908 a small group of research workers who had been studying cathode-ray phenomena in the Post Office Research Laboratory attacked the problem of developing a telephone relay of the cathode-ray type.[3] Possibly their thinking had been stimulated by the issuance of the von Lieben patent on such a device in 1906.[4] The machinery necessary for making and evacuating such tubes was purchased and installed, but unfortunately the group was broken up by staff changes shortly thereafter. Their work had been overshadowed by the possibilities of the mechanical amplifier, which promised quicker results even though the quality was poor.

Fig. 11-1. Brown's Type G telephone relay.

Interest in the thermionic repeater was aroused again in 1913. The work of de Forest, von Lieben and Reisz, Round, and others had brought the thermionic tube out of the research laboratory into the realm of commercial practicability. Fortunately, one of that small group of British Post Office engineers, dispersed in 1908, returned to the Research Laboratory about that time and resumed the suspended experiments. Samples of the valves of de Forest, von Lieben and Reisz, Round, and others were obtained and examined to see if they could meet the requirements of telephone work. New experimental valves were constructed, incorporating such special features as might adapt them to successful telephone use.

Fig. 11-2. The original British Post Office amplifying valve (Round type). Reproduced from *P.O.E.E.J.*, 1919.)

The Round type of "soft" valve seemed to have the best possibilities at first, and a number of these were produced in the laboratory. They were made somewhat larger than the original Round valves in order to handle the necessary power. Fig. 11-2 is a photo-

Fig. 11-3. British Post Office repeater using Round valve. (Reproduced from Paper 76, *Inst. P.O.E.E.*)

graph of one of these valves, the first type to be used in telephone service in England. The repeater in which it was used is shown in Fig. 11-3.

The essential features of the Round valve are: (1) the cathode is of the Wehnelt, or oxide-coated, type; (2) the grid is a fine mesh completely surrounding the filament; (3) the anode is a cylinder surrounding the grid; (4) there is a tubulation containing a wad of asbestos extending upward from the top of the bulb. This grid construction was adopted to prevent electrification of the inner surface of the glass bulb by electrons expelled from the filament, and the asbestos in the tubulation was used as a source of gas to increase pressure when the tube became hard. The asbestos gave off small quantities of gas when heat was applied externally to the tubulation.

These valves were considered rather stable in operation and gave a good quality of reproduction. When new they would start up from cold in about 3 seconds, but as they became older, whether used or not, the internal pressure decreased. If used in this condition, they required considerably more time to reach their full amplification. The pressure could be restored in most cases by heating the tubulation. The average life, when only moderate gains were required, was about 600 hours.[5]

These soft valves were difficult to manufacture with any degree of uniformity and were soon replaced by a "hard" or high-vacuum valve, the earliest form of which is shown in Fig. 11-4. This valve had either a tungsten or Wehnelt cathode, taking about 2 amperes at 8 volts. This cathode was supported on a U-shaped glass frame, which also carried the grid. This grid consisted of a nickel-gauze cap fitting over the frame carrying the cathode. The anode consisted of two nickel plates supported by glass arms on either side of the grid-cathode assembly. The valve was exhausted to such a vacuum that it showed no indication of ionization when worked at an anode potential of 400 volts.[6]

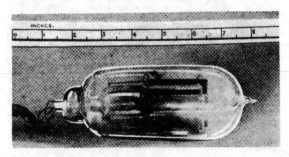

Fig. 11-4. Earliest type of high-vacuum telephone repeater valve used by British Post Office. (Reproduced from Paper 76, *Inst. P.O.E.E.*)

Fig. 11-5. Two forms of "Valve, Amplifying, No. 1" used by British Post Office as the first standard amplifying valve. The one at the right is the earlier construction.

The glass work of this valve was rather troublesome to make,[7] and subsequently the Post Office engineers inclined toward the use of a valve similar in structure to that developed by the French Télégraphie Militaire and called by them the TM tube. The adaptation of the TM tube arrived at by the British Post Office became the first Standard Repeater Valve and was officially known as "Valve, Amplifying, No. 1." Two forms of this valve are shown in Fig. 11-5, the one on the right being the earlier construction.

The filament of this valve was a fine spiral of tungsten wire. The grid was a somewhat more open spiral about ¼ inch in diameter, at first of tungsten and later of alloy wire, mounted concentrically with the filament. The anode was a spiralled helix of tungsten wire, mounted concentrically with the grid and filament, with a radial spacing of ¹⁄₁₆ to ⅛ inch. Later (1919) models of this valve used an anode made of sheet nickel, as shown at the left in Fig. 11-5. The bulb, spherical in shape, was mounted on a red fiber base which carried the four terminal connections. These were flat strips of brass, arranged to be clamped under binding posts on the repeater unit. This method of mounting was used in preference to the four-pin base of the TM tube because of the necessity of keeping contact resistances to a minimum. The anode terminal strip was painted red "for reasons that will be appreciated by anyone who touches it while the valve is in operation."[8] The repeater in which this valve was used was known as "Repeater, Telephonic, No. 2," shown in Fig. 11-6.

The filament of this valve was designed to give a total space current of not less than 10 milliamperes when a potential of 150 volts was applied between filament and grid-anode connected together. The normal operating range of the anode current was 1–2 milliamperes. The working temperature of the filament was chosen to give a working life of about 2000 hours.[9] The valve had a mutual conductance of 450 micromhos and an internal impedance of about 20,000 ohms. In order to insure obtaining a reasonably straight-line plate current–grid voltage curve, one of the requirements on this valve was that between grid voltages of −8 and 0, the mutual conductance must not vary more than 20 percent from the value at −4.5 volts—the grid bias existing in Repeater No. 2.

Fig. 11-6. "Repeater, Telephonic, No. 2." (Reproduced from *P.O.E.E.J.*, Apr. 1919.)

In order to insure meeting the other requirements, the proper filament current for each of these valves was determined for the individual valve.[10] This was done by putting the valve into a test circuit and increasing the filament current until the mutual conductance reached a predetermined value. At this point the filament voltage was noted, and thereafter the filament was operated at that voltage. The usual value of heating current was between the limits of 0.7 and 0.8 ampere, and the filament voltage was about 4.7 volts. Under these conditions the filament resistance was approximately ten times its resistance when cold. The usual anode voltage was 200–220 volts.

This is a brief delineation of the evolution of telephone repeater valves in Great Britain, starting with the Round type "soft" valve, which was being developed primarily for wireless use. All of the early British wireless valves were of the gaseous type and seem to have been inspired largely by the work of von Lieben and Reisz in Germany. It is true that Fleming had obtained at least one sample of the de Forest Audion as early as 1907, but we have no records

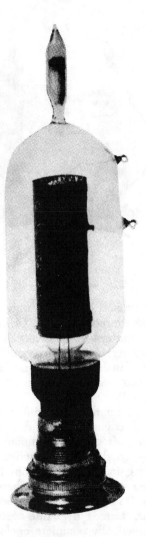

Fig. 11-7. Round Type C valve.

to show that he or anyone else in Britain was stimulated by it immediately. Here, as in France, it was rejected.

The first work in triode valve development in Great Britain seems
to have been done about 1911 by Captain H. J. Round of the British
Marconi Company. Little has been published concerning Round's
early work; hence it is difficult to trace with any degree of authority
the evolution of the Round valve. A patent agreement between
British Marconi and Telefunken was signed March 6, 1913. The two
companies decided to collaborate and divide responsibility for de-

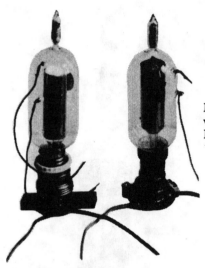

Fig. 11-8. Left: Round Type N with Edison medium screw base. Right: Round Type N with Ediswan bayonet base.

velopment. It was arranged that Round and C. S. Franklin should work on receivers and Telefunken engineers should concentrate on transmitters. Round speaks intimately of the work of Alexander Meissner of Telefunken in an article on wireless telephony published in 1915, but the article deals chiefly with circuits and applications, and no mention is made of the Round version of the LRS Relay.[11]

The Round valves differ from the Meissner form of the LRS Relay chiefly in details of design.[12] They were first employed by Round as high-frequency amplifiers, later as ocillators. They were remarkably good amplifiers when operated under optimum conditions. The gain obtainable from the Round Type C was equivalent to three stages of the best "hard" tube of that time, the French TM.[13] The Round Type C is shown in Fig. 11-7. The Round valves were characterized by oxide-coated cathodes, wire-mesh grids forming a practically complete enclosure of the cathode, a long tubulation containing means for adjusting the vacuum, and cylindrical anodes with a large ratio of anode-cathode to grid-cathode distance. The filamentary cathodes were usually hairpin shaped, with the hottest part at the top.

Round considered it necessary for stability of operation that the grid completely enclose the filament. If this was not done, the inside of the glass bulb would become charged by bombardment of electrons emitted from the filament. If the charge thus accumulated produced an appreciable electrostatic field at the filament, it would

Fig. 11-9. Marconi Type 27 receiver (1914–1918) using Round Type N valve.

be necessary to readjust the grid voltage to compensate. Hence, unless a completely enclosing grid was used, this rather critical parameter would require frequent readjustment—an undesirable operating limitation.[14]

There were a number of types of Round valves, and the nomenclature used to designate them is quite confusing. The Types C and T, both first produced in 1913,[15] may be taken as representative of the series. Two versions of the Type N, which was similar to the Type C, are shown in Fig. 11-8. The Marconi Type 27 Receiver (Fig. 11-9) used one of these Type N valves as a high-frequency amplifier. The Round Type T with multiple cathodes is shown in Fig. 11-10. Fig. 11-11 is a drawing of the internal structure of this tube, and Fig. 11-12 is a view looking downward with the tubulation removed showing this internal structure.

The Type N had a single lime-coated filament which operated with a filament current of 2.5 amperes,[16] 40–80 volts on the anode, and was used in the famous Marconi No. 16 circuit, which had a carborundum detector. The valve functioned in this circuit as a radio-frequency and audio-frequency amplifier, the circuit being of the reflex type. The Type CA valve was a variant of the Type N. This valve had an extremely fine mesh grid, operated with a filament current of 2.5 amperes, and anode voltages up to 200 volts.[17]

There were several variants of the Type T, some with coarse mesh, others with fine mesh grids, some with long tubulations, others without any tubulation at all. One of these was known as

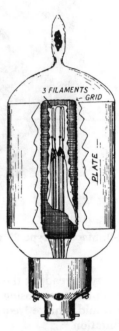

Fig. 11-10. Round Type T valve with multiple cathodes.

Fig. 11-11. Drawing of the internal structure of the Type T with multiple cathodes.

the Type TN. It operated with 2000 volts on the anode and 4 to 4.5 amperes in the filament at approximately 6 volts.[18] Another was the LT, considerably smaller than the other T types, with a three-pin base, similar to the TM base with one pin removed. This valve,

Fig. 11-12. Top view of the Round Type T valve, with tubulation removed, showing characteristic Round mesh-type grid.

Fig. 11-13. Round Type LT valve.

mounted in a receiving tube socket, is shown in Fig. 11-13. The grid and filament connections were on the socket, and the anode terminal was at the top of the valve. The LT operated at 1- to 1.2-amperes filament, and 1500 volts on the anode.[19] Other variants were the TF-HC-3F, a multiple-cathode tube with three cathodes, and the PF-HC-3F. In both these types, there was a tubulation at the top containing an amalgam instead of asbestos. Some of the TF-HC-3F valves had no tubulation (see Fig. 11-14).

The Type TN was used as the transmitting valve in the Marconi Short Distance Wireless Telephone Transmitter and Receiver made in 1914. It had the Type C valve in the receiving circuit.[20] This apparatus is shown in Fig. 11-15. These Round valves were manufactured by the Edison and Swan Electric Light Company.

The first actual use of the three-electrode valve in the British armed forces was by Round in December 1914 in a Marconi Direction Finder.[21] Many of the Round valves were utilized by the Royal Flying Corps (later the Royal Air Force) in the earlier wireless sets for plane-to-ground communication during World War I. Discussing their use shortly after the war, one of the RFC officers said:

> The soft valves used in the early days were provided with a regulating device in the form of a pip containing a crystal of asbestos or other mineral. This when heated reduced the vacuum in the valve. It was the custom to heat the pip before the flight took place but it often happened that when in the air one found that the valve had become too hard to oscillate. In or-

Fig. 11-14. Round Type TF-HC-3F valve without tubulation.

Fig. 11-15. Marconi short-distance wireless telephone transmitter and receiver. The valve in the gallows frame is the Round Type TN, used for transmitting. The one at the right rear is the Round Type C used for receiving.

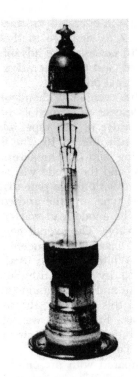

Fig. 11-16. The White valve.

der to overcome the danger of applying a naked flame a small electric heater was devised which could be placed over the regulating pip.[22]

The Round valves were in demand because of their high gain and power-handling capabilities in British communications equipment during World War I. They were difficult to manufacture and required highly trained wireless operators to get the most out of them. Concerning their manufacture Round wrote:

> I have mentioned that the production of valves at that time required special men. Even then it was a terrible process. Again and again we lost the knack of making good tubes owing to some slight change in the materials used in their manufacture. A thorough investigation was impossible, as all hands were out on the stations. On several occasions we were down to our last dozen tubes.[23]

Another soft tube used to a limited extent by the British armed services at that time was the White valve. It resulted from work done at the Cavendish Laboratory, Cambridge, under the direction of Sir J. J. Thomson. The earlier experiments were by Wright and Ogden, but the later developments were by G. W. White, which explains its designation.[24] White worked for some time on the possible applications of cold-cathode tubes and succeeded in making some which operated satisfactorily in wireless work.[25] These valves were not as sensitive as those of the hot-cathode type, although they did possess some advantages. No filament-heating battery was required, and their operation was not affected by small changes in the internal pressure.

White eventually abandoned the cold cathode and adopted an incandescent construction because of its superior sensitivity. A White valve of this type, which came into practical use in 1916, is shown in Fig. 11-16. The filament was of oxide-coated platinum, operating with 2.8 amperes. The grid was a disk of perforated copper, and the anode was a disk of amalgamated iron. The valve operated with anode potentials of 35–75 volts. The base was of the bayonet type, and the grid connection was brought out to the base shell. The anode lead was connected to a binding post at the top of the valve. The overall height of the valve was about 5¾ inches and the maximum diameter was about 2⅜ inches.

The White valve was used in the Mark III Amplifier, which was designed by the British Signals Experimental Establishment for field use and first manufactured in April 1917.[26] Two valves were used in this amplifier, the second being a de Forest Audion. The amplifier, Fig. 11-17, was of the high-frequency type employing regeneration and was intended for use with the Mark III Short Wave Tuner.

Compared with present-day standards, the soft valves made by Round and White were of relatively large physical size, as was

Fig. 11-17. Mark III amplifier using White valve and de Forest Audion.

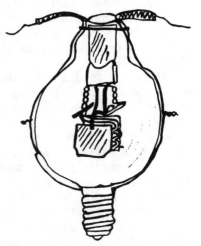

Fig. 11-18. Sketch of the
B.T.H. Audion.

the German LRS Relay; this was necessary to provide stability of
operation. Any reduction of the size of the valve meant a decrease
in the ratio of the volume of gas present to the area of the electrodes. Variations in the electrode temperatures would result in
larger changes in temperature and pressure of the residual gas.
The smaller the gas volume, the more erratic the behavior of the
valve.[27]

It was appreciated, even as these developments were carried out,
that the high-vacuum valve had great advantages in military work
because of the stability of its characteristics and the uniformity of
the manufactured product. Yet the soft valve possessed such a high
sensitivity that much development effort was expended in an attempt to make it a stable, reliable device, satisfactory for military
work where the skill of the operator could not be guaranteed.

The manufacture of soft valves was undertaken by the British
Thomson-Houston Company at Rugby during the summer of 1916.[28]
The first production was of the Audion type, but it had a much
better life expectancy. A sketch of this B.T.H. Audion is given in
Fig. 11-18. Serious difficulties were experienced in 1917,[29] and as
a result of investigation the Audion structure was abandoned. A soft
valve similar in construction to the French TM type was developed.
This was designated the R2 valve and at first was filled with nitrogen to a pressure of 0.06 millimeter of mercury. The pressure was
measured during manufacture by measuring the width of the "dark
space" in an auxiliary cold-cathode tube.[30] After development, the
specifications on this valve were released to several manufacturers,
and the first quantity production was achieved by the Osram-Robertson Works of the General Electric Company Ltd. in June 1917.

Difficulties were encountered in maintaining the gas pressure because of the absorption of the nitrogen by the electrodes. Later R2 valves were helium-filled to a pressure of 0.6 millimeter of mercury. The manufacture of the helium-filled R2 was begun in September 1917.

The filament of the R2 was of drawn tungsten wire. It was 0.79 inch long and 3.3 mils in diameter; it operated at 1.1 amperes with a potential drop of about 3.3 volts. The anode was of sheet nickel bent into the form of a complete cylinder, approximately 0.6 inch long and 0.35 inch in diameter. The grid was a helix of molybdenum wire 16 mils in diameter. It was wound with a pitch of 14 turns per inch, the internal diameter of the helix being about 0.18 inch. The anode operated at 20–40 volts, and the grid bias was adjusted by means of a potentiometer to obtain optimum operating conditions in actual use.[31] This valve was manufactured by General Electric (Osram), British Thomson-Houston, and Ediswan.

A modification of the R2, designated R2A, manufactured chiefly by Osram, was used in British naval installations during the last year of World War I. It marked the final development of the soft valve in England. One of these R2A valves is shown in Fig. 11-19. The R2A operated under the same conditions as the R2, except that it had a somewhat narrower range of anode voltage, 28–38 volts. Another soft valve used to a limited extent by the British Air Force was known as the Air Force Type D. This will be covered later.

Fig. 11-19. Osram R2A valve fitted with a candelabra base for use in British naval apparatus designed to use the de Forest Audion. This valve was usually supplied unbased; the user applied whatever base he required.

Before leaving the consideration of soft valves of British origin, mention should be made of the so-called NPL valve, described by Stanley in 1919 as follows:

> In this valve the plate was a thin sheet of circular metal, above this was the grid, consisting of a perforated sheet of metal, beyond which was the bowed tungsten filament. This was a bad design; the grid was too heavy and the flow of electrons from the filament was not uniform along its length, but was concentrated at the center. The design is now out of date. . . .[32]

Apparently this was a soft valve, since the characteristics given by Stanley show kinks ascribed by him to the presence of mercury vapor, and he records the presence of an amalgam on the anode. This is the only reference to this valve in my records. It is possible that the NPL was another designation for the White valve previously described. If the reader compares the description given by Stanley with the White valve shown in Fig. 11-16, he will note that if the White valve were mounted with its base uppermost, Stanley's words read rather well as a description of it.

The manifold difficulties in the manufacture and utilization of soft valves, because of the nonuniformity of the manufactured product and the erratic behavior of individual valves, eventually compelled the British armed services to adopt the hard valve. This was done despite the fact that their comparative insensitivity necessitated the use of multistage amplifiers. The exact time when this decision was reached is unknown. W. J. Picken of Marconi's Wireless Telegraph Company Ltd. first learned of hard valves in the autumn of 1914,[33] when he was in the United States working with Roy A. Weagant on transatlantic radio reception. They were using Audions, but their operation was tricky and results were uncertain. They obtained some samples of hard Audions which had been re-evacuated at Columbia University. These gave much better and more consistent performance. When Picken returned to England he brought back several of these hard Audions which "were received with great interest."

Gossling states that a study was made by the Admiralty of some "oscillions" imported from the United States in 1915, and that the most illuminating data were obtained in 1916 by H. M. Signal School at Portsmouth on re-exhausted Audions of the flat plate and zigzag-wire-grid type.[34] Later, in 1916, further study was made of a "pliotron" made by General Electric in the U.S.[35]

Meantime the British Thomson-Houston Co. had been studying the TM-type tube developed by the French Télégraphie Militaire.[36] From all this work came a high-vacuum receiving valve generally designated as the R-type valve, which was made by all of the British manufacturers beginning in 1916, although some makers used different designations. For example, the R-type made by Edison

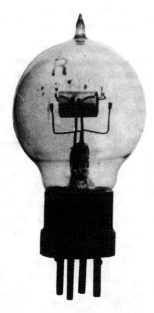

Fig. 11-20. Osram Type R valve.

and Swan was called the ES1. The R valve was widely used in its various embodiments. Fig. 11-20 shows the R valve made by Osram.

The R valve had an anode of sheet nickel, bent in the form of a cylinder about 0.625 inch long and 0.41 inch in diameter. The grid was an 11-turn helix about 0.2 inch in diameter, the wire being 0.005 inch in diameter. The filament was of tungsten and operated with about 0.7 ampere at 4 volts. The anode voltage was 30–100 volts, anode resistance 35,000 to 40,000 ohms, and amplification factor about 9. The earliest models of this valve had a simple helix form of grid patterned after the French TM tube. This proved to be very microphonic. Later valves had the grid stiffened by means of a catenary suspension. The base usually applied to the R valve was of the type originally used on the French TM tube. The outer metallic shell was copper or (later) brass, in some cases nickel plated. Originally the pins were held in a ceramic insert; later a molded insert was used. The R2 valve was a soft valve and has been previously covered. The author has found no record of an R3 valve.

It should be remembered that this valve development was being carried out during World War I. Engineers and scientists were working under pressure to satisfy the incessant demands for more and better communication equipment. The chief naval communications problem in the early part of this war was to get good continuous-wave (cw) reception over a wide band of frequencies.

Audions and other soft valves were used in naval installations as local oscillators in heterodyne cw reception. The Audion first came into prominence for naval work for this application. The extent of its use is indicated by the fact that there were 800 Audions of de Forest manufacture in service for the Admiralty in 1917. Small arc-generators had previously been used as local oscillators but were troublesome, and even the smallest which could be conveniently operated gave a much higher output than was desirable. The Audion and the Round valve operated satisfactorily over the entire frequency range to be covered but were short-lived and difficult to handle.

Up to this time British Thomson-Houston had been successful in the manufacture of R valves, but the standard R would not oscillate over the complete frequency range used in naval work. They now proposed to develop a hard valve to replace the Audion and the soft valves in use. The R4 valve was born of observations made by Mr. Edmundsen of B.T.H. in the course of this work. A number of the R valves were made up for trial, and by accident one of those experimental valves had a distorted filament. The distortion was such as to bring the filament and grid very close together. Edmundsen observed that this valve was very satisfactory in operation, being capable of meeting all the requirements for this application. But it was not reproducible. The R4 was an attempt to duplicate in a commercially manufacturable valve the characteristics of this "freak."

The grid diameter was made as small as possible, the diameter and pitch being chosen to accomplish the desired result. The anode was of nickel sheet about 0.006 inch thick bent into the form of a cylinder 0.36 inch in diameter and 0.68 inch long. The helical grid was of 0.006-inch-diameter molybdenum wire, wound with a pitch of 25 turns per inch, had an internal diameter of 0.14 inch and a length of 0.79 inch. The filament was of tungsten wire containing 1 percent thorium, about 3.5 mils in diameter and 1 inch long, crimped to eliminate tensile strains. The filament operated with about 1.1 amperes at 3.5–4 volts. The anode voltage ranged from 45 to 55 volts. This low anode voltage greatly relieved the requirements on the hardness of the vacuum needed.[37]

The first of these R4 valves made by B.T.H. had a life of about 1500 hours. Attempts were made by other manufacturers to improve the valve and attain longer life. This was finally achieved at the Osram-Robertson Works by the development of an extremely hard exhaust which could be obtained with a minimum of bombardment. The commercial product of these valves was long-lived, some lasting for 8000 hours, while the general run had a life of several thousand hours. In addition to the companies mentioned, the R4 was

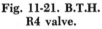

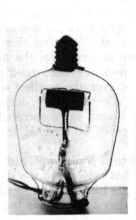

Fig. 11-21. B.T.H.   Fig. 11-22. The R4A   Fig. 11-23. The Os-
    R4 valve.   valve.   ram R4B valve.

also made by Ediswan and by the Stearn Lamp Company. Fig. 11-21 shows an R4 valve.

The R4 was redesigned about a year later to reduce the filament power required. The diameter and length of the anode were reduced, the pitch of the grid increased slightly, and the filament wire was changed to 2.4-mil-diameter thoriated tungsten. The redesigned valve was designated R4A and is shown in Fig. 11-22. It operated with a filament current of 0.46 ampere at 2.5–4 volts. The life of this valve was about 1500 hours. The filament operated at a somewhat higher temperature than that of the R4, and hence the valve was somewhat noisier.

The R4B (Fig. 11-23) was designed for use in amplifiers where the noise introduced by the R4A was objectionable. The element structure was practically the same as that of the R4A, except that the filament was of pure tungsten. It operated at the same filament current as the R4A but at a slightly higher voltage, the range being 3.4–3.9 volts. There was an R4C made by the General Electric Co. Ltd. beginning in 1919. It operated with 3.2–3.85 volts on the filament, and the anode voltage was 35–55 volts.

The final development of high-vacuum receiving valves of the R type for the British naval services during World War I was the R5, manufactured by the Z Electric Lamp Company (among others) (Fig. 11-24). It followed in its general design one of the high-vacuum receiving valves which had been previously developed by Captain Round. The first quantity production of the R5 did not come up to expectations, and the valve was redesigned to increase

Fig. 11-24. The Osram R5 valve, with shipping carton.

the ratio of saturation current to working current. With this change the valve was found to be satisfactory.[38]

The anode of the R5 was made of 6-mil nickel sheet, formed into a cylinder 0.36 inch long and 0.36 inch in diameter. The helical grid was composed of 14 turns of 4-mil molybdenum wire with a pitch of about 22 turns per inch and an internal diameter of 0.115 inch. The filament was of pure tungsten, approximately 2.5 mils in diameter and 0.87 inch long. It operated with a current of about 0.65 ampere at about 3.6 volts. The anode potential used was 30–60 volts. It may be noted from the photograph that this valve differed from the rest of the R series in its method of mounting. The bulb and cap used on this valve were developed by Captain S. R. Mullard for the Royal Flying Corps.[39] The ratio of diameter to length of the anode is greater than in the other valves of the R series. This was done to reduce the anode-grid capacitance of the valve. One drawback was found: leakage developed between the electrode leads outside the glass, because the cement used to attach the caps was hygroscopic.

The design of this valve was inadequate in other respects. The thin spring wire used to support the upper end of the filament lost its elasticity after heating, and the lack of spring action caused considerable filament breakage while the valves were still on the exhaust pump. The adjustment of spring tension was quite critical. If the tension was too great, the filament would break; if too small, it would sag and touch the grid.

Possibly the R6 never advanced beyond the experimental stage. The R7, made about 1920 by Mullard Radio Valve Company, operated at 3–3.7 volts on the filament and 30–100 volts on the anode. A sample of the R8 (Denman Cat. No. 112) is in the Science Museum, London. No information on its characteristics is available.

The R-type valves when used by the Admiralty were designated by the prefix letter N. Thus the Admiralty in ordering from suppliers would specify NR2 when they wanted R2, NR2A when ordering R2A, and so on.

Fig. 11-25. Air Force C valve, made by Osram.

Fig. 11-26. Air Force D valve, made by Osram.

There were at least two other valves made for use in British Air Force equipment which were similar mechanically to the R5. These were known as the Air Force C Valve and the Air Force D Valve. The Air Force C (Fig. 11-25) was made by Osram. The Air Force D (Fig. 11-26) was made by both Ediswan and Osram. The Air Force C was introduced about September 1918. It was a high-vacuum triode which had a pure tungsten filament and operated at 3 volts and 0.75 ampere. It had an amplification factor of about 6 and the anode resistance was 16,000–30,000 ohms. The anode voltages used were between 50 and 70 volts. The Air Force D, which was a soft tube used as a detector, was first employed about January 1919. It resembled the Air Force C in external appearance and mounting, but the anode was of larger diameter and the grid was of gauze rather than the helical wire type.

These valves were used in the Aircraft Tuner Receiver Type T10 and in the Ground Station Detecting Amplifier T-XII. The T10 used two C valves as high-frequency amplifiers, a D type as detector, and two C valves as low-frequency amplifiers. The T-XII used four C valves as high-frequency amplifiers and one D valve as detector.[40]

The design of the R5 was based on a high-vacuum valve which had first been produced for the British Marconi Company in 1916 by Captain Round and was designated as V24.[41] It is shown in Fig. 11-27. The V24 was intended specifically for use as a high-frequency amplifier valve. It had been found that it was impracticable to build satisfactory multistage high-frequency amplifiers using R-type and similar valves of the single-ended construction with the conventional four-pin base. The common type of multistage amplifier of that time was resistance-capacitance coupled, and the inter-electrode capacitances of the R tube and its holder represented a considerable shunt on the coupling resistances.

Accordingly, in designing the V24, Round strove to reduce these parasitic capacitances as much as possible by separating the leads as far as possible. He accomplished this by using a cylindrical bulb and bringing out the axial filament leads at opposite ends, while the anode and grid connections were brought out on small caps placed at opposite ends of a diameter. This valve, which had a spring-tensioned filament, operated with a filament current of 0.75 ampere at about 5 volts. The anode voltage used was 20–60 volts. The amplification factor was about 6, and the internal anode resistance 15,000–20,000 ohms. Six of these valves were used as high-frequency amplifier valves in the Marconi Type 55 amplifiers. These amplifiers could be obtained to cover the frequency range of 25–1000 kilohertz in three steps, 25–200, 100–600, and 300–1000 kilohertz. This equipment was widely used in marine work, and the

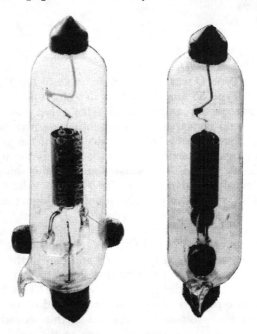

Fig. 11-27. Two views of the Marconi V24 valve.

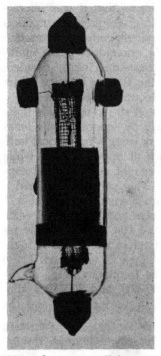

Fig. 11-28. Marconi Type Q valve.

V24 valve was still being made for replacement purposes in these amplifiers as late as 1937.

The Marconi Type Q was a companion valve to the V24. It was used in all the Type 55 amplifiers as a detector following the six stages of high-frequency amplification. This valve was similar to the V24 in external appearance and mounting, as may be seen in Fig. 11-28. It differed chiefly in the construction of the grid, which was a fine mesh gauze carried on two glass beads through which the filament leads passed. This valve had a higher amplification factor and internal impedance than the V24, the values being 50 and 150,000 ohms, respectively. It also required a higher anode voltage (up to 150 volts) for good operation.

The V24 and Q valves were first issued in 1916. Round thought that by the design of the V24 and Q types he had removed as much of the lead capacitance as was practicable and that further improvements could be made only by reducing the capacitance existing inside the valve between the grid and the anode. This he did by inserting a mesh-type grid between the spiral grid of the V24 and the anode. A positive voltage was applied to this second (shield) grid in order to draw the electrons through to the anode. This resulted in the F.E.1 valve, first issued in 1920. Fig. 11-29 is a draw-

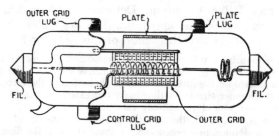

Fig. 11-29. Drawing of the F.E.1. valve. (Reproduced from H. J. Round, *The Shielded Four-Electrode Valve*, London, 1927.)

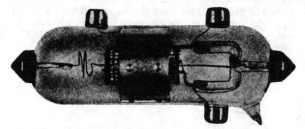

Fig. 11-30. The F.E.1. valve.

ing of the internal construction of the F.E.1 and Fig. 11-30 is a photograph of the F.E.1. It is somewhat larger than the V24, the glass being 1 inch in diameter and the overall length, including filament terminals, being 3⅝ inches.

The F.E.1 took a filament current of 1.5 amperes at 4.5 volts. The anode voltage was 24–100 volts. It was used in the Marconi Type-91

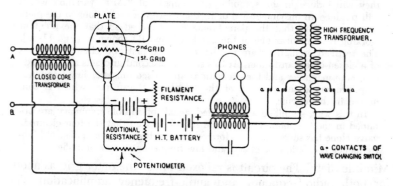

Simplified Diagram of Connections.

Fig. 11-31. Circuit diagram of the Marconi Type-91 four-electrode valve amplifying detector for ships. (Reproduced from Bulletin L163 of Marconi's Wireless Telegraph Co. Ltd.)

Four-Electrode Valve Amplifying Detector for Ships. Fig. 11-31 is the circuit diagram of this apparatus. The descriptive bulletin on this equipment states that the action of this detector is as follows:

> The high tension battery is connected in the second grid circuit and produces therein a normally steady current which is varied by the potential changes impressed on the first grid through the action of the incoming signals. The three inner electrodes thus carry out exactly the same functions as the three electrodes of an ordinary valve.
>
> The plate is connected, through the secondary winding of the high-frequency transformer, to a potentiometer shunted across the filament battery (the primary winding of the transformer is in the second grid circuit). By this means the plate potential can be varied between the limits of a few volts above or below that of the filament. Some of the electrons which are emitted from the filament pass through the second grid and fall on the plate; but, as the potential of this electrode is practically equal to that of the filament, very little current will flow in the plate circuit. The characteristic curve of this current with respect to the voltage [see Fig. 11-32] is very similar to that of a Fleming valve.

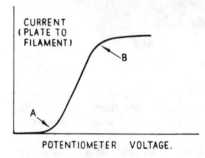

CURRENT (PLATE TO FILAMENT)

B

A

POTENTIOMETER   VOLTAGE.

Fig. 11-32. Characteristic curve of the Fleming valve. (Reproduced from Bulletin L163 of Marconi's Wireless Telegraph Co. Ltd.)

> Thus if symmetrical oscillations occur in the primary of the transformer they will induce in the secondary a symmetrical E.M.F. variation which will produce an unsymmetrical or rectified series of oscillations in the plate circuit, provided that the potentiometer is adjusted so that the point of working is on or near one of the bends (A and B) shown in [Fig. 11-32]. The rectified oscillations are fed back into the first grid circuit by means of a closed-core transformer. At this stage the second grid acts as the anode of a note magnifier and the oscillations are passed on, after low frequency amplification to the primary of the telephone transformer which is connected in this circuit.
>
> In this way, amplified and rectified signals of audible frequency are obtained in the telephone receiver and it will be seen that the four-electrode valve alone has successfully performed the functions of an amplifier of high-frequency oscillations, rectifier, and low-frequency or note amplifier.

Mirabile dictu! The circuit is reflexed to use the outer grid as anode for both radio-frequency and audio-frequency amplification. The plate is used only as the anode of a Fleming valve operating with the electrons which pass through the mesh of the outer grid. While it has the requisite four electrodes, the valve in no way functions as a screen-grid valve in this circuit.

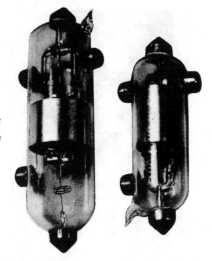

Fig. 11-33. Comparison of sizes of the F.E.1 and F.E.2 valves. The F.E.1 is at the left.

The F.E.1 was later followed by the F.E.2, which was smaller but had approximately the same operating parameters. The F.E.1 and F.E.2 are shown for comparison of size in Fig. 11-33. The F.E.2 may have been used as a screen-grid valve, since at least one source of tabular information states that, with an anode voltage of 50–100 volts, the voltage on the screen should be 30–50 volts.[42] However, Banneitz also gives identical mechanical dimensions for these two valves and uses Donisthorpe's paper as authority for his statement.[43] Since there is no mention of the F.E.2 in this paper, Banneitz' data are suspect.

Two other tubes manufactured by British Thomson-Houston are pertinent to this history. The first of these was the B.T.H. Type A. It was put into production about 1917 and was similar to the French TM except for the grid structure. The spiral grid was stiffened by means of a length of straight wire stretched between the grid support brackets. Each turn of the grid was strapped to this support wire by a fine wire interlacing. This reduced the microphonic noise. The anode of the Type A was of nickel sheet bent into a cylinder 0.63 inch long and 0.41 inch in diameter. The grid had 11 turns of 5-mil wire, the spiral being 0.2 inch in diameter and 0.67 inch long. The filament operated with about 0.72 ampere at 4 volts. As a low-frequency amplifier it usually operated with 50 volts on the anode and −4 volts on the grid. It is shown in Fig. 11-34A.

About 1918 the B.T.H. Type B (Fig. 11-34B) was also put into production. It was similar to the A but had a closer-mesh grid approximately 0.8 inch long having 23 or 24 convolutions. The vacuum

(A) *Type A.*   (B) *Type B.*

Fig. 11-34. B.T.H. Type A and B valves.

was harder, so the B valve could be used as a transmitter with up to 800 volts on the anode. When so used, the filament voltage was increased to 6 volts.

While this work is concerned primarily with receiving valves, the story of British Admiralty developmental work would not be complete without some attention being given to transmitting valves. Fig. 11-35 shows the construction of two typical Admiralty transmitting valves, and Table 11-1 gives further information concerning them.

World War I with its imperative demands for communications equipment brought about forced draft development in Great Britain as well as in the United States. When the need for valves became manifest, the British military communications officers could turn only to the incandescent lamp manufacturers for quantity production. These manufacturers, like the General Electric Company in America, made use of the materials and techniques with which they were familiar, and the background of the makers was reflected in the product. The British abandoned the oxide-coated cathode of Round and went to a tungsten filament, with which they were experienced. This channeled valve development along incandescent lamp lines in order to attain quantity production in the shortest possible time.

In the United States, where the high-vacuum tube was developed from 1913 on, the situation was different. For military purposes the U.S. Government had a source of supply in addition to incandescent lamp manufacturers. Western Electric had been making high-vacuum tubes for use in the telephone system before the war broke out. Western Electric engineers had followed a different path of

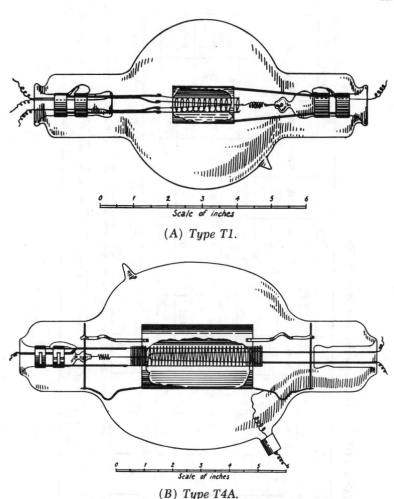

(A) *Type T1.*

(B) *Type T4A.*

Fig. 11-35. Two British Admiralty transmitting valves. (Reproduced from J.I.E.E., Aug., 1920, 59:67.)

tube development, their thinking being conditioned by their objective of ensuring the operation of their tubes over long periods of time. Complete reliability and uniformity of product and results were mandatory for successful commercial operation. In the quest of these essentials they had surveyed the possibilities and had focused their efforts on the oxide-coated cathode as being best suited to their needs. As a result of these parallel lines of development, excellent cathodes of both types—tungsten and oxide-coated—were available at the end of the war. The tungsten filament proved to be

Table 11-1. British Admiralty Transmitting Valves

Type	Filament			Anode diss. watts	Anode cylinder				Helix		Grid			Filament		
	Date	Volts	Amps		Lgth mm	Diam mm	Thick mm	Material	Lgth mm	Diam mm	Diam mm	Pitch t/cm	Material	Lgth mm	Diam mm	Material
T1	1917	13.2	4.2	150	45	27	0.2	Ni	55	10	0.2	2.6	W	120	0.195	W
T2A	1917	11.5	2.5	250	45	38	2	Ni	50	10	0.2	3.55	Mo	100	0.138	Th-W
T3	1918	17.5	5.4	250	65	38	0.2	Ni	—		Note 1		Mo	176	0.23	Th-W
T4	1918	17.5	5.2	450	71	45	0.2	Ni		17.5	0.2	4.6	Mo	176	0.23	W or Th-W
T4A	1918	17.5	5.2	450	85	45	2	Ni	120	17.5	0.2	Note 2	Mo	176	0.23	Th-W
T5	1919	5.6	1.6	20	18	11	0.15	Ni	24	5	0.15	5.8	Mo	28.5	0.096	Th-W
U1	1918	Rectifier—same as T1 except no grid														
U2	1918	18.0	6.2	450	85	45	0.2	Ni	Rectifier					177	0.250	W or Th-W

Note 1. The grid of the T3 consisted of a helix 95 mm long with a center section 65 mm long, and two end sections each 15 mm long. The pitch of the end sections is not given. The pitch of the center section is 4.6 turns/cm.

Note 2. The grid of the T4A consisted of a helix 120 mm long, composed of a center section 85 mm long, and two end sections each 17.5 mm long. The pitch of the center section is 14.5 turns/cm. The pitch of the end sections is 4.6 turns/cm.

particularly well suited for use in large transmitting tubes; the oxide-coated cathodes were used in low-power applications.

REFERENCES

1. B. Gherardi and F. B. Jewett, "Telephone Repeaters," *Proc. A.I.E.E.*, Oct. 1919, *38*:1255–1313.
2. A. C. Timmis, "Recent Developments in Long-Distance Telephony," *J. I.E.E.*, June 1936, *78*:601–628.
3. A. B. Hart, "The Telephone Repeater," *P.O.E.E.J.*, 1919, *12*:1–11.
4. R. von Lieben, "Kathodenstrahlenrelais," D.R.P. Nr. 179,807, application date Mar. 4, 1906, published Nov. 19, 1906.
5. C. Robinson and R. M. Chamney, "Gas Discharge Telephone Relays and Their Applications to Commercial Circuits," Part I of Paper 76, *Inst. P.O.E.E.*, p. 31.
6. *Ibid.*, p. 18.
7. C. Robinson and R. M. Chamney, "Technical Developments in Telephone Repeaters since 1917," Part II of Paper 76, *Inst. P.O.E.E.*, p. 65.
8. A. B. Hart, "Telephonic Repeaters," Paper 75, *Inst. P.O.E.E.*, pp. 11–12.
9. W. Noble, "The Long-Distance Telephone System of the United Kingdom," *J. I.E.E.*, 1921, *59*:389–408.
10. C. Robinson and R. M. Chamney, "Technical Developments . . . since 1917," pp. 68, 100.
11. H. J. Round, "Wireless Telephony," *Yearbook of Wireless Telegraphy, 1915*, pp. 572–582.
12. Bernard Leggett, *Wireless Telegraphy with Special Reference to the Quenched Spark System* (New York: E. P. Dutton, 1915), p. 164.
13. H. J. Round, "Direction and Position Finding," *J. I.E.E.*, 1919–1920, *58*: 224–257.
14. G. W. O. Howe, "The Marconi-Mullard Valve Patent Litigation," *Electrician*, May 11, 1923, *90*:500.
15. W. J. Picken, "Wireless Section—Chairman's Address," *J. I.E.E.*, 1941, *88*: 38–46.
16. H. M. Dowsett, *Wireless Telegraphy and Telephony: First Principles, Present Practice, and Testing* (London: Wireless Press, 1920), p. 131.
17. *Ibid.*
18. *Ibid.*
19. *Ibid.*
20. *Ibid.*, p. 143.
21. A. G. T. Cusins, "The Develoment of Army Wireless during the War," *Electrician*, Apr. 25, 1919, *82*:493–494. This is a condensed version of a paper of the same title which appeared in *J. I.E.E.*, 1920–1921, *59*:763–770.
22. C. E. Prince, "Wireless Telephony on Airplanes," *J. I.E.E.*, 1919–1920, *58*: 377–390.
23. Round, "Direction and Position Finding," p. 233.
24. B. S. Gossling, "The Development of Thermionic Valves for Naval Uses," *J. I.E.E.*, 1919–1920, *58*:670–703.
25. G. W. White, "The Discharge Tube Used as a Wireless Valve," *Electrician*, Oct. 22, 1915, *76*:103.
26. R. P. Denman, *Catalogue of the Collections in the Science Museum—South Kensington. Electrical Communication II. Wireless Telegraphy and Telephony* (London: HMSO, 1925), p. 44.
27. Leggett, *Wireless Telegraphy*, p. 165.
28. Gossling, "Development of Thermionic Valves," p. 674.

29. *Ibid.*, p. 685.
30. *Ibid.*, p. 686.
31. Denman, *Catalogue*, p. 38.
32. R. Stanley, *Text-Book on Wireless Telegraphy. V.II. Valves and Valve Apparatus* (2nd ed., London: Longmans, Green, 1919), pp. 174–176.
33. Picken, "Wireless Section," p. 39 (No. 15 above).
34. Gossling, "Development of Thermionic Valves," pp. 670, 674, 675.
35. C. L. Fortescue, "The Three-Electrode Thermionic Valve as an A.C. Generator," *Electrician*, Sept. 19, 1919, 82:294–295.
36. Gossling, "Development of Thermionic Valves," p. 679.
37. Denman, *Catalogue*, p. 38.
38. Gossling, "Development of Thermionic Valves," pp. 689–690.
39. *Ibid.*, p. 690.
40. J. Erskine-Murray, "Wireless in the Royal Air Force," *J. I.E.E.*, 1920–1921, 59:693–700. Lecture delivered May 14, 1919.
41. H. J. Round, *The Shielded Four-Electrode Valve* (London: Cassell & Co., 1927), p. 8.
42. F. Banneitz, ed., *Taschenbuch der drahtlosen Telegraphie und Telephonie* (Berlin: Julius Springer, 1927), p. 490.
43. H. deA. Donisthorpe, "The Marconi Four-Electrode Tube and Its Circuit," *Proc. I.R.E.*, Aug. 1924, 12:411–421.

Chapter 12

The Entrance of Industrial
Laboratories and Military Demands,
1910-1920: *Germany*

The early development of the telephone repeater in Germany followed much the same path as in Great Britain and the United States. Early in 1910 the firm of Siemens & Halske attacked the problem along the line of producing a receiver-microphone type of amplifying mechanism. They had secured the rights to the receiver-microphone repeater which had been developed in Great Britain by S. G. Brown. Using this as a basis, they succeeded in producing an improved mechanical repeater which could be adjusted to operate for some months without excessive maintenance.[1] This mechanical repeater is shown in Fig. 12-1. Its frequency response was not as good as desired, however, and the search for a better amplifier continued and brings us back to the work of von Lieben and his associates.

The diagrams in the German Patent 249,142 (Chapter 5) in all but one case show a ribbon cathode looped back and forth in the manner of an incandescent lamp filament of that time. This ribbon is oxide-coated and heated by a battery. In one suggested form the hollow mirror cathode and external magnetic control have been retained. Mention has been made previously of the reference in this patent to the work of de Forest, and the recognition by von Lieben of the potential amplifying characteristics of the Audion. Von Lieben and his associates had already had some experience in the use of a grid.

As noted in Chapter 6, de Forest, up to this time (1911), had not

Fig. 12-1. The Siemens & Halske mechanical repeater. (Reproduced
from *Siemens-Z.*, 1941.)

succeeded in utilizing the amplifying potentialities of the Audion.
This may possibly have been because of the use of improper coupling devices—the use of radio-frequency inductors and capacitors
—while trying to make it operate as a low-frequency amplifier. Otto
von Bronk, a Telefunken engineer, was more successful in this respect and in 1911 applied for a German patent (D.R.P. Nr. 271,059)
on the use of the "de Forest hot-cathode tube" as a *high-frequency
amplifier*.[2] He also obtained French, United States, Austrian, and
British patents on this arrangement,[3] which is shown in Fig. 12-2.

In August 1911 Robert von Lieben demonstrated to a group of
representatives of the leading German electrical manufacturers the
tube which he and Eugen Reisz and Sigmund Strauss had developed.

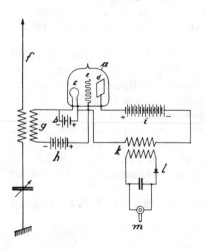

Fig. 12-2. Von Bronk arrangement
for using de Forest Audion as a
high-frequency amplifier. (Reproduced from D.R.P. Nr. 271,059.)

This demonstration, conducted in the Institut für physikalische Chemie der Universität Berlin, was so impressive that four of these companies—Allgemeine Elektrizitäts Gesellschaft (AEG), Siemens & Halske, Felton & Guilleaume Carlswerk, A. G., and the Gesellschaft für drahtlose Telegraphie mbH (Telefunken)—entered into a contract with von Lieben, Reisz, and Strauss for further development and jointly founded a laboratory called the Lieben Konsortium.[4] Siemens & Halske also entered into development work in their own laboratories, and the other three members of the syndicate set up a laboratory in AEG's Kabelwerke Oberschoenweide, with Eugen Reisz in charge. This laboratory opened March 1, 1912, and by July 12 submitted a progress report to the Reich Post Office. The engineers were given permission to use Reichspost facilities for field testing. Although the tests were not wholly satisfactory, the work continued.

The final form of the von Lieben tube, which came to be known as the LRS Relay or LRS Repeater, is shown in the German Patent 264,554,[5] the application date of which is October 15, 1912. This patent was issued to Telefunken, a subsidiary of AEG, which was one of the members of the syndicate. At the request of the Konsortium, Eugen Reisz presented a paper on this amplifier to the Elektrotechnische Verein on October 14, 1913, which was reported in detail in the *Elektrotechnische Zeitschrift*.[6] Reisz described the tube (Fig. 12-3) as follows:

> . . . g is the evacuated glass tube in which the three electrodes (cathode k, auxiliary electrode h, and anode a) are mounted. The auxiliary electrode extends over the entire cross-section of the tube and permits of current flow between the main electrodes through small openings, the main electrodes being connected to a direct current source. The cathode k consists of a thin platinum strip, wound in a zigzag fashion upon a glass rod, the metal surfaces being covered with a thin layer of barium and calcium oxides. The cathode is brought to a bright red heat (1000 °C.) by means of a battery of 30 volts.

Further details from other sources are as follows.[7] The cathode consisted of a strip of platinum about 1 meter in length, 1 millimeter wide, and 0.02 millimeter thick. The apertures in the auxiliary electrode (grid), which was an aluminum disk, were 3.5 millimeters in diameter. An amalgam was contained in the small side tube, which was used to enable the operator to maintain the pressure in the main tube at the proper level (about 0.01 mm Hg). Mercury vapor could be introduced when needed by heating the amalgam in the side tube. The anode was a spiral of aluminum wire about 2 millimeters in diameter. The anode battery was 220 volts, the anode current was 10–11 milliamperes, and the cathode heating current was about

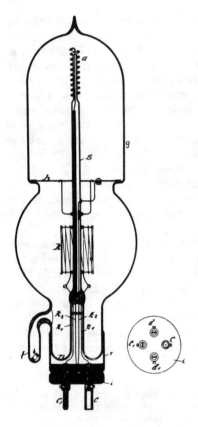

Fig. 12-3. Von Lieben mercury-
vapor repeater tube in final form.
(Reproduced from D.R.P.
Nr. 264,554.)

2 amperes. The amplification factor of the tube was about 33, and
a useful life of 1000–3000 hours was claimed.

In the earlier LRS relays the maximum diameter of the bulb was
4 inches, and the overall height was about 12 inches. Later a smaller
bulb about 7 inches high and 2 inches maximum diameter was
made.[8] Two types of bases were used. AEG-Telefunken tubes had
a metal clad base with four projecting pins so arranged that the
tube could not be incorrectly inserted into the socket. Tubes made
by Siemens & Halske had recesses in the base, the projecting pins
being in the mounting socket. Fig. 12-4 shows an LRS Relay made
by AEG-Telefunken, and Fig. 12-5 one made by Siemens & Halske.

When the LRS relay was in operation the bulb was filled with
the blue glow of ionized mercury vapor, except for a dark space
just above the grid. This tube was operated with a positive potential
on the grid, the potential being adjusted by means of a potentiometer. The most satisfactory operation was usually achieved when
the grid potential was adjusted so that the dark space extended

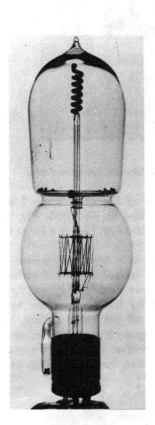

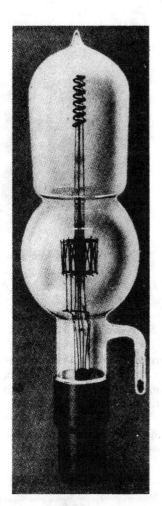

Fig. 12-4. Large LRS relay made by AEG-Telefunken, with perforated aluminum grid.

Fig. 12-5. Large LRS relay made by Siemens & Halske, with perforated aluminum grid.

from 1 to 2 centimeters above the grid. Some of the tubes had a graduated scale etched on the inside of the glass bulb, extending upward from the grid. This was probably used as a guide in making this adjustment.

The LRS relay was made not only in two sizes but also with two different types of grid, one a perforated aluminum disk, the other a wire mesh. The tube with the perforated aluminum sheet was intended for use as a "strong-current" amplifier[9] and the wire mesh

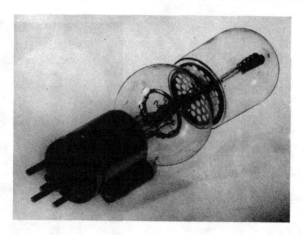

Fig. 12-6. Small LRS relay with perforated aluminum grid.

grid as a "weak-current" amplifier. One of the smaller von Lieben tubes of the strong-current type is shown in Fig. 12-6. Fig. 12-7 shows one of the weak-current type, while Fig. 12-8 is a large tube of this type.

The LRS relay was used for a time as a telephone repeater in Germany, but it was not satisfactory. It had several drawbacks. The relay was, like all ionization devices, undesirably noisy. The filament was subject to bombardment by the positive ions in the mercury vapor, which tended to knock off the oxide coating. Variations in the operating characteristics caused by external influences, such as temperature changes, were excessive. It was very sensitive to extraneous voltages which, if very great, caused paralysis of the

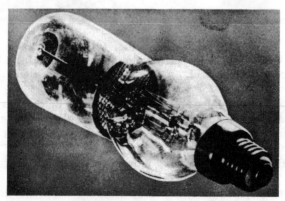

Fig. 12-7. Small LRS relay with wire mesh grid.

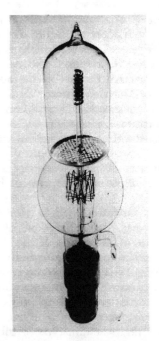
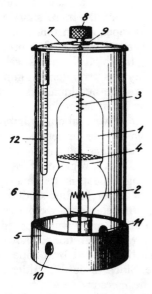

Fig. 12-8. Large LRS relay with wire mesh grid.

Fig. 12-9. Temperature regulator enclosure for LRS relay. (Reproduced from D.R.P. Nr. 293,460.)

tube. Most of these disadvantages are common to all devices which use mercury vapor. The introduction of this vapor had the effect of reducing the internal impedance of the instrument and permitting the use of larger anode currents than had been previously obtained in vacuum tubes. It also simplified the design of the auxiliary apparatus, such as the input and output transformers.

Some of the difficulties were improved in practice by enclosing the tube in a temperature regulator as shown in Fig. 12-9. This arrangement was made the subject of a German patent in 1914,[10] but it was a makeshift solution which only partially overcame the difficulties.[11] This LRS relay was used on some long nonloaded openwire circuits such as those connecting Königsberg (Prussia), Frankfurt (Main), Cologne, Danzig, and elsewhere before World War I.[12]

After the outbreak of the war there was an urgent demand for reliable, good-quality communication between battle areas and the headquarters of the army and navy. As early as 1914 circuits using the LRS relay repeaters were in use to connect the Eastern Front with Berlin and the Western Front. Conversation was carried on successfully between the headquarters at Luxembourg and the Hindenburg army in East Prussia, a distance of about 750 miles. This was accomplished by the use of a single repeater in Berlin. As the fighting fronts advanced, this single repeater proved inadequate, and the rapidly increasing length of circuits required the use of several repeaters in tandem. This necessitated the use of the four-wire type of circuit (first proposed by a Dutch engineer, Van Kesteren) in which the tubes were used for unidirectional amplification only. By this arrangement good speech transmission was maintained between the headquarters staff and Constantinople as well as with the armies in Macedonia, Rumania, and Russia. By the end of the war there were about a hundred repeaters of both two-wire and four-wire types in service which had sufficed to take care of the urgent military demands.

In 1914 a program of research was instituted with a view to adapting repeaters to general civilian use, particularly on cable circuits. After further studies were made of the action of the LRS relay, the elements were rearranged and a concentric cylindrical element assembly was adopted.[13] See Fig. 12-10. The mercury vapor filling was still retained, however, which meant that the operating difficulties caused by temperature variations were still to be overcome. Since these difficulties could be conquered only by eliminating the mercury vapor, the change to a high-vacuum type of tube was decided upon. The first attempts in Germany were actually made by the Telefunken Company with the cooperation of Professor M. Pirani in the incandescent lamp factory of Siemens & Halske.[14] One of these tubes is shown in Fig. 12-11.

Before leaving our consideration of von Lieben and his gaseous repeater, it should be mentioned that he was honored by the Austrian government by being pictured on a postage stamp. The stamp is one of the Charity Series of Commemorative Semi-Postals, issued in 1936 (Scott #B131).

The first hard tube developed by Siemens & Halske was the Type A, shown in Fig. 12-12, originally intended for use as a telephone repeater. The first of these tubes was delivered in the autumn of 1916. Military requirements took precedence, and the tubes were incorporated into amplifiers for eavesdropping on enemy conversations in the field.[15] The construction of these tubes at first leaned heavily on the de Forest Audion. As will be seen in Fig. 12-12A, the first attempt had a plane anode supported horizontally, a spiral wire grid pressed into glass rods, and a bowed tungsten filament. The first improvement was to substitute a punched metal grid for the spiral wire. This modification (Fig. 12-12B) tended to produce greater uniformity in the product. The production model is shown in Fig. 12-12C. About 50,000 of the A tubes were made.[16] This tube operated with a filament current of 0.52 ampere, an amplification

Fig. 12-10. Modified LRS relay with concentric cylindrical element assembly. (Reproduced from *Arch. Gesch. Math. Naturwiss. Tech.*, 1931.)

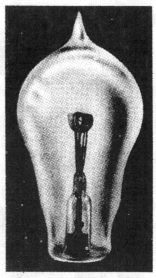

Fig. 12-11. First high-vacuum tube produced at the incandescent lamp factory of Siemens & Halske. (Reproduced from *Arch. Gesch. Math. Naturwiss. Tech.*, 1931.)

factor of about 14, anode resistance of 120,000 ohms, and a mutual conductance (slope) of about 120 micromhos.

The next step in the German quest for a satisfactory telephone repeater tube was completed in 1917. Three stages of its development are shown in Fig. 12-13. This was the Mc tube, which had a higher mutual conductance (slope) than the A. The amplification factor was about 6.7, the anode resistance about 10,000 ohms, and the mutual conductance (slope) about 700 micromhos. Fig. 12-14 shows a telephone repeater of World War I vintage which was equipped with Mc tubes.

The Mc tube operated with 2.1-amperes filament current at about 4 volts, had a space current of 10 milliamperes, with 220 volts on the anode, and gave an output of about 60 milliwatts.[17] The U-shaped electrode configuration was selected for the Mc in order to eliminate the necessity of putting tension on the filament to insure its position in a concentric cylindrical element assembly.[18] The filament was slightly arched in the direction of the open side of the U.

The K6 (Fig. 12-15) is similar electrically to the Mc tube, and was developed by AEG-Telefunken. The significant difference was in the filament, which operated with 1.1 ampere at 7 volts. The K6 followed more closely the design of the original de Forest Audion.

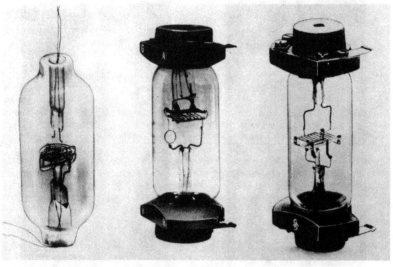

(A) *First attempt.*   (B) *Improvement.*   (C) *Production*
                                                           model.

**Fig. 12-12. Development series of Siemens & Halske Type A. (Repro-
duced from Veroff. NachrTech., 1935.)**

It too was double ended but had end fittings similar to those on the
Siemens & Halske Mc. In the K6 tube the filament was hairpin
shaped and was surrounded by a zigzag grid wound on formed
glass arbors. Both filament and grid were supported from the lower
press. The anode, shaped like an inverted U, was supported from
the upper press and fitted rather closely over the grid filament assembly.[19] The K6 tube was used in the final stages of the AEG K4
Amplifier shown in Fig. 12-16.

The Mc and K6 tubes were not only used in military amplifiers
but in the German civilian telephone network in the immediate postwar years. The output of these tubes was greater than that required
in ordinary repeater work, and they were subsequently replaced
about 1920 with smaller tubes especially designed for repeater use.
For this purpose equivalent tubes were made by several manufacturers, among them Siemens & Halske, AEG, Süddeutsche Telefon-
Apparate-, Kabel-, und Drahtwerke A.G. (a subsidiary of Felton &
Guilleaume), C. Lorenz, and Dr. Erich F. Huth Gesellschaft. With
the exception of those made by Huth, which had plane-parallel electrodes, all these tubes had cylindrical electrode systems.

The Siemens & Halske BF may be taken as an example of these
repeater tubes. The development of the series (Fig. 12-17) was
started in 1920 and the final design was evolved in 1922. It was the

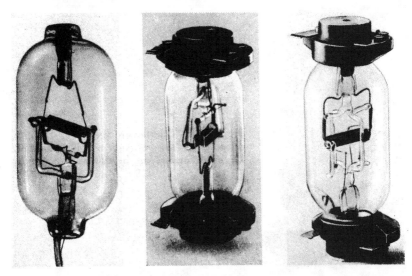

Fig. 12-13. Development of Siemens & Halske Mc telephone repeater tube. (Reproduced from *Veroff. NachrTech.*, 1935.)

Fig. 12-14. Repeater P rls 13 using Siemens & Halske Mc tubes.

Fig. 12-15. Telefunken K6 tube. (Reproduced from A. Forstmann and E. Schramm, *Die Elektronenröhre*, Berlin: R. C. Schmidt, 1927.)

Fig. 12-16. The AEG K4 amplifier using K6 tubes in the output stage. (Reproduced from J. Zenneck and H. Rukop, *Lehrbuch der drahtlose Telegraphie*, 5th ed., Stuttgart, 1925.)

first Siemens & Halske tube to be developed from the ground up specifically to meet the rigid requirements of a telephone repeater, and it was the standard in all Reichspost amplifiers from its introduction in 1922 until 1925. The cylindrical electrode system and quadriform glass supporting structure for the electrodes were carefully worked out to achieve exact maintenance of relative electrode spacings. It was found to have low sensitivity to microphonic disturbance caused by mechanical shock.[20]

In addition to the telephone repeater tubes described above, there was another type used during World War I by the Reichspost Ministerium in terminal amplifiers. This was a double-grid tube produced by Dr. Walter Schottky of Siemens & Halske.[21] The second grid was placed between the filament and the control grid to neutralize space charge. Two varieties were made, one by Siemens & Halske, Type 110 (Fig. 12-18), the other by AEG-Telefunken, the K26 (Fig. 12-19).[22] The K26 later became the RE26 (Fig. 12-20).

The filament current was 0.55 ampere at 3.2 volts for the 110 type, and 0.55 ampere at 4.0 volts for the K26. These tubes operated with both anode and inner grid voltages of 16–24 volts. The amplification factor was about 6 and the internal impedance about 9000 ohms. The mutual conductance (slope) was about 350 micromhos. The slope of the 110 was somewhat greater than that of the K26.[23] The

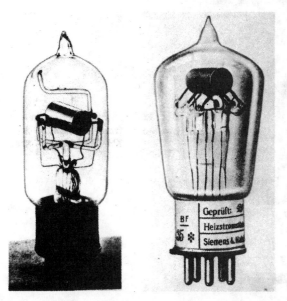

Fig. 12-17. Development series of the Siemens & Halske BF tube. (Reproduced from *Veröff NachrTech.*, 1935.)

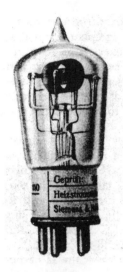

Fig. 12-18. Siemens & Halske 110 tube. (Reproduced from *Veröff. NachrTech.*, 1935.)

Fig. 12-19. AEG-Telefunken K26 tube. (Reproduced from Forstmann and Schramm, *Die Elektronenröhre.*)

Fig. 12-20. Telefunken RE26 tube. (Reproduced from F. Banneitz, ed., *Taschenbuch der drahtlosen Telegraphie und Telephonie*, Berlin, 1927.)

output was small, but these tubes were particularly adapted to the production of the desired gain at low anode potentials. This was essential for their use in military work, because the terminal amplifiers were self-contained portable devices operated from their own batteries. After the war these amplifiers fell into disuse, as there was no further need for the gain they produced.

As in the case of long-distance telephony, the first tube used by Germans in wireless telegraphy was the LRS relay. In 1913 Alexander Meissner built an oscillator using the LRS relay (see Fig. 12-21) for use in heterodyning the incoming carrier of continuous-wave telegraph signals from transmitting stations using high-frequency alternators as generators. This was applied in the marine receivers on German ships.[24] When World War I broke out, the German passenger liner S.S. *Vaterland* was docked in New York. It was promptly interned by the U.S. Government. When the U.S. entered the war on April 6, 1917, this ship was expropriated, renamed U.S.S. *Leviathan*, and remodeled for use as a troop carrier. All the German wireless equipment on board was removed and replaced with U.S. equipment. Fig. 12-22 shows the heterodyne oscillator which was found on this ship, and Fig. 12-23 the high-frequency amplifier used to boost incoming signals (if necessary) before heterodyning.

Some of the earliest types of AEG-Telefunken high-vacuum tubes have been covered in connection with telephone repeater development. By early 1914 Telefunken had standardized the use of high-vacuum tubes for radio reception. Two of the earliest of these standard tubes, the EVN94 and the EVN129, are shown in Fig. 12-24. These tubes had a construction similar to the Siemens & Halske A

Fig. 12-21. A. Meissner's first heterodyne oscillator, built in May 1913. (Reproduced from *25 Jahre Telefunken*, Berlin, 1928.)

—plane anode, spiral grid, and bowed filament (in this case, helically wound tungsten wire). The EVN129 had metal plates on each side of the filament. These functioned to prevent emitted electrons from reaching the walls of the glass bulb to which they might be impelled by the magnetic field set up by the filament current.[25]

The first application of these tubes was in the EV89 amplifier (Fig. 12-25), first produced in 1914.[26] The EVN129 was originally developed for use as a heterodyne oscillator; it was also used as a low-powered transmitting tube in sets of the type shown in Fig. 12-26, which were first made in June 1915. The designation EVN indicates that the tube was intended for use in a receiver (E = *Empfanger*) as an amplifier (V = *Verstärker*) at low frequencies (N = *Niederfrequenz*).[27] The EVN171 (Fig. 12-27) was another tube also intended for use in low-frequency amplifiers. It operated with a filament current of 0.5–0.55 ampere at 2.7 volts and 80–100 volts on the anode. It had an amplification factor of about 10, a mutual

Fig. 12-22. Heterodyne oscillator using LRS relay, found on the S.S. *Vaterland*.

Fig. 12-23. High-frequency amplifier found on the S.S. *Vaterland*.

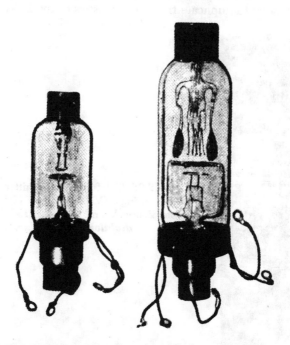

Fig. 12-24. Telefunken EVN94 (left) and EVN129 (right) tubes.
Reproduced from *Proc. I.R.E.*, Feb. 1922.)

Fig. 12-25. Telefunken EV89 amplifier, using EVN94 tubes. (Reproduced from Zenneck and Rukop, *Lehrbuch der drahtlose Telegraphie.*)

conductance of about 100 micromhos, and an internal resistance of about 100,000 ohms.[28]

Telefunken engineers had decided by 1914 to change to a cylindrical element assembly. One of the first of these tubes, made for use in the EVE211 amplifier, was designated EVE173 (Fig. 12-28). It was intended to duplicate the characteristics of the EVN171, and

Fig. 12-26. Telefunken transmitter, made in 1915, using EVN129 tube. (Reproduced from Zenneck and Rukop, (*Lehrbuch der drahtlose Telegraphie.*)

Fig. 12-27 (Left). Telefunken
EVN171 tube.

Fig. 12-28 (Right). Telefunken
EVE173 tube.

for a time both tubes were made, but eventually the EVN171 was abandoned. The earlier EVE173s had nickel anodes and grids. The grid was made of thin nickel ribbon and had a longitudinal stiffening rib of nickel. About 1918, because of the shortages of material in Germany, these tubes had anodes of copper and in some cases grids of copper as well. The copper was chemically treated to eliminate surface impurities and to make the tubes uniform in operating characteristics.[29] Not long after the EVE173 was put into production the Telefunken system of nomenclature was changed, and German receiving tubes were denoted by the prefix RE (*Röhre Empfanger*), transmitting tubes by RS (*Röhre Sende*), and two new types were added—RG (*Röhre Gleichrichter*) for rectifiers and RV (*Röhre Endverstärker*) for output tubes.[30]

The RE11 (Fig. 12-29) was being produced in quantities of 250 per day in 1918.[31] This tube, like most of its predecessors, was operated with an "iron-wire in hydrogen" ballast resistor in the filament circuit. One of these ballast resistors is shown at the left in Fig. 12-29. This tube had a tungsten filament of about the same characteristics as that of the EVE173 (0.55 ampere at 2.8 volts) but operated at an anode voltage of 40–70 volts, had an amplification factor of 8, and a mutual conductance of 120–150 micromhos—slightly higher than that of the EVE173.[32] It was a general-purpose tube.

The RE16 (Fig. 12-30) was another general-purpose tube bearing a close resemblance to the EVE173. This tube was used chiefly as a detector for cw work.[33] The extent of its use may be gauged by the fact that in the summer of 1918 Telefunken was producing them at the rate of 1000 per day.[34] Its filament took 0.5–0.6 ampere at 4.0 volts. The usual anode voltage was 65 volts, and the mutual conductance about 200 micromhos, the internal resistance being about 24,000 ohms. Its characteristics in general resembled those of

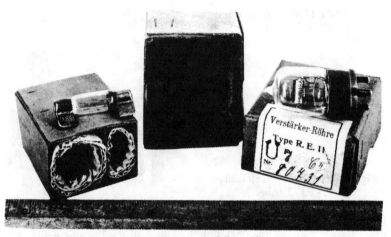

Fig. 12-29. The RE11 tube with ballast resistor.

the French TM, although it required less filament power. The normal anode current was about 1 milliampere.

In addition to his work on the telephone repeater tube, Schottky, among others, expended considerable research effort during this period on multiple-grid tubes. He realized at an early date that

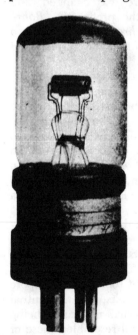

Fig. 12-30. The RE16 tube. The top is painted red. (Reproduced from E. Nesper, *Der Radio-Amateur: Broadcasting*, Berlin, 1923.)

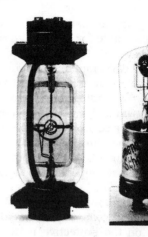

Fig. 12-31. Development of the SS (Siemens-Schottky) tube. Left: early development model. Right: commercial tube. (Reproduced from *Veröff. NachrTech.*, 1935.)

there were limits to the amplification which could be attained by the use of a triode, and set out to produce a tube which would be capable of high amplification with the low anode potentials available in army field equipment. Schottky investigated the possibilities of modifying the high-vacuum triode by the insertion of additional electrodes. He patented the "space charge" grid in 1915[35] and the "protective-network" grid in 1916.[36] His first patent on a multiple-electrode tube was applied for on June 1, 1916, and covered a tube designated by him as a "protective network" (*schutznetz*) type.[37] Another of his patents, applied for on January 24, 1917[38] was issued on a tube with a space-charge grid. In this tube grids were made of strips of sheet metal with their edges turned toward the cathode.

The first multiple-electrode tubes produced were tetrodes of the protective network type, known as the SSI, SSII, SSIII. An early development model and the final design of the SSI are shown in Fig. 12-31. The earliest construction of this type is shown at the left in the figure. The electrode assembly was cylindrical, the grids were of the "squirrel cage" type, and two presses were used. The cold electrodes were slotted so that it was possible to insert the filament assembly into the cold-electrode assembly after fabricating the two separately. The production model was single ended with a glass "star" supporting the electrode system.

The protective network was a grid inserted between the control grid and the anode. These tubes differed from the later-developed "screen-grid" type in that no attempt was made to use the additional grid to minimize the direct electrostatic capacitance between the anode and the control grid. This difference is relatively unimportant for low-frequency work, but it is of great importance in high-frequency applications. As Schottky himself pointed out, these tubes were not suitable for use at high frequencies.[39]

The SSI was first manufactured in 1917. It had a tungsten filament which took 0.38 ampere at 2.5 volts. The anode potential was 35 volts and the potential of the protective network was 12 volts. When so operated, the amplification factor was about 33 and the mutual conductance was about 400 micromhos.

The SSII, also known as the 97,[40] was a lower-powered, lower-gain tube operating with a filament current of 0.25 ampere at 2.2 volts, and with 10.5 volts on both the anode and the protective network. It had an amplification factor of 30 and a mutual conductance of 30 micromhos.

The SSIII, also known as 114, drew a filament current of 0.55 ampere at 3.2 volts, and operated with 125 volts on the anode and 45 volts on the protective network. It had an amplification factor of about 100 and a mutual conductance of 250 micromhos. The internal resistance was 400,000 ohms.

In addition to the SS series of double-grid tubes, Schottky also developed tubes with three grids. Fig. 12-32 shows a double-ended development model using slotted electrodes. The tube on the right in this illustration is a commercial design of the single-ended type.

Meantime, development of receiving triodes for radio use went on. While the scope of this work will not permit detailed consideration of all such types or even all such tubes produced by any particular manufacturer, some of those most likely to fall into the hands of the tube collector will be considered. Only one other Telefunken receiving tube, the RE20 (Fig. 12-33), will be considered at this point. The photograph shows two embodiments, the one at the left being the earlier. It had two grids; the inner one is a space-charge grid. The tungsten filament operated with 0.5 ampere at 2.8 volts. Both anode and space-charge grid operated at 12–18 volts, the

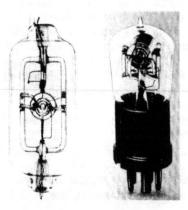

Fig. 12-32. Development of the Schottky triple-grid tube. Left: development model. Right: commercial tube. (Reproduced from *Veröff. NachrTech.*, 1935.)

Fig. 12-33. Two RE20 tubes. Left: earliest construction. Right: improved version. (Reproduced from *Telefunkenztg*, 1920.)

space current being 2–3 milliamperes.[41] The amplification factor was about 7 and the mutual conductance about 330 micromhos.

The development of transmitting tubes for radio work was carried on in parallel with that of receiving tubes. The first tube designed for transmitter work by Telefunken was the RS1 (Fig. 12-34), which was first used in a military application. This was a transmitter for use in the trenches and the plate power was supplied by a hand-cranked generator. The filament supply was a 12-volt storage battery. The RS2 and RS3 were little used and hence of no great importance. The RS4 was a higher-powered tube developed for use in a navy transmitter. It had an output of 50–75 watts with 1000–2000 volts on the anode. The filament took 3 amperes at 9 volts.

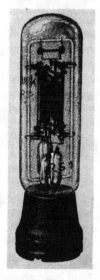

Fig. 12-34 (Left). Telefunken's first transmitting tube, the RS1. (Reproduced from *Telefunken Fest.*, 1928.)

Fig. 12-35 (Right). Telefunken RS5 tube.

The RS5 (Fig. 12-35) was an RS4 with improved characteristics and was in production (twenty-five tubes per day) in the summer of 1918. It operated with a filament current of 3 amperes, but various sources give the filament voltage different values—from 8 to 12 volts. When the RS5 was operated with 400 volts on the plate, the output was about 5 watts; when 600–800 volts were used on the plate, the output was 10 to 20 watts. The RS5 was also made by Siemens &

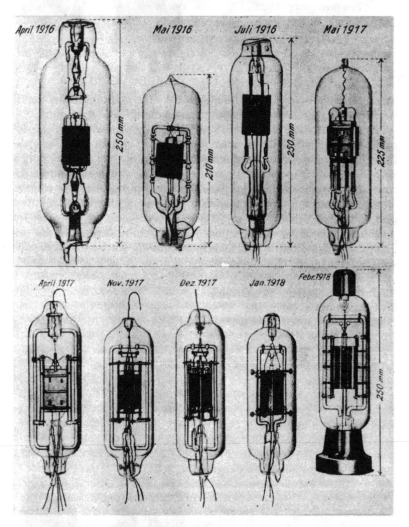

Fig. 12-36. Evolution of the Telefunken RS17. (Reproduced from E. Niemann, *Funkentelegraphie fur Flugzeuge*, Berlin, 1921.)

Halske. All these transmitting tubes are characterized by excellent glasswork in their internal construction.

The RS4 had been adapted to meet certain needs and became the RS5. The RS4 was adapted again for still greater power output and became the RS17, the evolution of which is shown in Fig. 12-36. This was a larger tube of the same general construction. The maximum power output was 200 watts. The filament current was 4.5 amperes at 12 volts, and the anode voltage required for 200-watt output was 3000 volts. The production rate of this improved tube was five per day in the middle of 1918.

In addition to the major companies whose work has been covered, there were a number of smaller manufacturers who also produced tubes during this period, chiefly for the German armed services. Many of these companies no longer make tubes. Their plants and archives have suffered the vicissitudes of two wars and enemy occupation, so that information on their products is difficult to obtain and fragmentary at best.

The largest of these manufacturers was the Süddeutsche Telefon-Apparate-, Kabel-, und Drahtwerke A.G., of Nurnberg. This company started making the type K6 receiving tube (Fig. 12-37) and the type ST12 (Fig. 12-38) tube in 1918. These tubes were made for carrier-current apparatus used on high-voltage transmission lines.[42] The ST12 (Fig. 12-38) shows the effect of metal shortages. The interior portion of the base in which the connecting pins are

Fig. 12-37. TKD K6 tube. (Reproduced from Forstmann and Schramm, *Die Elektronenröhre.*)

Fig. 12-38. TKD ST12 tube.

mounted is wood and the base shell is sheet iron with poor nickel plating. TKD was the trademark used in the company's early production. After the K6, all their receiving tubes bore VT numbers. From 1920 on, they used the trademark Te-Ka-De, and their tube production continued until 1956. Most of their tube archives were destroyed by enemy action in World War II.

Tubes were also made during World War I by Dr. Erich F. Huth, GmbH, of Berlin, which in 1923 became Huth Gesellschaft für Funkentelegraphie, mbH, and this company was taken over in 1926 by Telefunken and Lorenz (now Standard Electric Lorenz A.G.). Huth made both receiving and transmitting tubes. The earlier Huth tubes were designated by RE numbers and had cylindrical element assemblies. One of these, the RE32, is shown in Fig. 12-39. The use of the cylindrical element assembly involved them in patent difficulties, so they changed their construction and used plane-parallel electrodes. At this time they changed their tube designations to LE numbers. Fig. 12-40 shows the LE219, a tube with a filament which

Fig. 12-39. Huth RE32
receiving tube.

Fig. 12-40. Huth LE219
receiving tube.

took 0.5 ampere at 3.0 volts, an anode voltage rating of 40–80 volts, amplification factor of about 20, and mutual conductance of 200 micromhos.[43] All the Huth receiving tubes were characterized by tipless spherical bulbs and comparatively large bases.

Fig. 12-41 shows the Huth RS15, a 5-watt transmitting tube for use in an aircraft transmitter. A larger 2-kilowatt output tube, for a smiliar application and designated the RS30, is shown in Fig. 12-42.

Fig. 12-41. Huth RS15 5-watt transmitting tube (1917). (Reproduced from Niemann, *Funkentelegraphie für Flugzeuge.*)

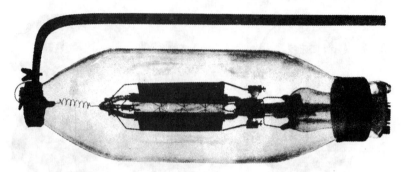

Fig. 12-42. Huth RS30 2-kilowatt transmitting tube (1917). (Reproduced
from Niemann, *Funkentelegraphie für Flugzeuge.*)

This tube was about 16 inches high and 4½ inches in diameter;
it operated with about 3000 volts on the anode.[44]

Studiengesellschaft Auer, later Auergesellschaft GmbH of Berlin,
was another supplier of tubes during World War I. All of their factories and administration buildings were lost in air raids in the last
days of World War II. Whatever remained after the raids was seized
by the Russians, since their plants were in the Russian zone.[45] Auer
made both receiving tubes (Fig. 12-43) and transmitting tubes (Fig.
12-44). The anode of this tube was made of fine molybdenum wire
in the form of a very dense gauze applied against the inside of the
bulb.[46] The filament took 2.85 amperes at 12 volts, and the anode
voltage was 400 volts.[47]

Fig. 12-43 (Left). Auer receiving
tube. (Reproduced from Nesper,
Der Radio Amateur.)

Fig. 12-44 (Right). Auer MW6
transmitting tube. (Reproduced
from E. Nesper, *Handbuch der
drahtlosen Telegraphie und Telephonie*, Vol. II, Berlin, 1921.)

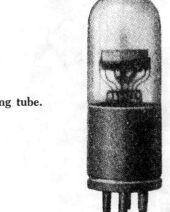

Fig. 12-45. C.H.F. Müller receiving tube.

C. H. F. Müller, GmbH, made X-ray tubes before World War I. In 1916 they began developing electronic tubes at the behest of the German government, at first making receiving tubes such as the hand-made one shown in Fig. 12-45. The tube shown operated with a filament current of 0.5 ampere and an anode voltage of 80 volts. The amplification factor was about 7.7, the internal resistance was 25,000 ohms, and the mutual conductance was about 310 micromhos.[48] In 1918 Müller received orders for 400 transmitting tubes and set up a "radio" department to produce tubes in quantities. Two samples of these—MSI and MSII—are shown in Fig. 12-46. The MSI was rated at 250 watts output at 2000 volts on the anode, and the MSII at 500 watts with the same anode voltage. In 1924 the "radio" department became a separate corporation, Radioröhrenfabrik, GmbH, and C. H. F. Müller went back to making X-ray tubes. A few months later, Radioröhrenfabrik GmbH changed its name to Valvo, GmbH, which still exists and is now known as Philips Valvo Werke.

C. H. F. Müller moved several times subsequent to the founding of Radioröhrenfabrik—from Hamburg to Berlin, then back to Hamburg, where its location changed several times. During World War II the factories and offices (with their archives) in both Berlin and Hamburg were almost completely destroyed by bombings. Hence, little documentation exists on their early work on vacuum tubes.

J. Seddig of Würzburg also supplied tubes to the German armed forces during World War I. These tubes were all designated RJW and bore a serial number etched on the tipless glass bulb. Fig. 12-47 shows five tubes which might be called a developmental series. The tube at the extreme left (Serial No. 512) is the earliest type. It

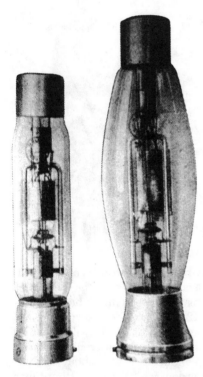

Fig. 12-46. Müller MSI (left) and MSII (right) transmitting tubes.

has massive end mountings similar to the early Siemens & Halske types A and Mc, and Telefunken's K6.

Later, as shown by the next tube to the right (Serial No. 8065), the construction was changed to utilize the Telefunken version of

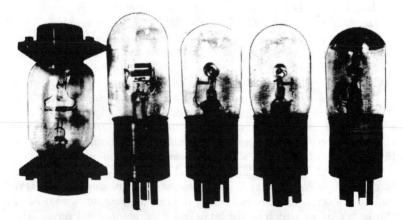

Fig. 12-47. Seddig RJW receiving tubes.

the four-prong brass base. The kind of metal used in the dark anode is unidentified but is thought to be nickel or iron. The sheet metal anode is formed into an almost complete cylinder, which has tabs extending downward toward the press. Each tab has two holes. In assembly the two sets of holes are aligned and fastened with wire in the manner of a staple, with the ends twisted together. The grid is a spiral of copper wire held in a single-ribbon clamp on one side. This clamp has two heavy supporting wires, one at each end, which are molded into glass supports. This results in a rigid element assembly with little chance of distortion by mechanical shock.

The middle tube (Serial No. 36698) has a copper anode and grid and an iron base shell. Its electrical characteristics are similar to the Telefunken EVE173. The next tube (Serial No. 78977) has a copper plate and grid, but the grid is of smaller diameter than those in the preceding tubes. Its characteristics approximate those of the Telefunken RE16. The tube at the extreme right (Serial No. 64768) is similar in construction to the middle tube (36698). It has red varnish on the top and a paper band with the word Tafunk on the base. The date on the label is 7-19-22. This is apparently a selected tube for use as a heterodyne oscillator in some particular circuit.

Early RJW tubes operated with a filament current of 0.55 ampere and with 80 volts on the anode. Under these conditions the amplification factor was about 8.3, the internal impedance 46,000 ohms, and the mutual conductance about 180 micromhos.[49]

C. Lorenz, A.G., started manufacturing tubes in Vienna. By 1920 they had moved to Berlin-Templehof. The exact date of relocation is unknown, because their early records were totally destroyed in World War II. Fig. 12-48 shows two of their tubes made in Vienna. The one at the left has a flat spiral electrode system and the one at the right a cylindrical electrode system using a gauze grid. Fig. 12-49 shows a two-stage low-frequency amplifier equipped with the earliest type of Lorenz tubes. These tubes were unsatisfactory on two counts. The gases occluded in the electrodes were slowly freed when the tubes were in service, and the unstretched filament was affected

Fig. 12-48. Lorenz receiving tubes made in Vienna. (Reproduced from Nesper, *Handbuch der drahtlosen Telegraphie und Telephonie*.)

Fig. 12-49. A Lorenz amplifier using two tubes of the type shown at the left in Fig. 12-48.

by mechanical vibrations and shock. This latter resulted in considerable noise in the output circuit.

Fig. 12-50 shows the progressive changes made in the structure. Fig. 12-50A shows the filament stretched between its support points. The grid is a spiral of wire held between rigid supports, and the anode is of molybdenum gauze on the inside of a glass cylinder which also supports the grid mechanically. This assembly had an improved mechanical stability. The next improvement (Fig. 12-50B) was the replacement of the gauze anode in the glass cylinder with a cylindrical sheet metal anode, still in a glass cylinder. This change resulted in the elimination of practically all noise in the output circuit.[50]

Fig. 12-50C shows the next modification: the anode consists of two bent metal plates in contact with the inner wall of the supporting glass cylinder, and the grid is a spiral which has been flattened into an elliptical shape. Fig. 12-50D illustrates another type of assembly where the grid is a spiral, concentric with the filament, and the anode is a pair of metal plates fastened in the glass cylinder. The latter two designs were not as good electrically as the design of Fig. 12-50B and were not produced commercially.

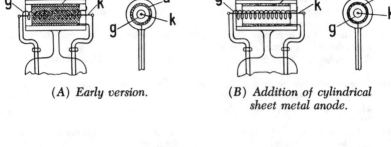

(A) Early version.

(B) Addition of cylindrical sheet metal anode.

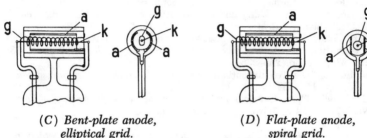

(C) Bent-plate anode, elliptical grid.

(D) Flat-plate anode, spiral grid.

Fig. 12-50. Steps taken to improve Lorenz tubes. (Reproduced from Jb. Radioakt., 1920.)

Lorenz also made transmitting tubes of 10- and 20-watts output during this period, but no detailed information concerning them is available. Information on several other tube manufacturers in Germany who may have started in 1920 is fragmentary. They will be covered in a subsequent chapter on German tubes made during the period 1921-1930.

REFERENCES

1. C. Gruschke, "Die Entwicklung der Fernsprechverstärker," *Siemens-Z.*, Mar. 1923, 3:113–119.
2. Gesellschaft für drahtlose Telegraphie, "Empfangsenrichtung für drahtlose Telegraphie," D.R.P. Nr. 271,079, Klasse 21a, Gruppe 68, application date Sept. 2, 1911, publication date Mar. 3, 1914.
3. Gesellschaft für drahtlose Telegraphie, "Receiving Station for Wireless Telegraphy and Telephony," Brevet d'Invention No. 456,788, application date Apr. 17, 1913, published Sept. 4, 1913. See also U.S. Patent No. 1,087,892 of Jul. 21, 1914; Austrian Patent 63,593 of Feb. 25, 1914; British Patent 8821 of 1913.
4. G. A. Fritze, "Wie die Verstärkerröhre vor 20 Jahren in die praxis eingefuhrt Werde," *Europ. Fernsprechdienst*, Jan. 1934, pp. 38–42.
5. Gesellschaft für drahtlose Telegraphie, "Entladungsröhre mit glühender Kathode und eingeschlossenem dampflieferndem Korper," D.R.P. Nr. 264,554, Klasse 21g, Gruppe 20, application date Oct. 15, 1912.

6. Eugen Reisz, "Neues Verfahren zur Verstärkung elektrische Ströme," *Elektrotech. Z.*, Nov. 27, 1913, *34*:1359–1363. See also *Electrician*, Feb. 6, 1914, 72:726–729.

7. J. Scott-Taggart, *Thermionic Tubes in Radio Telegraphy and Radio Telephony* (London: Wireless Press, 1921), pp. 62–63.

8. H. Thurn, *Das drahtlose Telegraphieren und Fernsprechen mit Hilfe von Kathodenröhren* (2nd ed., Berlin: Dietz, 1920), p. 7.

9. G. Eichhorn, "Tonverstärker," *Jb. drahtl. Telegr.*, 1914, 8:446–458; see p. 458.

10. Gesellschaft für drahtlose Telegraphie, "Arrangement for Cathode Ray Tube, for Operating as Amplifying Relay," D.R.P. Nr. 293,460, Klasse 21g, Gruppe 4, application date Aug. 23, 1914, publication date June 25, 1919.

11. Otto von Bronk, Die historische Entwicklung der Elektronenröhre in der drahtlose Telegraphie," *Telefunkenztg*, Sept. 1928, pp. 7–19; see p. 12.

12. E. Hopfner, "Entwicklung und gegenwartiger Stand der Verstärkertechnik in Deutschland," *Elektrotech. Z.*, Feb. 14, 1924, *45*:109–113.

13. Karl Skowronnek, "Die Entwicklung der Elektronenverstärker-Röhre (Lieben-Röhre)," *Arch. Gesch. Math. Naturwiss. Tech.*, 1930–1931, *13*: 225–276; see pp. 255–256.

14. H. Rukop, "Die Telefunkenröhren und ihre Geschichte," *Telefunken Fest.*, 1928, pp. 114–154; see p. 116.

15. C. Nebel, "Die Entwicklung der Siemens Fernsprechröhre," *Veröff. NachrTech.*, 1935, *5*(No. 4):215–226; see p. 216.

16. *Ibid.*, p. 216.

17. F. Vogel and A. Haag, "30 Jahre Siemens Fernsprechverstärker," *Siemens-Z.*, Jan.-Feb. 1941, *21*:26–36; see p. 27.

18. Nebel, "Siemens Fernsprechröhre," p. 221.

19. C. W. Kollatz, *Die Fernsprechtechnik* (Berlin: Georg Siemens, 1922), p. 247.

20. Nebel, "Siemens Fernsprechröhre," p. 222.

21. W. Schottky, "Über hochvakuum Verstärkerröhre. III Teil. Mehrgitterröhren," *Arch. Elektrotech.*, 1919, *8* (No. 9):pp. 299–328.

22. A. Gehrts, "Elektronenröhren–Kennelinien und Betriebsdaten," *Taschenbuch der drahtlosen Telegraphie und Telephonie*, F. Banneitz, ed. (Berlin: Springer, 1927), pp. 475–500.

23. *Ibid.*, pp. 476, 479.

24. A. Meissner, "The Development of Tube Transmitters by the Telefunken Company," *Proc. I.R.E.*, Feb. 1922, *10*:3–23.

25. *Ibid.*, p. 5.

26. Rukop, H. "Die Telefunkenröhren," p. 115.

27. *Ibid.*, p. 118.

28. J. Groskowski, trans. Teyssier, *Les lampes à plusieurs électrodes et leurs applications en radiotechnique* (Paris: Etienne Chiron, 1925), p. 126.

29. Rupert Stanley, *Textbook of Wireless Telegraphy. V.II. Valves and Valve Apparatus* (London: Longmans Green, 1919), pp. 187–188.

30. Martin, "Telefunken Röhrentypen," *Telefunkenztg*, Sept. 1923, *4*:51–55.

31. Rukop, "Die Telefunkenröhren," p. 49.

32. Gehrts, "Elektronenröhren," p. 476.

33. A. E. Harper, "Amplifying Bulbs," *QST*, Feb. 1921, *4*:27–28.

34. Rukop, "Die Telefunkenröhren," p. 49.

35. Siemens und Halske A. G., "Kathodenstrahlröhre mit Glühkathode," D.R.P. Nr. 310,605, Klasse 21g, Gruppe 11, application date Mar. 19, 1915, publication date Aug. 6, 1920.

36. D.R.P. Nr. 388,775, application date May 31, 1916.

37. Siemens und Halske A.G., "Vakuumverstärkerröhre mit Glühkathode und Hilfselektrode," D.R.P. Nr. 300,617, Klasse 21g, Gruppe 11, application date June 1, 1916, publication date Jul. 12, 1921.

38. Siemens und Halske A.G., "Durchbrochene Zwischenelektrode für Glühkathodenröhren," D.R.P. Nr. 300,191, Klasse 21g, Gruppe 11, application date Jan. 24, 1917, publication date Jul. 5, 1921.

39. Schottky, "Mehrgitterröhren," p. 320.

40. B. Pohlmann and A. Gehrts, "Werdegang einer Verstärkerröhre," Elek. NachrTech., Mar. 1925, 2:65–74.

41. J. Zenneck, and H. Rukop, Lehrbuch der drahtlosen Telegraphie (5th ed., Stuttgart: Ferdinand Enke, 1925), p. 756.

42. Werk und Wirken—50 Jahre Te-Ka-De (Nürnberg, 1962), p. 52.

43. Groskowski, Les lampes à plusieurs électrodes, p. 127.

44. E. Niemann, Funkentelegraphie für Flugzeuge (Berlin: Carl Schmidt, 1921), p. 140.

45. Letter from V. Kröger of Auergesellschaft GmbH to the author, dated Jan. 27, 1966.

46. Groskowski, Les lampes à plusieurs électrodes, pp. 133–135.

47. E. Nesper, Handbuch der drahtlosen Telegraphie und Telephonie, Vol. II (Berlin: Springer, 1921), p. 53.

48. H. G. Möller, Die Elektronenröhren und ihre technischen Anwendungen (2nd ed., Braunschweig: Vieweg, 1922), pp. 48, 50.

49. Ibid., p. 49.

50. C. R. Forth, "Neuere Formen von technischen Elektronenröhren," Jb. Radioakt., 1920, 17:174–178.

Chapter 13

The Entrance of Industrial Laboratories and Military Demands, 1910-1920: *The Netherlands, Russia, Australia, Italy, Denmark, Japan*

THE NETHERLANDS

During this period the pressure for electronic development was not as great in the Netherlands as in other European countries because the Netherlands was not directly involved in World War I. Nevertheless, the Netherlands military authorities were alert to the progress in new communications systems and investigated whatever fell into their hands.

On November 15, 1917, Army Lieutenant Tolk and Navy Officer DuBois were sent by the Netherlands Ministry of War to the Metaldraadlampenfabriek "Holland," a small company in Utrecht. As the name indicates, Holland made wire incandescent lamps. The officers requested the manager, K. M. E. Schuurman van Strijen, to make a series of radio tubes in secret. They gave him a Telefunken EVN94, taken from a German hydroplane which had landed in the Netherlands, asked him to analyze it and make one with similar electrical characteristics. The daily progress of the first Holland tube is recorded in the notes kept by Engineer F. B. A. Prinssen, to whom the work was assigned. Following are excerpts taken directly from his notes of 1917:

Nov. 15   Request received from the Netherlands Ministry of War. Engineer F. B. A. Prinssen ordered to make tubes. Filament measurements resulted in determining that the current needed was 0.53 ampere, and with an "iron wire in hydrogen" ballast resistor it operated from a 4 volt storage battery. There were two filaments, one of which was a spare. Anode voltage was 90 volts.

Glassworker Smith made model which was pumped by Prinssen. When the filament was lighted and 90 volts applied on the anode, a bluish glow appeared and the gas was removed by putting phosphorus in the pump tube. The Gaede mercury pump did not produce the requisite vacuum.

Nov. 16   The impossibility of reaching the wanted vacuum was probably due to gases coming out of the nickel anode and grid. The electrodes of the next model were treated by heating them in an atmosphere of hydrogen at 300 °C. followed by heating in a vacuum to 715 °C. A mercury vapor pump of the Langmuir type was used. This second model had lead-out wires of molybdenum because they contained no gas. [Prinssen obtained a Dutch patent on this feature: No. 9II 1918 5176.]

Nov. 22   Tube operated successfully with 120 v. on the anode without any trace of blue glow. This tube is the first Dutch high-vacuum tube.

Nov. 23   This tube and two others were taken by Lt. Tolk to the Netherlands Postal Telegraph and Telephone laboratory at The Hague and were tried out in a Telefunken receiver taken from a German mine sweeper. It was tested as a detector and audio amplifier. Then an amplifier was built using Holland #1, #2, #3 and ENV94 as the fourth.

Dec. 1   The amplifier was used in a successful test over an artificial line simulating the line between The Hague and Berlin. Paris also received. Tolk sent enthusiastic telegram to "Holland."

Dec. 7   "Holland" tube #19 double tube with two grids and two anodes, separately switchable, longest life, much improvement.

Dec. 10   Demonstration with 4 Holland tubes, the multielectrode tube in the 4th stage. Very good results.

Dec. 11   Tube made with cylindrical anode and grid.

Dec. 14   Demonstration with Holland tubes in receivers and amplifiers with good results. Tests witnessed by Dr. Egidius, president of the Holland Co. and Dr. Koomans of PTT.

Dec. 14–22   First orders from the Dutch Navy received.

The dates given in the extracts above are confirmed in the report made by Lt. Tolk to his superiors.

Fig. 13-1 shows one of the early Holland tubes. This company made tubes for the open market beginning in 1923 and went out of business in 1928. In 1929 the last president of the Holland Company,

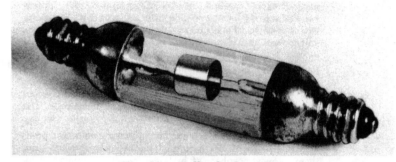

Fig. 13-1. Holland tube, 1917.

Mr. Boogardt, founded the Apex Lamp Works, which is still producing incandescent lamps.

The year 1917 marks another significant development in the Netherlands. There was at The Hague a small factory where crystal radio receivers and radio parts were produced under the firm name Nederlandse Radio-Industrie. The manager of this enterprise was Ir. Hanso Hericus Schotanus à Steringa Idzerda. Engineer Idzerda went to N. V. Philips Gloeilampenfabrieken at Eindhoven with a sample triode, which we assume was a de Forest Audion of the double-element type, and asked them to duplicate it. Reluctantly they agreed to do so but only after Idzerda contracted to buy at least 180 tubes per year. The first experimental tubes were made toward the end of 1917. The tube was identified as the Philips-Ideezet, the latter half of the name being the Dutch pronunciation of the first three letters of *Idz*erda. The element structure of the Ideezet was essentially the same as that of the Audion.

The first production Ideezets were delivered early in 1918. They were enthusiastically received, and the amateur demand was so great that Idzerda sold over 1200 by December 1918 (see Fig. 13-2). The Ideezet was a "soft" tube. Fig. 13-2 shows one which is marked "0.25 amp. Max 4 volts" on one end cap and "P-25v" on the other. The filament is of tungsten. The anodes are of nickel, approximately ⅜ inch square. The filament leads come out on one base, the grid and anode connections on the other.

By July 1, 1919, Philips, recognizing the potential, was offering for sale independently of Idzerda three versions of this tube. They differed chiefly in their filament characteristics. The filament of the Ideezet Type A operated at 4 volts, 0.25 ampere; Ideezet Type B at 2 volts, 0.5 ampere; and Ideezet Type C at 4 volts, 0.5 ampere. The Ideezet apparently made its debut in the United States early in 1920. In the March 1920 issue of *QST* results of tests made on one of these tubes rated at 0.25-ampere, 4-volts filament indicate that

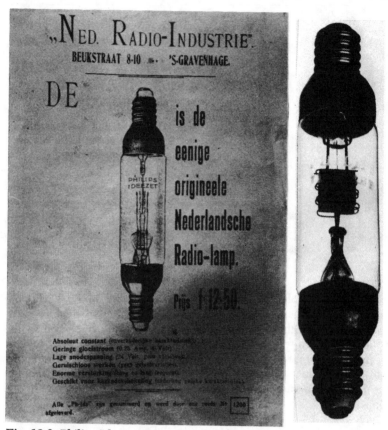

Fig. 13-2. Philips Ideezet Type A, 1918, with advertisement stating that 1200 have already been sold.

it attained normal brilliance and operated quite satisfactorily as a detector at 0.125 ampere.[1] The anode voltage applied was 19 volts. The tube tested was supplied by a representative of Philips, but the name Ideezet does not appear in the article.

By July 1919 Philips had also developed a hard transmitting tube known as the Zendlampe. The filament of this tube operated with 1.6 ampere at 6 volts. The anode voltage was 400–500 volts and the output was between 5 and 10 watts.

In 1918 a receiving tube was offered for sale to Dutch radio amateurs in a magazine advertisement.[2] The advertiser was N. V. Bal, of Breda. Samples of two varieties of this tube are shown in Fig. 13-3. Note the difference in the size of the electrodes, and note that these tubes are marked "Bal Breda" on one end and "Pope" on the other end. They carry the same labels, and no other infor-

Fig. 13-3. N.V. Bal detector tubes, 1918. The one at the left is the earlier construction.

mation is available. The name Pope is the mark of N. V. Pope's Draad- en Lampenfabrieken, of Venlo. According to their records they produced light bulbs in Holland before Philips but never made radio tubes.[3] Pope was taken over by Philips around 1920 and is an important wire and cable manufacturer in Europe. It is possible that they made radio tubes prior to affiliation with Philips, though the records are not extant. Pope brand tubes are now made by Philips.

RUSSIA

After the revolution of 1918 and during the period 1918 to 1921, all radio engineering work in Russia was necessarily carried out by Russian scientists and enigineers in complete isolation from the scientific work done elsewhere. It was accomplished under very difficult circumstances because of the disturbed conditions of Russian industrial enterprises.

The Institute of Russian Radio Engineers was founded on March 31, 1918, with a charter membership of thirty-four scientists and engineers who associated themselves in this organization to facilitate their work.[4]

The Peoples Commissariat of Posts and Telegraphs established a radio laboratory at Nijni-Novgorod at which development work on radio projects was carried out. This included the development of vacuum tubes. One of the engineers at this laboratory, M. A. Brontsch-Brujewitch, had learned in 1917 of the French TM tube.

Fig. 13-4. Russian PR1 tube. (Reproduced from *Gedenkenboek N.V.V.R.*, 1926.)

He attempted to develop a similar tube at the shops of a radio station at Twer, where he had been stationed. He was transferred to the radio laboratory at Nijni-Novgorod and continued his work. Toward the end of 1919 he brought out a receiving tube which was the only tube available in Russia for a period of about two years.[5] This tube was designated PR1 and is shown in Fig. 13-4.[6] The anode was of aluminum, for no other material could be obtained at that time.[7] The base was similar to that of the French TM. The electrical characteristics are not available.

AUSTRALIA

Tube manufacture in Australia was initiated by Amalgamated Wireless (Australasia) Ltd. in Sydney in 1920. The tube they produced was a soft triode with a double filament, designated the Expanse B Valve (Fig. 13-5). Its production continued to about the end of 1923.

The designation Expanse was chosen because at the time it was produced the A.W.A. Ltd. was associated closely with the British Marconi Company, which was then using a trademark consisting

Fig. 13-5. The Expanse B valve made by Amalgamated Wireless (Australasia) Ltd. about 1920.

of the word Expanse enclosed in a laterally elongated diamond. This trademark was adopted by the subsidiary A.W.A. Ltd. to apply to the tube which they started to make. It was later modified by adding the letters SY for Sydney below the word Expanse. Each tube had a serial number stamped on the anode. The use of the suffix B seems to indicate that there was a predecessor. There is some evidence to support this, because a similar tube minus the molded end-caps has been found. It was known simply as "Expanse double filament." The instruction sheet supplied with the Expanse B is interesting: it not only instructs the purchaser how to use the tube but also contains a section on how *not* to use it (see Fig. 13-6).

ITALY

The only vacuum tube development in Italy during this period was that of Quirino Majorana, who devised a modification of the de Forest Audion which he named an Electronic Deviator. He described this in a note to the Accademia dei Lincei in 1912.[8] He obtained a German patent on this arrangement,[9] which is depicted in Fig. 13-7. It is similar in construction and dimensions to the de Forest Audion except for the grid, which has been replaced with two comb-shaped electrodes with their prongs alternating in the same plane. This was the first use of co-planar grids, and we do not find it again for twenty years. Majorana's device was intended for use as a wireless detector; its possible use as a telephone relay was suggested by Max Iklé,[10] although Majorana had expressed doubts that this could be done.[11]

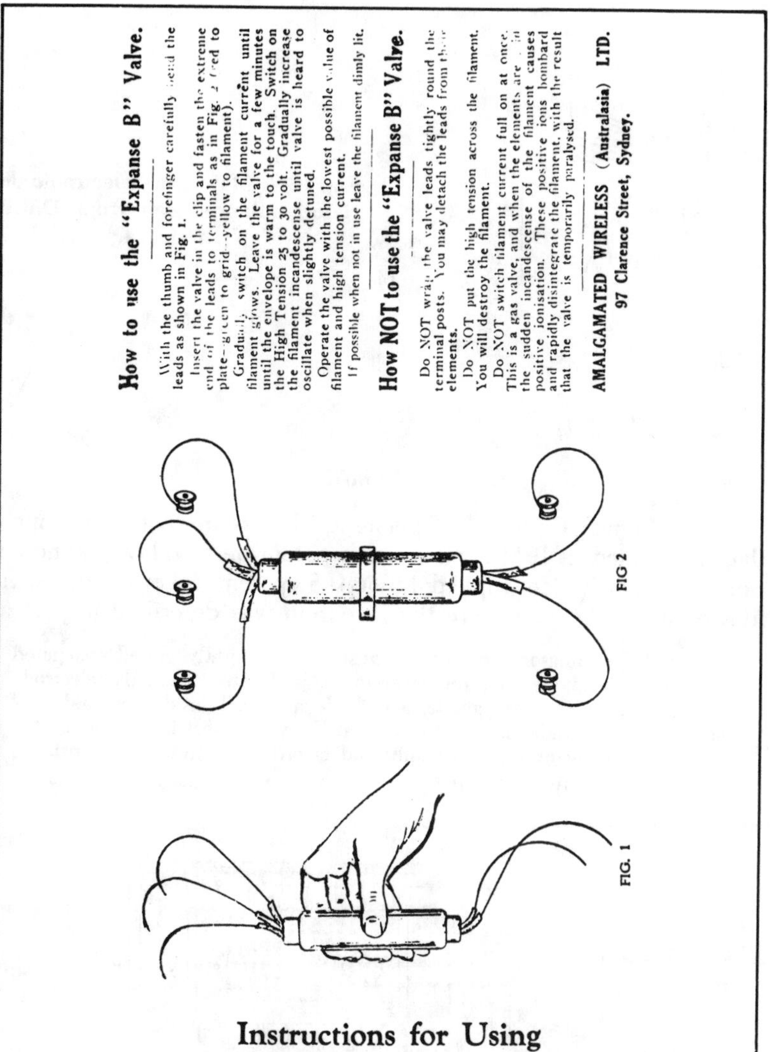

How to use the "Expanse B" Valve.

With the thumb and forefinger carefully hold the leads as shown in Fig. 1.

Insert the valve in the clip and fasten the extreme end of the leads to terminals as in Fig. 2 (red to plate—green to grid—yellow to filament).

Gradually switch on the filament current until filament glows. Leave the valve for a few minutes until the envelope is warm to the touch. Switch on the High Tension 25 to 30 volt. Gradually increase the filament incandescence until valve is heard to oscillate when slightly detuned.

Operate the valve with the lowest possible value of filament and high tension current.

If possible when not in use leave the filament dimly lit.

How NOT to use the "Expanse B" Valve.

Do NOT wrap the valve leads tightly round the terminal posts. You may detach the leads from the elements.

Do NOT put the high tension across the filament. You will destroy the filament.

Do NOT switch filament current full on at once. This is a gas valve, and when the elements are cold the sudden incandescence of the filament causes positive ionisation. These positive ions bombard and rapidly disintegrate the filament, with the result that the valve is temporarily paralysed.

AMALGAMATED WIRELESS (Australasia) LTD.
97 Clarence Street, Sydney.

FIG 2

FIG. 1

Instructions for Using

EXPANSE "B" VALVE
Pat. No. 1769—2-9-20

Manufactured by
Amalgamated Wireless (Australasia) Limited
97 Clarence Street, Sydney

Fig. 13-6. Instruction sheet for the Expanse B valve.

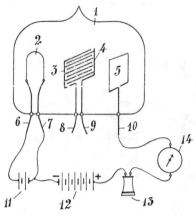

Fig. 13-7. Majorana's electronic deviator. (Reproduced from D.R.P. Nr. 281,014.)

DENMARK

Eric Magnus Campbell Tigerstedt, a Russian living in Copenhagen, applied in 1914 for a German patent on a "relay for undulatory currents."[12] He applied for a U.S. patent covering the same device in 1916,[13] and there the invention was described in part as

A relay for undulatory current comprising an airtightly closed evacuated container, an anode mounted therein, a perforated auxiliary electrode arranged inside the said anode, a cathode arranged inside the said auxiliary electrode and adapted to be heated by an electric current and a mantle consisting of a magnetically and electrically conducting substance surrounding the said container.

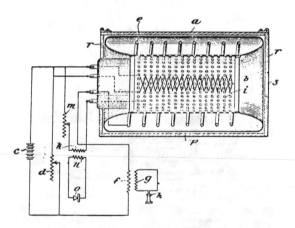

Fig. 13-8. The Tigerstedt telephone relay arrangement using magnetically and statically shielded concentric electrode assembly. (Reproduced from U.S. Patent No. 1,212,163.)

Fig. 13-8, reproduced from the U.S. patent, shows the Tigerstedt tube in a circuit arranged for use as a telephone repeater. The spiral wire *e* is the anode, the perforated cylinder *i* is the grid, and the helically wound element *b* is the cathode. The patent does not name the material of which the airtight evacuated container is made. The shield consists of a cylinder *p* closed by two end plates *r*, in one of which there is a hole *s* "through which the relay can be watched during its working." The arrangement is intended to amplify the output of the microphone *o* and feed it into the telephone receiver *h*. The author has found no records to indicate that this tube was ever made commercially.

JAPAN

A tube of special interest is shown in Fig. 13-9: it is believed to have been made in Japan before 1921. The sample in the author's collection bears the etched markings ANNAKA-AAB-5 and P.V.-30.

As may be seen in Fig. 13-9, this is a cylindrical unbased tube, a triode with a double filament. At one end are the three filament leads and the grid lead. The plate lead is brought out at the opposite end. The tube is about 1⅛ inches in diameter and 3¾₁₆ inches long. The cylindrical anode is about ¹¹⁄₁₆ inch in diameter and ⅞ inch long with a longitudinal gap about ⅛ inch wide. The grid is a spiral of wire, seven turns, approximately ¼ inch in diameter and ⅞ inch long. The grid has two longitudinal bracing wires not welded to the grid but exerting pressure to keep the grid in position. One of these bracing wires is insluated from the grid by what appears to be a glass tube. This brace also functions as the mid-tap on the filament. The portions of the lead-out wires in the presses appear to be of platinum. The low plate voltage specified (30 volts) would seem to indicate that this is a comparatively soft tube. It might have been patterned after the American AudioTron, but its structure was greatly improved mechanically.

How could the AudioTron have fallen into the hands of the

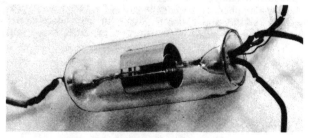

Fig. 13-9. Annaka AAB-5 triode.

Japanese in those days? One explanation might be found in a quote from a taped interview with Walter Schare, who worked for de Forest at Highbridge. "Before the war, when I was a salesman for de Forest I had a standing order with the Mitsui Company, located in the Metropolitan Life Building, for two pieces of everything de Forest sold. One was taken apart, the other kept intact. I don't know what they did with them." Possibly another Japanese merchant had a standing order for "two of everything" Cunningham sold. In 1918 Japan was the leading manufacturing and trading nation of all Asia.

The Japanese Chamber of Commerce in New York has no record of the Annaka Company. The archivist of the Museum of the Japanese Broadcasting System carries on the search.

REFERENCES

1. "A Dutch Amateur Valve," *QST*, Mar. 1920, 3:17.
2. *Radio Nieuws*, Apr. 1, 1918.
3. Letter of Aug. 4, 1971, from Cl. Receveur of N. V. Pope's Draad- en Lampenfabrieken to the author.
4. V. Bashenoff, "Progress in Radio Engineering in Russia, 1918–1922," *Proc. I.R.E.*, June 1923, 11: 257–270.
5. C. Zaitseff, "The Nijni-Novgorod Radiolaboratory of the Name of Lenine," *Gedenkenboek N.V.V.R., 1916–1926*, ed. J. Corver (Zutphen, Netherlands: Nauta, 1926), pp. 382–393.
6. Bashenoff, "Progress . . . in Russia," p. 258.
7. Zaitseff, "The Nijni-Novgorod Radiolaboratory," p. 384.
8. Quirino Majorana, "Su di an nuovo tipo di rivelatore di onde elettromagnetische fondate sull'emissione elettronica dei fili incandescenti," *Atti Accad. Lincei*, 1912, 5th Ser. 21:274–277.
9. Quirino Majorana, "Empfänger für drahtlose Telegraphie und Telephonie, bestehend aus einer Röhre mit darin angenordnetem kathodischen Glühdraht und positiv geladener Metallplatte," D.R.P. Nr. 281,014, Klasse 21a, Gruppe 70, application date Oct. 10, 1912, publication date Dec. 4, 1914.
10. Max Iklé, "Majorana's neuer Wellendetektor," *Jb. Draht. Telegr.*, 1912, 7:462–468.
11. Majorana, "Nuovo tipo di rivelatore," p. 277.
12. Aktieselkabet "Anod" in Kristiana, "Relais für undulierende Ströme," D.R.P. Nr. 314,805, Klasse 21g, Gruppe 4, application date June 27, 1914, publication date Oct. 5, 1919.
13. Eric Magnus Campbell Tigerstedt, "Relay for Undulatory Currents," U.S. Patent No. 1,212,163, application date Oct. 19, 1916, issued Jan. 9, 1917.

Chapter 14

The Early Days of Broadcasting, 1920-1930: *United States (Western Electric)*

As was done for the period from 1910 to 1920, the period from 1920 to 1930 has been divided into four chapters for the United States. Thus, this chapter covers developments by Western Electric during this period. Chapter 15 is devoted to de Forest, Chapter 16 to General Electric, Westinghouse, and RCA, and Chapter 17 to the independents.

At the end of World War I, when the demands of the U.S. armed services became negligible, engineers of the Western Electric Company's New York Engineering Department focused their attention on the further development of vacuum tubes for telephonic and other low-frequency applications. The injunction resulting from the Fleming–de Forest suit prohibited their use of the triode tube only at radio frequencies. The subsequent step-by-step innovations illustrate the teamwork of engineers. Each step was the culmination of attention to multitudinous details of construction and materials, meticulous measurements, and exhaustive performance testing.

Since the tube collector knows a tube chiefly by its appearance, in this chapter physical characteristics, significant changes in construction, and markings will be emphasized.

Beginning in 1913, in order to coordinate the work of the engineering staff of Western Electric, consecutive alphabetical designations were given to tube development projects. These letters, strictly laboratory identification for new devices, were official designations until manufacturing specifications were issued. An engineer having a letter assigned to his project could reserve a code number for his manufacturing specification. Some tubes for which code numbers were reserved never went into production. In like manner some letters were never coded. This accounts for the gaps and lack of continuity of code numbers and letters.

Briefly, to assist the collector: Types A and B—never coded; C—never coded, replaced by H; D—201A with three-pin base, 201B with four-pin base; E—205 series; F—never coded; G—211 series; H—103A; I—212 series; J—203 series; K—202A reserved but specification never issued; L, M—101 series; N—215A; NN—221A; O—104 series; P—not coded but a few were made as VT-3 for the U.S. Signal Corps; Q—104C; R—not coded; S—204A, but never in production; T, U—experimental, never coded; V—102 series; W—famous for Arlington–Paris tests, code 204B reserved but specification never issued; X, Z—variants of W, never coded; Y—never made.

There is no uniformity in the use of dashes on markings. The VT-1 may be marked VT1. The carton labeled 215A may contain a tube etched 215-A. The letters were essentially colloquial designations used by the engineers but were also frequently used in correspondence and on drawings. Officially they were abandoned when code numbers were assigned, but the official action could not break habits. Thirty years later engineers were still referring to the 101D as an L tube, and the 101F would always be the "half-ampere L tube."

The delineation of the Western Electric 101-type tube continues from Chapter 6. These were by far the best of the early tubes. They were made exclusively for telephone service where uniformity, reliability, and long life were the essential requirements. They are a striking example of the achievement of organized research producing a tube for service in a highly specialized application. The 101 tubes are still being used in telephone repeater stations.

Late in 1919 the patent markings applied to the base shell of the 101B were as follows:

PAT. IN U.S.A.

1–15–07	TWO PATENTS
2–18–08	4–27–15
10–17–16	12–19–16
12–17–18	

PATS. APPLIED FOR

Early in 1921 the patent date 10-5-20 was added to this marking.

Work was continuously being carried on to improve the characteristics of this tube, especially in the matter of power required for the filament. By 1921 theoretical studies and laboratory tests indicated that the filament power could be reduced without sacrificing the other characteristics. Late in 1921 the 101B was superseded by the 101D, and the manufacture of the 101B was discontinued in 1924.

The 101D was the same as the 101B except for the filament. The

101B required 1.30 amperes, whereas the first of the 101D tubes operated at a filament current of 1.15 amperes. The filament of the 101D, not twisted, had a platinum-nickel core instead of the platinum-iridium previously used. In order to readily distinguish these lower-current tubes from their predecessors, the tips were colored green by the application of lacquer. This practice was continued on the 101D until 1924.

The first production of the 101D tubes had the code marking etched on one side of the bulb in letters approximately ¼ inch high (Fig. 14-1) and had the serial number etched on the opposite side. These tubes bore the following patent markings on the base:

PAT. IN U.S.A.
1-15-07   TWO PATENTS
2-18-08   10-17-16
12-19-16   10-5-20
PATS. APPLIED FOR

Early in 1922 this marking was discontinued, and the standard type of marking was applied on the base, both on the shell and in the wax. Soon the patent marking was changed to read as follows:

PAT. IN U.S.A.
1-15-07   12-27-18
2-18-08   1-27-20
10-17-16   10-5-20
12-19-16
PATS. APPLIED FOR

Early in 1923 the policy of the American Telephone & Telegraph Company was changed, and the vacuum tubes were sold directly

Fig. 14-1. The earliest type of 101D repeater bulb, 1921.

Fig. 14-2. The 101D with Western Electric
marking.

to the operating companies instead of being leased to them. The
marking on the base "Property of the American Tel. & Tel. Company" was discontinued. Henceforth they were marked "Western
Electric—Made in U.S.A." followed by the code number and patent
dates (Fig. 14-2).

In 1925, in order to effect economy in manufacture and permit
the use of the same base shell on all tubes, identification was applied to the bulb in a single band. Late in 1925 the design of the
101D was changed and called for a molded base, but the code and
patent markings were applied to the tube in a single band around
the bulb as before (Fig. 14-3). The metal bases were difficult to
manufacture to the close dimensional limits required, the filling wax
tended to soften and flow under extreme high temperature conditions, and the micarta inserts on which the base contact pins were
mounted frequently absorbed moisture.

The first molded base having soldering tabs on the contact pins
was used for about a year and then was replaced with one having
a new type of pin. Each lead-out wire from the bulb was threaded
through an axial hole in its contact pin and soldered on the outside.
The same sort of contact pin is still in use on 101-type tubes. In
order to reduce the variation in resistance between the tube pin
and the socket spring, all 101-type tubes (including the early metal-
base shell) were equipped with precious-metal contact tips on the
base pins.

The practice of magnesium flashing to aid in obtaining the requisite high vacuum in the bulb was introduced just before the change

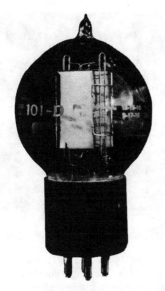 

Fig. 14-3. The 101D with molded base and markings on bulb.   Fig. 14-4. The 101D with metal base and magnesium flashing.

from metal to molded base. Fig. 14-4 is a flashed tube with a metal base. Some 101 tubes were still made without flashing for special applications.

By 1927 intensive studies of filament materials and their characteristics had been made, and methods of manufacture had been improved. A new filament which required only 0.5-ampere current at approximately 4 volts was developed, representing a great increase in efficiency and consequently a lower operating cost. A new repeater tube was designed around this filament with about the same plate characteristics as the 101D. At the same time the mechanical structure of the element assembly was entirely redesigned. The anode was changed to a completely enclosed type, the grid became a continuously wound flattened spiral, and the spacing between the elements was greatly reduced. The tube was known familiarly as the "half-ampere L tube" and officially as the 101F Vacuum Tube (Fig. 14-5). The 101F was used in the newly developed telephone repeaters. The 101D was continued in production for replacement in the older equipment.

In April 1927 the U.S. Patent Law was revised and required that the patent marking on any article made under a patent issued after that date should consist of the patent number rather than the date of issue, as heretofore. An article made under patents issued prior to the effective date of change in the law could be marked with

Fig. 14-5. The earliest form of the 101F vacuum tube.

Fig. 14-6. The 101D and 101F vacuum tubes with markings containing patent numbers instead of patent dates.

either the date of issue or the patent number. In accordance with the provisions of this law the markings on the bulbs of the 101D and 101F were changed in 1928 from dates of issue to patent numbers (Fig. 14-6).

In 1929 the practice of magnesium flashing the 101D was discontinued. Minor changes in design were made, which included the

Fig. 14-7. A 101F with the code number stamped on molded base.

relocation of the plate lead and the use of a shielded grid lead-in wire. About the same time, the system of putting the code marking in depressed characters on the base was adopted (Fig. 14-7). The patent markings were applied to a paper strip which sealed the carton in which the tube was packed.

The steps of development outlined above and in Chapter 6 resulted in a reduction of filament current from 1.6 amperes for the 101A to 0.5 ampere for the 101F and an increase in operating life from 400 hours for the 101A to 40,000 hours for the 101D. Truly a remarkable achievement! The construction of the 101D and the 101F remained unchanged up to the end of 1930. Further improvement continued but is beyond the scope of this work.

As development progressed on the 101, corresponding improvements were made on the 102 and 104 types. Originally the 101, 102, and 104 tubes were known as Telephone Repeater Elements. When Western Electric started producing tubes for the U.S. Government in World War I, it was considered desirable to distinguish them from tubes made for the telephone system. Accordingly, tubes for Bell System applications were known as Repeater Bulbs and those for so-called Non-Associate Use, as Vacuum Tubes. Repeater bulbs had code numbers in the 100 series, the others in the 200 series. This procedure was continued until 1922. About the middle of 1922 the term "repeater bulb" was abandoned, and all such tubes were called vacuum tubes, as noted in Chapter 6.

The distinction between Bell System and Non-Associate tubes

Fig. 14-8. The 208A and 209A vacuum tubes.

Fig. 14-9. The 102DW and 104DW vacuum tubes.

was still maintained in the code numbers. For example, the 208A tube was the same as the 101D but was supplied for Non-Associate use. The 209A was the same as the 102D, and the 210A was the 104D. The 208A and 209A are shown in Fig. 14-8. Late in 1922, to reduce cost, the 200 series was abandoned and replaced by the telephone system equivalent, with the letter W added, becoming

Fig. 14-10. The 205B vacuum tube. It is the same as the VT-2 except for the markings.

101DW, 102DW, and 104DW. See Fig. 14-9. In May of 1923, these in their turn were replaced by corresponding tubes without the W suffix. The distinction between Bell System and Non-Associate tubes disappeared.

Some of the tubes developed for the U.S. armed services were adapted to civilian use. One of these was the Signal Corps VT-2, the Western Electric designation for which was 205B Vacuum Tube (Fig. 14-10). The manufacture and sale of this power amplifier tube to the public continued until about 1924, when it was replaced by the 205D. The chief improvement was the filament, which was better electrically and differed from its predecessor in that it was plane instead of twisted. In all 205 types, including the VT-2, the bayonet locking pin was set at 45° from the position used in other Western Electric tubes. This was done to prevent accidental burnout should a lower-powered tube, such as the 101 or 102, be inserted into a socket intended for the 205 tube.

In the early 1920s there arose a demand for higher-powered tubes for public address systems and radio transmitters. This need stimulated the development of two series of power tubes familiar to those acquainted with the early days of broadcasting. One was known in the laboratory stage as the Type G, the other as Type I.

The Type G was one variety of the tube which later became known as the "50 watter," the progenitor of the Western Electric 211A and others of the 211 series. Three of these experimental Type G tubes are shown in Fig. 14-11. The Type G went through various structural changes before one commercially suitable was adopted and designated 211A (Fig. 14-12).

Fig. 14-11. Three experimental Type G tubes.

Fig. 14-12 (Left). The 211A
vacuum tube.

Fig. 14-13 (Right). The 211D vacuum tube with metal base.

The 211A operated with a filament current of 3.4 amperes at 9–10 volts. The anode voltage was usually about 750 volts and the anode current 40 to 80 milliamperes. The amplification factor was about 12 and the internal anode impedance 3000–4000 ohms. The operating life was about 300 hours. The base was originally designed by the Western Electric engineers for the Type K tube in 1917. Eventually this base was adopted as standard for all 50 watters by Western Electric and other manufacturers. The 211A was designated by the U.S. Navy as the CW-1818 and by the U.S. Signal Corps as the VT-4. The 211A was first made commercially late in 1921.

The 211-type tubes were designed for operation at a fixed value of filament current, and the value of filament voltage was determined by the filament resistance. They were usually operated, however, from a constant voltage source. Hence they were classified at the time of manufacture into five groups, and the classification was indicated by a letter etched on the bulb at the end of the serial number—A, B, C, D, or E. This was done so that when two or more were required to operate with their filaments in parallel from the same source, tubes suitable for operation at the same filament voltage could be selected (e.g., two As).

The 211A was replaced about the middle of 1924 by the 211D, which had a different filament. The characteristics of the new filament were sufficiently controllable so that the classification of tubes in accordance with their filament resistance was no longer necessary to their operation in parallel, and thus no classification letter was needed. One of the earlier 211D tubes is shown in Fig. 14-13. Note that the code and patent markings are applied to the bulb in baked enamel lettering. This tube was assigned VT-4B by the Signal Corps and CW-1818A by the Navy.

In 1926 the 211E was introduced. It differed from the 211D in that it was designed primarily as an audio-frequency amplifier. It had small spirals incorporated in the grid and plate leads (Fig. 14-14), which acted as high-frequency chokes, discouraging the tendency for high-frequency parasitic oscillations to occur in the circuit in which such tubes were operated in parallel.

The Type I tube, the forerunner of the 212 series of Western Electric tubes, was rated at 250 watts. Fig. 14-15 shows two of the experimental models of the Type I tube, and Fig. 14-16 shows a commercial model designated 212A. The 212A was about 13⅝ inches high and 3⅝ inches in diameter. It functioned as either an oscillator or a modulator. The filament current was 6.25 amperes at 12.5–14 volts. The nominal anode voltage was 1500 and the anode current 100–150 milliamperes. The amplification factor was about 16 and the internal anode impedance about 2000 ohms. The code and patent markings were on the base. This tube was assigned the designation CW-1819 by the Navy and VT-6 by the Signal Corps.

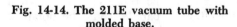

Fig. 14-14. The 211E vacuum tube with molded base.

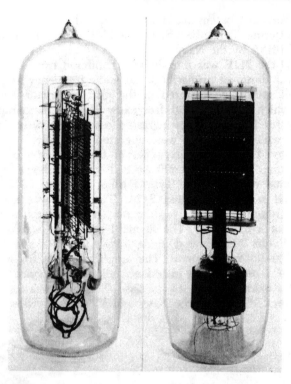

Fig. 14-15. Experimental I tubes.

As in the case of the 211As, the 212As bore a letter designation following the serial number to indicate filament resistance. In addition they bore a ½-inch high number (1, 2, 3, or 4) etched on the bulb a short distance above the base. This numeral was determined by the anode impedance of that particular tube. The classification was such that satisfactory operation in parallel could be obtained with two tubes whose classification numbers did not differ by more than one. A class-1 tube would operate satisfactorily with another class 1 or a class 2, but not with a class 3 or 4. A class-2 tube would operate satisfactorily in parallel with class 1, 2, or 3, but not with a class 4, and so on.

The 212A was replaced in 1924 by the 212D (Fig. 14-17). The 212D tubes were classified in accordance with anode impedance in the same way as the 212A, but the use of a new filament made classification according to filament resistance unnecessary.

Companions to the 211 and 212 series were the rectifier tubes of the 214 and 219 series. They were essentially the 211 and 212 types with the grid omitted and the filament-anode spacing reduced. The

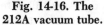
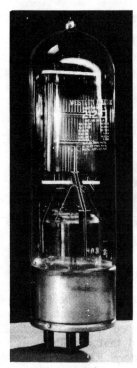

| Fig. 14-16. The | Fig. 14-17. The | Fig. 14-18. The |
| 212A vacuum tube. | 212D vacuum tube. | 214A vacuum tube. |

214A (Fig. 14-18) was the rectifier counterpart of the 211A. It was first made commercially about the middle of 1922. The 219A was first made commercially in 1923. In 1926 the 214A and 219A were replaced by the 214D and 219D respectively. The change was primarily in the filament. These tubes continued to be made into the 1930s.

Possibly the best known of the Western Electric tubes in the middle 1920s was the 216A, which was intended for use with amplifiers of small public-address systems and similar low-power applications. It was first made in 1922. It was essentially a 101D with wider tolerances in the characteristics, and the element structure resembled the VT-1. As originally sold, the tube had a paper band wrapped around the bulb, just above the base, which carried the following restrictive legend: "216A—Licensed for use only as a part of the Western Electric loud-speaking telephone outfit" (Fig. 14-19). Late in 1922 this paper band was discarded, and the restrictive legend was steel stamped on the base shell (Fig. 14-20). About the middle of 1926 the metal base was replaced by a molded plastic base. The

Fig. 14-19. An early 216A vacuum tube.

grid was changed from ladder type to a continuously wound flat-tened-spiral type. This arrangement was continued beyond 1930.

Three 216As were used in the Western Electric 7A Amplifier, which was so designed that the filaments could be operated on 60-cycle ac. The Western Electric 2A Current Supply Set provided ac for the filaments and incorporated a rectifier and filter to supply the necessary anode voltage. Two half-wave rectifier tubes, designated 217A, were utilized. The 217A was similar to the 216A but had no grid and the anodes were close to the filament (Fig. 14-21).

The 104A, covered in Chapter 6, was replaced by the 104D in 1922. It had an improved filament like that of the 101D.

The 223A, similar to the 104D but having a slightly heavier filament, appeared in 1922. This was designed for applications which called for more power than could be obtained from the 104D, but less than the output of the 205D.

Another Western Electric tube of this period, the 215A, is of special interest to collectors. To the Signal Corps it was the VT-5; to the Navy it was first the CW-1344 and later CW-38015. This was the original "peanut" tube, so called because it was about the size of a peanut. The 215A, originally known as the Type N vacuum tube, was the outgrowth of work which had been done during World War I by H. J. van der Bijl.

Van der Bijl had undertaken the task of designing for the U.S. Army a tube which had the lowest possible filament power requirement for use in battery-operated trench sets. The development

Fig. 14-20. The 216A vacuum tube with restrictive legend stamped on the metal base.

of the P tube, designated VT-3 by the Signal Corps, was not completed by the time the war was ended, and only a few were made. The VT-3 (Fig. 14-22) is about the size of the VT-1. The filament of the VT-3 operated with 0.2 ampere from a 2-volt storage cell, the voltage required being 1.8–2.1 volts. A total of 1000 VT-3s were made and delivered to the Signal Corps. It was never assigned a Western Electric code number nor made commercially.

Using the experience gained in the work done on the VT-3, Western Electric engineers designed the first commercial Western Electric tube having a concentric cylindrical element assembly. The first photograph of this tube, Type N, the 215A, still unbased, was made in November 1919 (Fig. 14-23). The filament was a single

Fig. 14-21. The 217A vacuum tube.

strand mounted vertically, the grid a spiral wire, and the anode a cylinder. Fig. 14-24 shows two variants of the early construction, the difference being chiefly in the bulb size. The tube shown at the left in Fig. 14-25 is the next variant. The spirally coiled filament tension spring has been replaced by a single bent wire. These early constructions were very sensitive to mechanical disturbances. This was to some extent overcome by modifying the element structure to include a glass reinforcing bead, as shown in the tube at the right in Fig. 14-25.

All of these earlier 215-type tubes had metal bayonet locking pins inserted in the molded base. The first pins had flat ends; later the ends were rounded. Subsequently it had a new base with a molded bayonet pin, as seen in Fig. 14-26. This illustration also shows that the size of the glass reinforcing bead has been increased. Fig. 14-27 shows the tube's various markings. The tube at the extreme right is flashed with magnesium.

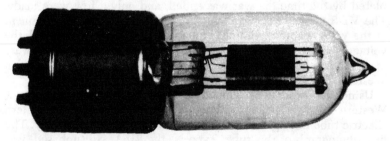

Fig. 14-22. The VT-3 vacuum tube.

Fig. 14-23. First photograph of the
Type N tube.

In 1927 the 239A (Fig. 14-28), a modification of the 215A, was introduced. It was equipped with a small UX base and a sturdier element structure for applications where low response to mechanical shock was all-important.

In the low-filament-power field two other tubes were brought out, the 230D in 1925 and the 231D in 1926. These were used in the same applications as the well-known RCA UV199 and UX199 types and are shown in Figs. 14-29 and 14-30. The 221D and 235D, first

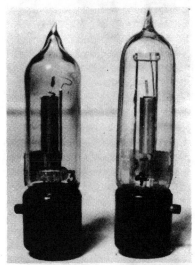

Fig. 14-24. Left: earliest type of the 215A vacuum tube. Right: later model with larger bulb diameter.

Fig. 14-25. Left: model of 215A vacuum tube with redesigned filament tension spring. Right: later model with small-diameter glass bead added for stiffening the element assembly.

Fig. 14-26. The 215A vacuum tube with glass envelope removed. This illustration shows the increased size of the stiffening glass bead and the molded bayonet pin.

Fig. 14-27. Type 215A vacuum tubes with various types of markings visible.

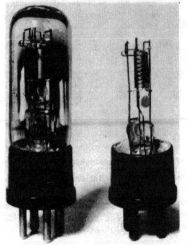

Fig. 14-28. The 239A vacuum tube. Left: complete tube. Right: element assembly.

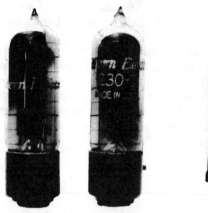 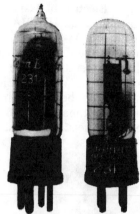

Fig. 14-29. The 230D vacuum tube.   Fig. 14-30. The 231D vacuum tube.

Fig. 14-31. The 221D and 235D vacuum tubes.

made in 1926, were general-purpose tubes designed primarily for Northern Electric of Canada, a Bell System affiliate. They were similar to the RCA UV201A and RCA UX201A, respectively, and are shown in Fig. 14-31.

It was during the 1920s that tubes with indirectly heated cathodes capable of operation on ac came on the market. Such tubes were not new to the Western Electric engineers, for in 1913 some of their earliest tube development work had been done along these lines. At that time there was little or no thought of using ac energy for cathode heating; the aim was to develop telephone repeater

Fig. 14-32. Nicolson's "Experimental Audion No. 1000" with indirectly heated cathode.

elements. Battery power was not only readily available in the telephone plant, but less liable to service interruptions than ac power. The advantage of having all of the cathode surface at the same potential was realized. This meant that electrons from all parts of the cathode would be equally utilized for the production of space current.

In the earliest years these tubes were known as "unipotential" or "homopotential" cathode devices, and work on their development was started in November 1913 by A. M. Nicolson of the Western Electric Engineering Department. By June 1914 he had devised a nickel sleeve, coated with cathode material, having a heater inside. One of Nicolson's experimental tubes, made in July 1914, is shown in Fig. 14-32. In April 1915 he applied for a patent on this construction, and the patent, No. 1,459,412, was issued on June 19, 1923. There are twenty-seven claims in this patent which pretty well cover the indirectly heated cathode type of tube. Claim 4 reads as follows: "A thermionic translating device comprising an insulating tube, a coating of thermionically active material on the outside of said tube, and a heating element within said tube."

Fig. 14-33. Indirectly heated cathode Western Electric vacuum tubes. Left to right: 244A triode, 245A tetrode, 247A early type with solid anode, 247A later type with mesh anode.

Development of indirectly heated cathode tubes for Non-Associate applications, such as talking motion pictures and public address systems, was begun late in 1927. In 1929 three tubes, using Nicolson's basic design, were put into production. These were the 244A and 247A triodes and the 245A tetrode (Fig. 14-33). All of these tubes had heaters which operated at 2.0 volts with a current of 1.4–1.75 amperes, the average current being 1.6 amperes. All were designed for anode voltages of 90–150 volts. Amplification factors were 10 and 15 for the 244A and 247A respectively. All had UY-type bases and pear-shaped bulbs. The control grid of the 245A was brought out to a cap on the top of the bulb. All of these heater-type tubes (which were adopted for early aircraft beacon receivers) were available from Western Electric Company until 1975.

Chapter 15

The Early Days of Broadcasting, 1920-1930: *United States (De Forest)*

Early in the 1920s changes took place in the de Forest organizations. The West Coast firm, Lee de Forest, Inc., of San Francisco, was taken over by the Moorhead Laboratories, Inc.[1] The De Forest Radio Telephone and Telegraph Company of Jersey City, New Jersey, continued to operate on the East Coast. Its advertisements offered both transmitting and receiving apparatus, but little emphasis was placed on Audions.

By this time de Forest had started to work on a sound picture system which he called Phonofilm. In 1921 he ceased active participation in radio development, turned the operation and control of the De Forest Radio Telephone and Telegraph Company over to Charles C. Gilbert and Randall Keator, and went to Germany, where he set up a laboratory and devoted himself entirely to making sound picture systems and equipment. This was the beginning of ten years of chaos for de Forest's company.

In 1923 de Forest sold his controlling stock in the De Forest Radio Telephone and Telegraph Company to Detroit industrialists headed by Edward Jewett of the Page Motor Car Company.[2] In 1924 the company was reorganized as the De Forest Radio Company. Gilbert continued as president and de Forest was retained as consultant. In 1926 Arthur D. Lord became president.[3] The company went into receivership that same year, and Lord was appointed receiver in equity by the Chancery Court of New Jersey on June 24, 1926. In 1927 Powell Crosley, Jr. was president. In 1928 the firm went bankrupt. It was reorganized in the period 1928–1930 under James W. Garside as president, and the executive offices were moved from Jersey City to a new plant in Passaic. At this time two engineers, formerly with Westinghouse, joined the technical staff: Allen B. Du Mont as chief engineer and Victor Q. Allen as his assistant. Both were experienced in automated manufacture and testing of vacuum tubes. Charles G. Munn took over the presidency in 1930 and was replaced in November 1931 by Leslie M. Gordon. De Forest Radio Company went into receivership in 1933, and its assets were bought by RCA. For a short time thereafter some RCA tubes bore the marking RCA-de Forest. All of these changes affected the company adversely.

In 1923 the De Forest Radio Telephone and Telegraph Company advertised a new line of receiving tubes in the September issue of *Radio Broadcast*. The ad appeared in the Advertisers Section (the pages of which were unnumbered) and offered for sale three tubes designated DV1, DV2, and DV6A. The V indicated that the bases were the UV type. These were the first of a series which was continued by the De Forest Radio Company after its reorganization late in 1924.

The DV1 and DV6A were made only for a short time, but others were added. By early 1925 the series consisted of the DV2, DV3, DV3A (base similar to the UV199), and DV5. By 1926 (after the advent of the UX base), the DV3A was discontinued and the DV7, DL2, DL4, DL5, and DL7 had been added. The letter L signified that the tube had a UX-type base with "long" pins. In 1927 all the DVs offered in 1926 were dropped. The DV3A was reinstated, and the DL3, DL9, DL14, DL15, and DR were added. The DR was a half-wave power rectifier. The D-01A made its appearance in 1927. Representative samples of these tubes are shown in Fig. 15-1.

The first new de Forest transmitting tube in this period, the Type H, was advertised in January 1926.[4] It was an unbased tube with widely separated leads for use at frequencies as high as 300 megahertz. Like all de Forest transmitting tubes made up to this time, it was rated on input rather than output. The maximum permissible input was 150 watts. The filament took 2.35 amperes at 10 volts. Maximum permissible anode voltage was 3000 volts, and maximum anode current was 50 milliamperes. Type HR, the rectifier counterpart of the H, was not advertised until some months later.[5] The HR had the same filament as the H. The maximum anode potential was given as 2000 volts rms, and the anode current 250 milliamperes maximum. Types H and HR are shown in Fig. 15-2. One HR was capable of supplying anode power to four Hs.

Later that year the De Forest Company introduced a new transmitter tube. There was some confusion in the nomenclature of the advertising pamphlet. The cover contained a picture of the tube captioned "The NEW Type R," but the text on the following pages

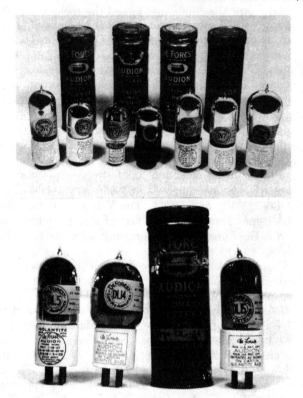

Fig. 15-1. Representative samples of de Forest tubes. In the upper row (left to right) are the DV2, DV3, DV3A, DV3, DV5, DV7, and D-01A. In the lower row, the DL5, DL14, and DL15 are shown. Metal shipping containers are shown for both series.

describes it as the RO. According to this ad, it would fit any standard 50-watt tube socket. It was rated at 300 watts input and was said to be capable of operation up to about 120 megahertz. Anode voltages up to 2500 volts were permissible. The anode terminal was at the top of the tube. It had a "long-life" tantalum filament. A companion modulator tube, the Type RM, was also described.

This printed sheet described two other triodes designated types D and P. The Type D (Fig. 15-3) was a low-power oscillator. It was neither fitted nor intended to be used as an amplifier or modulator. For these two functions the Type DM was supplied, and the rectifier was the DR. All were single-ended tubes with UX isolantite bases. Type P or PO was rated at 250 watts output. This was the first De Forest Radio Company transmitter tube to be advertised with its rating according to output instead of input. It was

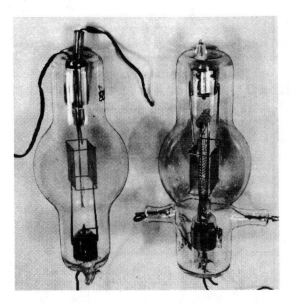

Fig. 15-2. The de Forest Types H and HR.

designed for use in broadcasting stations and for amateurs desiring powerful sets. The corresponding PM modulator and PR rectifier were also available.

The constants of these tubes are given in Table 15-1.

All the D, DN, and DL types were identified by a paper sticker on the glass bulb. The paper, however, did not adhere well, and

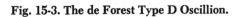

Fig. 15-3. The de Forest Type D Oscillion.

Table 15-1. Functional Characteristics of de Forest Oscillions

	Oscillators				Modulators			Rectifiers		
	D	H	RO	PO	DM	RM	PM	DR	HR	PR
Filament voltage, volts	7.5	10.0	10.0	15.0	7.5	10.0	15.0	7.5	10.0	15.0
Filament current, amperes	2.0	2.35	3.60	6.0	1.25	3.60	6.0	1.25	2.35	9.0
Plate voltage, volts dc	500	500 to 2000	2500 average	2000	500	2500	2000	—	—	—
Plate voltage, volts ac	—	—	—	—	—	—	—	550	2200	3000
Plate current, milliamperes dc	60*	50 to 100*	120*	250*	35	40	55	60	200 maximum	750
Grid bias, volts	—	—	—	—	−51	−220	−70	—	—	—
Grid leak, ohms	25,000**	18,000†	10,000‡	20,000§	—	—	—	—	—	—
Voltage drop, volts	—	—	—	—	—	—	—	40 at 35 ma	300 at 200 ma	800 at 750 ma
Maximum input, watts	30	150	300	500	17.5	150	250	—	—	—
Minimum wavelength, meters	2	1	2.5	2.5	—	—	—	—	—	—
Amplification factor	12	12	20	25	6.5	8.5	10	—	—	—
Price, $	9.00	18.00	35.00	110.00	9.00	35.00	110.00	7.50	16.00	90.00

* with tube oscillating

	**	†	‡	§
200 meters =	25,000	18,000	10,000	20,000 ohms
80 meters =	36,000	25,000	15,000	36,000 ohms
40 meters =	50,000	36,000	25,000	40,000 ohms

Fig. 15-4. Samples of the de Forest 400 series of receiving tubes.

once the sticker disappeared it was impossible to identify the tube without testing (a source of great irritation to tube collectors). Neither the size of the bulb nor the material of the base is positive identification. After the size of the bulb on the DL7 was changed, it looked exactly like the DL14. Without labels the DL9, D, and DR were identical. The exception to all this was the DV3A—it was the only one which had a UV199-type base.

By March 1930 the system of nomenclature had again been changed.[6] Receiving tubes were given numbers in the 400 series

Fig. 15-5. Samples of the de Forest 500 series for use in transmitter assemblies.

(Fig. 15-4) and transmitting tubes in the 500 series (Fig. 15-5). The other digits of the designation were the same as the ones used on the tube's RCA counterpart; that is, the de Forest 427 could be used where an RCA 227 was called for, and the de Forest 511 could replace the RCA 811.

REFERENCES

1. "Moorhead Represents De Forest Co. in West," *Pacif. Radio News,* Mar. 1921, *2*:255.
2. "New Ownership Marks Final Big Step in De Forest's Success," *De Forest's Standby,* May 1923, *1*:1 ff.
3. Obituary of Arthur D. Lord, *N.Y. Herald Tribune,* June 16, 1944.
4. De Forest Radio Co. advertisement in *QST,* Jan. 1926, *10*:1.
5. De Forest Radio Co. advertisement in *QST,* Oct. 1926, *10*:77.
6. De Forest Radio Co. advertisement in *QST,* Mar. 1930, *14*:96.

Chapter 16

The Early Days of Broadcasting,
1920-1930: *United States (General Electric,*
Westinghouse, and RCA)

In order to set the stage for this story it is necessary to review the founding of the Radio Corporation of America.

When the United States entered World War I the transatlantic radio telegraph station at New Brunswick, New Jersey, was taken over by the U.S. Navy. This station was owned by the Marconi Wireless Telegraph Company of America, which was controlled by the British Marconi Company. The station was equipped with a 50-kilowatt Alexanderson alternator installed by the General Electric Company for demonstration purposes. The Navy wanted the 50-kilowatt unit replaced by the 200-kilowatt alternator which was nearing completion at General Electric. American Marconi refused to finance this change. Because of the dire war situation, GE, at its own expense, installed the 200-kilowatt alternator and remodeled the entire system to make full use of its capabilities, thereby providing the Navy Department with the only reliable transoceanic communication system from June 1918 to March 1, 1920, when the station was returned to its owner.

Anticipating the day of return of this powerful station, British Marconi, in March 1919, opened negotiations with GE for the purchase of twenty-four Alexanderson alternators, fourteen for American Marconi and ten for British Marconi, with exclusive rights to their use. The transaction was practically concluded when a report of the proposal reached the Navy Department. On April 5, 1919, Rear Admiral W. H. G. Bullard, Director of Communications of the

Navy, and Commander S. C. Hooper, of the Bureau of Engineering of the Navy Department, visited the officers of the GE Company. Admiral Bullard pointed out that such a sale would result in foreign interests maintaining a monopoly on worldwide communications for an indefinite period. He asked them, as patriotic Americans, not to make it impossible to form an American communications company powerful enough to meet competition of foreign interests. He proposed that GE organize an American radio-operating company, controlled wholly by American interests, which could exploit the advantages of the Alexanderson alternator in worldwide communications.

The GE Company ceased negotiations with the British Marconi Company and proceeded to work out plans for the proposed corporation. The master plan included the purchase of Amercian Marconi and the rights to use much other equipment and many types of circuits, some of which were owned or controlled by organizations other than American Marconi. The officers of GE moved swiftly. Tentative agreements were made, each one being contingent upon the confirmation of all. The parts of the puzzle dovetailed.

On October 17, 1919, GE caused to be organized under the laws of the State of Delaware the company known as the Radio Corporation of America. In the certificate of incorporation it was provided that "No person shall be eligible for election as a director or officer of the corporation who is not at the time of such election a citizen of the United States."[1] On November 20, 1919, the American Marconi Company was officially merged with the Radio Corporation of America. It continued to exist for legal purposes to wind up its affairs but ceased to function as a communications corporation. On this same date a cross-licensing agreement was effected between RCA and GE. On July 1, 1920, a cross-licensing agreement was concluded between GE and A.T.&T. By another agreement of the same date these rights were extended to RCA and the Western Electric Company. A similar cross-licensing agreement between RCA and Westinghouse Electric and Manufacturing Company was signed on June 30, 1921.

It should be borne in mind that RCA was formed as an operating company for the purpose of providing ship-to-shore and transoceanic communication. It had no manufacturing facilities until the formation of a subsidiary company, RCA Radiotron, Inc., in 1930. Up to that time it functioned as a distributing agent for apparatus (including vacuum tubes) made for it by GE and Westinghouse.

The first receiving tubes marketed by RCA were the UV200 Detector and the UV201 Amplifier (Fig. 16-1). They were announced in November 1920 and advertised for sale in the December issues of radio magazines.[2] The ads stated that these tubes were the prod-

Fig. 16-1. The Radiotron UV201 amplifier tube. The tube at the left was made by Westinghouse Lamp Company and the one at the right by General Electric. The carton in the center is General Electric.

ucts of work done in the Research Laboratory of General Electric and were being sold for amateur and experimental use only. In the UV designation U signified that it was an apparatus unit and V that it was a vacuum tube. This system of significant tube coding broke down rather soon. In the first RCA catalogue, dated September 1921, there was offered for sale the UV712 Audio Frequency Intervalve Transformer.

In the first production the UV200 and UV201 tubes were structurally identical. Both had tipped, pear-shaped bulbs. The UV200 was argon-gas filled at a pressure of about 0.05 millimeters of mercury. The UV201 had a vacuum as high as the pumps could produce. The bases were of sheet brass with a ceramic insert in which the contact pins were imbedded. Both tubes operated with a filament current of 1 ampere at 5 volts.

The marking "Radiotron-Model UV-200 [or UV-201]—Patented—Licensed for amateur or experimental use only" was rubber-stamped on the base in black ink. The ads mentioned above showed the word Radiotron etched on the bulb, but the author has never seen a tube so marked. The emblem of the Radio Corporation ⓡ was etched

Fig. 16-2. Change in RCA emblem, as shown on cartons.

on most of these early tubes, as was the emblem of the manufacturer. This same ⓡ appeared on the cartons in which the tubes were packed. The base marking on most of the tubes which have survived is almost illegible because of discoloration of the brass, and cleaning the brass usually results in the removal of the rubber stamp marks as well. The trademark was replaced by ⓡ in September 1922. Subsequently this etching was discontinued and replaced by a circular paper label carrying the same marking. A similar change in the trademark was made on the cartons (Fig. 16-2).

One exception to this system was the marking of tubes for Cunningham, who became a distributor of RCA tubes (see Chapter 9). According to his agreement with RCA, the tubes he sold were to be marked as he directed and were to bear no RCA identification. Cunningham used C numbers instead of UV, and CX instead of UX. The early tubes shipped to him had a C etched on the bulb in place of the RC and the later RCA etching. This applied to the marking of the cartons also.

Westinghouse Electric and Manufacturing Company and its subsidiary, Westinghouse Lamp Company, joined the RCA consortium in June 1921 and contracted to make tubes for RCA. Westinghouse had earlier engaged in tube development and was familiar with the techniques of manufacture. Records show that the first shipment from W. E. & M. Co., WD11 tubes, was received by RCA in January 1922; the second shipment from the same source, WR21 tubes, was received in February; the third shipment, UV201 tubes, was received in April. RCA also received a shipment of UV201 tubes in April from Westinghouse Lamp Company, but the UV201 tubes from the two Westinghouse plants were not similar in appearance or characteristics.

For the information of collectors, W. E. & M. tube development followed the cylindrical assembly idea. Their so-called type UV201 had a cylindrical plate, spiral grid, and a bulb like the WR21, 1¼ inches in diameter extending about 2½ inches above the UV base shell. The anode was ¼ inch in diameter and ⅞ inch long. It looked like an oversize WR21. It operated with a filament current of 0.8 ampere at 4 volts. See Fig. 16-3. Some of these tubes had Shaw bases. The base bore the black rubber-stamped marking "Radiotron-Model UV-201—Patented—Sold for amateur and experimental use only" on one side and "Westinghouse Elec. & Mfg. Co." on the other, each set of markings in a rectangular enclosure. About 3200 of these UV201 tubes were made between April and September 1922, when production of this tube ceased. It was not interchangeable with those made by the Westinghouse Lamp Company or General Electric; it resembled neither in appearance or in filament characteristics.

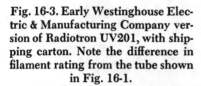

Fig. 16-3. Early Westinghouse Electric & Manufacturing Company version of Radiotron UV201, with shipping carton. Note the difference in filament rating from the tube shown in Fig. 16-1.

Some of the earliest Westinghouse tubes were stamped on the base "Manufactured for the Radio Corporation of America by Westinghouse Lamp Company U.S.A." in addition to the Westinghouse emblem etched on the glass. These tubes also had the word Radiotron in an arc rather than in a straight line parallel to the base. Even after the practice of etching the maker's name on the glass was discontinued, this arched marking continued to be used.

The GE UV200 and UV201 tubes had tungsten filaments which operated at 5 volts and took a current of 1 ampere. The widespread use of storage batteries in automobiles had brought about standardization, and the three-cell lead battery became the best available source of power for filament operation. This battery when discharged gave about 5.5 volts. It was thought best to allow 0.5 volt for drop in the battery connecting wires and the wiring in the set. When the battery was fully charged a filament rheostat could be adjusted to keep the current at the rated value. The operating temperature in these tubes was about 2400 K.

During 1920 the Harrison Works of General Electric by accident used some tungsten filament wire which contained thoria for the manufacture of UV201 tubes. It was found that a small percentage of these thoriated filament tubes operated satisfactorily when the filament voltage was reduced to one-half of the rated value. This resulted in the reduction of the filament temperature to about 1950 K. Intensive investigation ensued, and thoriated filaments were developed which had an electron production efficiency of the order

Fig. 16-4. Westinghouse E. & M. Co.'s Aeriotrons WR21D and WR21A, with packing cartons. The 21D, with lacquered tip, is at the left.

of 75 milliamperes per watt, whereas the tungsten filament used in the UV200 and UV201 had an electron production efficiency of only about 1.75 milliamperes per watt.

In the meantime Westinghouse was also engaged in developing receiving tubes. The first was the Aeriotron WR21 (Fig. 16-4), which was installed in the Westinghouse Aeriola Grand Receiver. This receiver was first advertised in 1922.[3] The WR21 had a small base with four long pins, all of the same diameter. There were two types, the WR21A and the WR21D. At first both were marked WR21, but the WR21A had a clear glass tip, while the tip of the WR21D was coated with green lacquer. The filament took 0.8 ampere at about 4 volts. The Aeriola Grand required one WR21D and three WR21A tubes. A WB800 Ballast tube was connected in the filament circuit of these WR21-type tubes to insure that the rated filament current was not exceeded when power was supplied from a 6-volt storage battery. Manufacture of these tubes was discontinued in September 1922.

The Aeriotron WD11 (later Radiotron WD11) in Fig. 16-5 was originally developed by Westinghouse for use as a detector in their Aeriola Sr. Receiver, which also appeared in 1922.[4] The WD11 was the first of the Westinghouse broadcast type of tubes to have an oxide-coated filament, which operated with 0.25 ampere at 1.1 volts. The tube could be operated on a single dry cell for filament power. It had a small base with four long pins. The anode pin was larger in diameter than the others to insure proper positioning in the socket. The WD11 worked satisfactorily at an anode potential

Fig. 16-5. Westinghouse E. & M. Co.'s Aeriotron WD11, with packing
carton. Note the lime getter on the press.

of 22.5 volts. The early Aeriotron WD11 did not use a "getter." In
later production the Radiotron WD11 had a lime getter applied
on both flat sides of the press just below the lead-out wires. The
WD12 was the same electrically as the WD11 but was made with
a UV-type base. It was introduced in 1923 and discontinued in
1926. It was replaced by the WX12 in 1925.

At GE research had continued on the thoriated filament. The
first tubes made with this filament were 50-watt power tubes for
the Navy. For general use the first thoriated filament tubes were
the UV199 and UV201A. The UV199 (Fig. 16-6) was intended for
equipment which was powered by dry batteries. The first production samples were made in October 1921 at the Harrison Lamp
Works. They had a thoriated filament 0.9 mil in diameter and operated at 0.135 ampere at 3.0 volts. In December 1921 a change was
made to use 0.6-mil wire, thus producing a 0.06-ampere filament.
This tube had a total emission of about 6 milliamperes, which was
the same as the UV201.

The UV199 was announced at the New York Radio Show in December 1922, but it was not available to customers until about the
middle of April 1923. Difficulties arose with this tube. When it was
used with three new dry cells, the available filament voltage was
4.5 volts. If the excess voltage was not absorbed, the thoriated filament was soon deactivated. This was a hazard of improper adjustment of the filament rheostat, and there was a tendency on the
part of the listener to turn up the rheostat to get maximum output
from the tube. As a protective measure, the filament was lengthened
to correspond to 3.3 volts. These tubes could still be operated with
dry cells which had been in service until their voltage dropped to

Fig. 16-6. Radiotron UV199 tube.

1.1 volts—the end of their useful life. The base of the UV199 was about 1 inch in diameter with pins about ⅛ inch long. Contact was made on the end of the pins by springs in the socket. No other RCA tube was made with this base.

Production of the tipless UV199 began about March 1924. The brass base was superseded by a molded base in the fall of 1924. Tubes made at Nela Park had a phosphorous getter and those from Harrison had magnesium. In April 1925 the UV199 was superseded by the UX199, announced August 1, 1925. Production continued up to 1931, although after 1927 few new receivers were built to use it. Nickel-plated contact pins were introduced in 1927.

The UV201A, which was announced at the same time as the UV199 at the New York Radio Show in December 1922, had been designed to utilize a thoriated filament in the existing UV201 structure and to replace the UV201. The electrode assembly of the UV201 was somewhat larger than that of the UV199, so manufacturing modifications were relatively simple. Work on production procedures was started in Nela Park and Harrison in April 1922 and progressed rapidly. In October 1922 manufacture of the UV201 was discontinued and production of the UV201A was initiated. There were sufficient stocks of the UV201 on hand to meet demands for some months. The UV201A sprang into instant popularity because it required only 0.25 ampere at 5 volts, one quarter of the filament power of the UV201. By August 1923 it was sold more widely than any other tube. Its life was satisfactory and production was free from trouble.

Late in 1923 the anode and grid structure of the UV201A were changed to increase the mutual conductance of the tube. This involved narrowing the anode structure to bring it closer to the grid, which increased the anode-grid capacitance. At the same time, the anode support arrangement was modified to eliminate the necessity of cutting away portions of the anode and bending these tabs out and around the vertical support wires. In the improved framework the vertical edges of the anode were extended far enough to be clamped to the support wire for the full length of the anode.

About this time the neutrodyne type of receiver (invented by L. A. Hazeltine) was becoming popular. It depended on the neutralization of the effect of the grid-anode capacitance of the tube; this was accomplished by inserting small neutralizing capacitors in an external circuit. These could, of course, be readjusted to provide the necessary balance. The Nela Park factory continued to manufacture UV201A tubes of the older construction for a considerable time after the Harrison plant started turning out tubes of the new design, and both tubes bore the same designation—causing some confusion for a few months. Replacement tubes in neutrodyne receivers had to be identical or the set had to be reneutralized.

The tipless construction and molded base were introduced in the UV201A at the time these same changes were made in the UV199 in 1924. Soon after this, the phosphorus getter was abandoned at Nela Park and magnesium getter was used on all tubes. In August 1925 the UV201A was withdrawn from the market and replaced by the UX201A. The UX201A base had a bayonet pin to adapt it to sockets designed to hold UV201As.

About the middle of 1925, the UX112 and UX120 (Fig. 16-7) were brought out in response to the growing demand for higher outputs. They were advertised in October 1925.[5] In the fall of 1924 work had begun on the design of the UX120, which was intended for sets equipped with UV199 tubes. Manufacture started in June 1925, and it was announced in September 1925. The UX120 operated at a filament voltage of 3.3 volts with a current of 0.135 ampere. The output was about 0.11 watt when operated at an anode voltage of 135 volts.

The UX112 was developed by Westinghouse as an output tube for battery-operated sets equipped with UX201A tubes. It had a 5-volt, 0.5-ampere filament of the oxide-coated type. At the recommended anode voltage of 157 volts, the output was about 0.20 watt. The UX112 was made for only a short time. It was replaced in 1927 by the UX112A, which took only half the filament power.

The design of the UX171 (Fig. 16-8) was started early in 1925. It followed the construction of the UX201A rather closely and had a thoriated tungsten filament operating at 5 volts and 0.5 ampere.

At the maximum recommended anode voltage of 180 volts, it would deliver 0.7 watt output. In October 1925 it was adopted by RCA but was not advertised or sold to the public until June 1926.[6] In November 1926 it was replaced by the UX171A, which had an oxide-coated filament operating with 0.25 ampere at 5 volts.

At the time the UX171 was brought out (May 1926), RCA also announced a new detector tube, the UX200A, to replace the UX200.

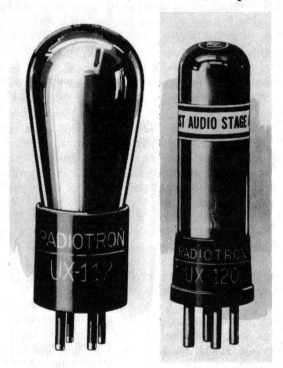

Fig. 16-7. Radiotron UX112 and UX120 tubes.

The new tube contained caesium vapor instead of the argon gas of the UV and UX200, resulting in much more stable operation and an increase in sensitivity. Manufacture on RCA orders started in April 1926. The UX200A had a thoriated filament which took 0.25 ampere at 5 volts. It continued in production into the 1930s.

Development of the UV210 started in May 1922 at GE to meet RCA's need for such a tube in loudspeaker systems. In 1924 it was first incorporated in the Rice-Kellogg form of dynamic loudspeaker which was marketed in 1925 as Radiola Model 104 loudspeaker. Early in 1924 the Navy began to use the UV210 in transmitting service. Because of its long life (15,000 hours) the UV210 became

Fig. 16-8 (Left). Radiotron
UX171 tube.

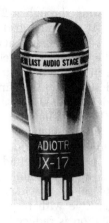

Fig. 16-9 (Right). Radiotron
UX210 tube.

part of the GE carrier-current receiving equipment and the RCA transoceanic receiving apparatus that same year.

The UV210 had a carbonized thoriated tungsten filament which took 1.25 amperes at 7.5 volts. The maximum recommended anode voltage was 425 volts. Anode current was 18 milliamperes. Power output was about 1.5 watts. It was used as an output tube in some Radiola receivers. The UV210 became the UX210 (Fig. 16-9) early in 1925, was announced by RCA in September 1925 and advertised in October 1925.[7] It is interesting to note that the tube shown in this ad is referred to as the UX210A, although the tube is plainly marked UX210. According to early records, no UX210A was ever produced.

The next development in high-power audio output tubes was the work of Westinghouse. It began in the summer of 1926, was announced as the UX250 in February 1928, and was made available to the public shortly thereafter. It had an oxide-coated filament which took 1.25 amperes at 7.5 volts (the same filament power as the UX210). Maximum recommended anode voltage was 450 volts. The anode current was 55 milliamperes, and the undistorted power output was 4.65 watts. This was more than three times the output of the UX210. It was similar to the UX210 in appearance but was larger.

In 1923 GE engineers started to develop a tube similar to the UV201A but which had a much higher amplification factor, specifically designed for resistance-capacitance coupled amplification. It was submitted to RCA engineers the same year. It was adopted in the latter part of 1926, designated the UX240, and announced in February 1927.[8] The amplification factor of the UX240 was 30 (about four times that of the UX201A). The thoriated filament was the same as that of the UX201A. It required an anode supply voltage of 180 volts, operating through a 250,000-ohm coupling resistor in the anode circuit. At the usual grid bias of −3 volts the anode current was about 0.2 milliampere; hence the effective anode voltage was 130 volts. The mutual conductance was 200 micromhos. The UX240 continued in production into the 1930s.

The last tube designed for dc filament operation by GE engineers during the period 1921–1930 was a four-element screen-grid type, the UX222 (Fig. 16-10). The electrostatic capacitance between the anode and grid of a three-element tube causes a feedback of energy from the anode circuit to the grid circuit which may produce instability. By placing a screen around the anode through which the electrons can pass, and maintaining the screen at radio-frequency ground, this troublesome capacitance can be greatly reduced. If the screen is made positive with respect to the filament, some of the space-charge limitation is reduced and a lower anode-filament impedance results. Extensive experimental work was done on the UX222 during 1924 and 1925. In July 1926 samples were submitted to RCA, and the designation was assigned in November. Production on a small scale was started in February of the following year at Nela Park, and the UX222 was announced by RCA in October 1927.

The two filament terminals and the anode terminal were connected to their proper prongs on the base, and the screen or outer grid was connected to the grid prong of the base. The inner (control) grid was connected to the cap on the top of the tube. The thoriated filament took 0.132 ampere at 3.3 volts. When the UX222 was operated as a screen-grid tube with the maximum recommended voltage of 135 volts on the anode, +45 volts on the screen, and −1.5 volts on the inner grid, the anode current was 1.5 milliamperes and the screen current 0.15 milliampere. Under these operating conditions, the amplification factor was 300, and the mutual conductance 350 micromhos.

Fig. 16-10. Stages in the assembly of the Radiotron UX222.

Early in 1926 there arose a demand for receiving tubes which could be operated with alternating current on the filaments. In receiving tubes of this sort it is important that the difference of potential between the ends of the filament be kept low. The ac hum in such a tube, in general, comes from two sources: one source is the voltage difference between the ends of the filament which produces a varying electrostatic field to which the emitted electrons are exposed; the other is the action of the varying magnetic field set up by the filament current on these same electrons. These two effects are opposite and tend to nullify each other. Establishment of the proper balance between current and voltage can thus hold the hum to a minimum.

In September 1926 RCA asked their manufacturing companies to work on an ac tube. Two months later Westinghouse submitted samples of the tube designated UX226. The samples were structurally the UX201A, had oxide-coated filaments which took 1.05 amperes at 1.5 volts, and a total emission of about 100 milliamperes. With a recommended maximum anode voltage of 180 volts and a grid bias of −13.5 volts, the anode current was about 7.5 milliamperes. At an anode voltage of 135 volts (maximum recommended for the UX201A), the UX226 produced 6 milliamperes current as compared with 3 milliamperes for the UX201A, with both operated at the same grid bias. The mutual conductance of the UX226 was 1100 micromhos compared with 800 for the UX201A under the same conditions. The amplification factors were about the same. The UX226 was announced in September 1927 and advertised (C-326) by Cunningham in December.[9] In appearance the UX201A and the UX226 were identical except for the markings. The UX226 was first used in both the radio- and audio-frequency amplifier stages of the Radiola 17. However, it could not be used as a detector. This problem was solved by the development of an indirectly heated cathode tube in time to advertise the Radiola 17 in the fall of 1927.

H. W. Freeman, of Westinghouse Electric & Manufacturing Company, in an article published in December 1922, described an indirectly heated cathode tube which was double ended.[10] A. M. Nicolson, of Western Electric, constructed indirectly heated cathode tubes in 1914 (see Chapter 6). In July 1925 samples of Freeman's tube were submitted to RCA. In April 1926 more samples were obtained. In June 1926 the designation UX225 was assigned to this tube (Fig. 16-11), and RCA placed orders for 1000 tubes at each of the three tube factories. During November Westinghouse suggested the use of a five-pin base to eliminate the necessity for the double-ended construction. In April 1927 the heater-type tube was adopted for detector applications, and the five-pin base was approved. With the adoption of this base the designation UX225 was

**Fig. 16-11. Proposed Radiotron
UX225 tube.**

changed to AY225 and then for commercial reasons to AY227, and
finally to UY227 (Fig. 16-12). On May 21, 1927, the UY227 was
announced in New York newspapers. Prior to this publicity there
had been a premature announcement of the UX225 on March 24,
1927, in a New York newspaper, and rather extravagant claims were
made for it.[11] These claims were denied by the sales managers of
both RCA and Cunningham in an interview published in *The New
York Times* on March 26, 1927.

The heater of the UY227 operated with 1.75 amperes at 2.5 volts.
When operated as a condenser-grid leak detector, the usual anode
voltage was 45 volts. When used as an amplifier with 180 volts on
the anode and −13.5 volts grid bias, the anode current was about
5 milliamperes. Under these conditions the amplification factor was
about 9, the mutual conductance was 1000 micromhos, and the
anode resistance 9000 ohms.

The first UY227s had sheet-metal anodes and were subject to grid
emission difficulties. Westinghouse engineers suggested that the
use of a mesh anode would eliminate this trouble, and the change
was soon made. Shipments to RCA began early in the summer of
1927, but the production was prone to failure in operation—open
circuits developed in the heater element. After a year of work on
the design and substitution of materials, the problem was eliminated.

Fig. 16-12. Radiotron UY227 tube.

The UY227 was announced several months before the UX222 tetrode, which was of the dc filament type. It at first seemed possible to make an ac-operated tetrode by substituting the heater-cathode assembly of the UY227 for the filament of the UX222, but the solution was not so simple. The power dissipated in the heater-cathode of the UY227 was about 4.4 watts, whereas that of the filament of the UX222 was only 0.44 watt, one-tenth as much. Such an increase in dissipation would result in grid emission and the increase in cathode area would increase the mutual conductance. Hence an increase in screening would be required to avoid the possibility of oscillation. Work was begun on the ac screen-grid tube in November 1927. By the end of the year a few samples were available. In July a set incorporating these samples was submitted for approval, and the tube, designated the UY224 (Fig. 16-13), was announced on April 20, 1929.

The heater-cathode combination of the UY224 was the same as that of the UY227. The UY224 operated as an amplifier with 180

Fig. 16-13. Radiotron UY224 tube.

Fig. 16-14. Radiotron UX245 tube.

volts on the anode, −1.5 volts on the inner (control) grid, and 75 volts on the outer (screen) grid. Under these conditions the anode current was 4 milliamperes, the amplification factor about 420, the anode impedance 400,000 ohms, and the mutual conductance 1050 micromhos. The direct capacitance between anode and control grid was less than 0.01 picofarad.

One other receiving tube worthy of note was introduced in March 1929. This was an audio-power output tube, intermediate between the UX171A and the UX210. It was designated UX245 (Fig. 16-14). Development was started by Westinghouse in June 1928, and most of the later work was also done by Westinghouse. The oxide-coated filament operated at 2.5 volts (ac or dc) and took 1.5 amperes. The anode was of sheet nickel, carbonized to facilitate radiation. When operated with 180 volts on the anode, with −34 volts on the grid, the anode current was about 25 milliamperes and the power output about 0.8 watt. The tube had an amplification factor of 3.5, anode resistance of 1900 ohms, and mutual conductance of 1900 micromhos. (These figures are approximate.)

The next tubes to be considered are the rectifiers of the early 1920s. The first of these, shown in Fig. 16-15, resembles the UV201 construction with the grid omitted. Whether it was intended for use as a low-power, low-frequency rectifier or as a substitute for the Fleming valves used in Marconi shipboard equipment is uncertain. Specimens of this tube which the author has seen bear no markings on the base or bulb. The element structure is similar to the early UV200 and UV201.

The first half-wave rectifier tube, the Kenotron Rectifier UV216 in Fig. 16-16, was originally advertised for sale in July 1921 and appeared in the first RCA catalogue, dated September 1, 1921.[12] This tube had a pure tungsten filament, designed for 2.35 amperes

Fig. 16-15 (Left). An experimental Westinghouse rectifier or Fleming valve.

Fig. 16-16 (Right). Kenotron UV216.

at 7.5 volts. It was intended for use in an anode-current supply unit for the 5-watt UV202 transmitting tube. The UV216 could operate with 550 volts ac on the anode and supply 20 watts at 350 volts dc. The filament emission was about 100 milliamperes.

In the fall of 1924, GE started working on a thoriated-tungsten filament for this tube. The improved product was first assigned the designation UV216A, but this was soon changed to UV216B to prevent confusion with the Western Electric 216A. By August 1925 the tube was in production and was on the market on September 1, 1925, as the UX216B.[13] The thoriated filament of the UX216B operated with 1.25 amperes at 7.5 volts. The filament emission was about 350 milliamperes. The maximum recommended anode voltage was 550 volts, and the maximum dc output current was 65 milliamperes. When operated under maximum conditions, the pulsating voltage at the input to the smoothing filter was about 470 volts dc. The UX216B was in production for about two years and was then superseded by the UX281.

The Kenotron UV217, a "50-watt" size tube, appeared on the market about the time the UV216 was announced. Both tubes were half-wave rectifiers. The UV217 (Fig. 16-17) had a pure tungsten filament, operating with a filament current of 6.5 amperes at 10 volts. It provided maximum energy at dc output potentials of 900–1100 volts. The maximum permissible anode potential was 1250 volts ac, and the maximum dc output was 150 watts. The UV217 was replaced about March 1926 by the UV217A, which had a thoriated filament taking 3.25 amperes at 10 volts. The maximum peak inverse voltage rating of the UV217A was 3500 volts, and the peak anode current was 0.6 ampere.

The UV217B was introduced in December 1926 but was replaced the following month by the UV217C, which had the same filament as the UV217A and also the same output current rating—0.6 ampere. It differed from the UV217A in that the peak inverse voltage rating was 7500 volts—more than twice that of the UV217A. It continued in production into the 1930s.

Fig. 16-17. Kenotron UV217.

Fig. 16-18. Rectrons UX213
and UV196.

Two small full-wave rectifiers came on the market in 1925, the Westinghouse UV196, and the GE UX213 (Fig. 16-18). The UV196, according to the ad in *Radio News*, October 19, 1925, was designed for the Dubilier Super-Ducon B Eliminator. It had two filaments, each connected to a pair of base terminals. The single anode was connected to the base shell. The filaments operated at 4.25 volts and each filament took 0.55 ampere. The maximum permissible voltage between the filaments was 440 volts ac and the output current was 50 milliamperes. The UV196 was the inverse of the UX213.

The UX213 was the first full-wave rectifier offered for sale by RCA. Work on this tube was started late in 1923, with the original objective being to produce a rectifier capable of supplying about 10 milliamperes at 90 to 100 volts. During the course of development, the requirements for voltage and power output changed drastically upward and revisions were made to meet the new needs. In December 1923 (before the UX base was adopted) the designation Rectron UV213 was assigned to this tube. In March 1924 there was another upgrading of the output requirements, and the UV213 went back to the drawing board. The final design was arrived at in the summer of 1924—a tube supplying 65 milliamperes at 160 volts dc at the output of the smoothing filter. It was announced by RCA as the UX213 in September 1925. It had a short commercial life and was superseded in May 1927 by the UX280.

Westinghouse had been developing a new full-wave rectifier of higher capacity than the UX213. The work was completed in April 1927, and the tube was designated the UX280. It was announced by RCA the following month. The filament of the UX280 (Fig. 16-19) was of the oxide-coated type, designed for operation under

Fig. 16-19. Radiotrons UX280 and UX281.

the same filament conditions as the UX213; that is, 2 amperes at 5 volts. The filament emission was in excess of 400 milliamperes. The rated maximum output current was 125 milliamperes, almost twice that of the UX213. The maximum recommended ac voltage per plate was originally 300 volts but was later increased to 350 volts. In order to assist in the dissipation of heat and reduce the tendency toward back emission, the anodes were carbonized.

The UX281 (Fig. 16-19) was also a Westinghouse development. Work was started on this half-wave rectifier early in 1927 and progressed rapidly. By May it was completed and the designation UX281 was assigned; it was announced shortly thereafter. The UX281 had an oxide-coated filament operating at the same voltage and current as the UX216B (1.25 amperes at 7.5 volts). The filament emission was about 600 milliamperes. The maximum recommended anode voltage was 700 volts ac. The maximum dc output current was 85 milliamperes, at which 620 volts dc were produced at the smoothing filter input. This tube superseded the UX216B.

Space limitations of this work restrict consideration of transmitting tubes of the early 1920s to those most likely to fall into the hands of tube collectors—tubes produced largely for use in amateur radio stations.

Power tubes were announced by RCA early in March 1921 and were listed in the RCA catalogue of September 1, 1921.[14] At the time of the announcement only the UV202 was available, but the press release stated that the UV203 would be available later in March, and the UV204 would be on sale some time in April 1921.

The UV202 (Fig. 16-20) was similar in construction to the early UV201 but larger—about 2⅛ inches in diameter and 5 inches high. It was rated at 5 watts output, a conservative rating, and had a

Fig. 16-20. Radiotron   Fig. 16-21. Radiotron   Fig. 16-22. Radiotron
UV202 tube.   UV203 tube.   UV203A tube.

tungsten filament which took 2.35 amperes at 7.5 volts. The normal anode voltage was 350 volts and the anode current 45 milliamperes. It had an amplification constant of 8, and an output impedance of 4000 ohms. This tube was beloved by the amateurs, who built transmitters with as many as six UV202s operating in parallel.[15] The UV202 was discontinued in 1925. It was replaced in the amateur field by the UV210, and later by the UX210, the latter having been announced on September 1, 1925.[16]

The UV203 (Fig. 16-21), the "50 watter," announced in March 1921, was advertised in April and appeared in the RCA catalogue of September 1, 1921.[17] It had a cylindrical bulb approximately 2 inches in diameter and an overall height of 7½ inches. The filament was of tungsten, operating with 6.5 amperes at 10 volts. The normal anode voltage was 1000 volts, and the anode current was 150 milliamperes. The amplification constant was about 15. It was claimed that "several" of these tubes could be operated in parallel because of their uniformity. Manufacture of the UV203 was discontinued in 1926, and it was replaced by the UV203A.

The UV203A (Fig. 16-22), announced in the summer of 1923, differed from the UV203 in several respects. The filament was of thori-

Fig. 16-23. Radiotron
UV204 tube.

Fig. 16-24. Radiotron
UV204A tube.

Fig. 16-25. Radiotron
UX250 tube.

ated tungsten, taking 3.25 amperes at 10 volts. The amplification factor was 25. The bulb was larger, $2\frac{5}{16}$ inches in diameter, and the overall height was $7\frac{7}{8}$ inches. The maximum permissible anode voltage was 1250 volts, and the maximum anode current was 175 milliamperes. Maximum anode dissipation was 100 watts. It was a higher-output tube than the UV203, which it replaced. The UV203A was still in production in 1931.

The last transmitting tubes to be considered are the UV204 and its successor, the UV204A. The UV204 (Fig. 16-23), was announced in March 1921.[18] It was double ended and required special mountings. As originally made, the center section of the bulb was spherical, about $4\frac{3}{4}$ inches in diameter. The overall length, including terminals, was $14\frac{3}{8}$ inches. The bulb of later UV204s and UV204As had a cylindrical center section $5\frac{1}{16}$ inches in diameter and approximately 5 inches long. The UV204 had a tungsten filament which required 14.75 amperes at 11 volts for its operation. The normal anode voltage was 2000 volts, and the amplification factor was 25. This tube continued to be made until some time in 1926.

Fig. 16-26. Radiotron UX852 tube.

The UV204A (Fig. 16-24) appeared in the summer of 1923. The thoriated filament took 3.85 amperes at 11 volts. As made originally, the bulb had a maximum diameter of $5\frac{1}{16}$ inches. This was reduced later to $4\frac{7}{16}$ inches. The maximum permissible anode voltage was 3000 volts, maximum anode dissipation 250 watts, and the maximum anode current was 275 milliamperes. The output of two of these tubes as a Class-B audio amplifier with 2000 volts on the anodes was 600 watts. The UV204A was still in production in 1931.

The UX250 was developed by Westinghouse. It was adopted by RCA early in 1927, announced in February 1928, and made available to the public a short time later. This was an audio power output tube advertised for use as a modulator and amplifier in low-power radiotelephone transmitters. The UX250 (Fig. 16-25) had an oxide-

Fig. 16-27. Two versions of the Radiotron UX864: the one at the right has a low loss insulating compound in the base.

Fig. 16-28. Cunningham CX330, CX331, and CX332 tubes.

coated filament which took 1.25 amperes at 7.5 volts. The recommended maximum anode voltage was 450 volts, the anode current was 55 milliamperes, and the output was 4.65 watts.

As amateur radio enthusiasts began using higher frequencies, a need arose for tubes capable of operation at such frequencies. The de Forest Type H (Chapter 15) appeared in January 1926. In May 1927 RCA announced a similar tube, the UX852 (Fig. 16-26) which was mounted in a standard UX base. The filament ratings of these two tubes were the same—2.35 amperes at 10 volts. The anode voltage of the UX852 was 2000 volts normal, whereas the Type H was 1000–3000 volts. The Type H was rated at 150 watts input; the UX852 was rated at 75 watts output. The grid lead came out at one end of each of these tubes. The anode lead came out of the opposite end of the Type H tube, and the anode lead of the UX852 was brought out through a side arm. Both tubes were said to be capable of operation up to 300 megahertz.

In 1928 increased activity in aviation brought about an urgent need for reliable aircraft communication. Airplane vibration caused noise in the receiver because of microphonic effect in the tubes. Engineers in the research laboratories of both GE and Westinghouse worked independently to solve the problem, but they developed tubes which were almost identical. The composite of all their effort was the sturdy nonmicrophonic tube—the UX864—which was adopted by RCA in the fall of 1928 (Fig. 16-27). It had a filament rating of 1.1 volts and 0.25 ampere. The maximum anode voltage was 135 volts and the anode resistance was 12,700 ohms. The amplification factor was 8.2.

During 1928 and 1929 both manufacturing companies were engaged in developing new designs of dry battery tubes. Three types of tubes were produced—general-purpose, loudspeaker, and screen-grid tubes. All were 2-volt filament tubes. They were announced by RCA Radiotron Company in June 1930. The RCA230 (general purpose) had a filament current of 0.06 ampere, a recommended anode voltage of 90 volts, and anode resistance of 11,000 ohms. The amplification factor was 9.3. The RCA231 (loudspeaker) had a filament current of 0.13 ampere, a recommended anode voltage of 135 volts, and an anode resistance of 4100 ohms. The amplification factor was 3.8. The RCA232 (screen grid) had a filament current of 0.06 ampere, a recommended anode voltage of 135 volts, and an anode resistance of 950,000 ohms. The amplification factor was 610. Fig. 16-28 shows the Cunningham equivalents of these three tubes.

REFERENCES

1. *Report of the Federal Trade Commission on the Radio Industry* (Washington, D.C.: GPO, 1924), p. 19.
2. See *QST*, Dec. 1920, 4:95; *Pacif. Radio News*, Dec. 1920, 2:114; *Radio News*, Dec. 1920, 2:409.
3. RCA Catalogue "Radio Enters the Home," June 1, 1922, pp. 29–33, 49.
4. *Ibid.*, pp. 18–20, 49.
5. RCA advertisement, *QST*, Oct. 1925, 9, back cover.
6. "New Tubes," *QST*, May 1926, 10:33.
7. RCA advertisement (n. 5 above), p. 40 and back cover.
8. R. S. Kruse, "Radiotron CX-340 UX-240," *QST*, Apr. 1927, 11:26–30.
9. Cunningham advertisement, *QST*, Dec. 1927, 14, inside front cover.
10. H. W. Freeman, "A Practical Alternating-Current Radio Receiving Set," *Elect. J.*, Dec. 1922, 19:501–505.
11. "The Facts about the A.C. Tube," *Radio Broadcast*, June 1927, 11:91.
12. RCA advertisement, *QST*, Jul. 1921, 4:91. RCA Catalogue "Radio Apparatus for Amateur and Experimental Use," Sept. 1, 1921, p. 24.
13. "New RCA Tubes," *QST*, Oct. 1925, 9:40–41.
14. "The Power Tubes Arrive," *QST*, Mar. 1921, 4:18–19. See also *QST*, Apr. 1921, 4:113; *Pacif. Radio News*, May 1921, 2:321; *Radio News*, Mar. 1921, 2:672; RCA Catalogue "Radio Apparatus," p. 23.
15. H. H. Tilley, "How I Operate UV-202 Radiotrons," *QST*, Feb. 1924, 7:37–38.
16. See "New RCA Tubes" (No. 13 above).
17. RCA advertisement, *QST*, Apr. 1921, 4:113. See RCA Catalogue "Radio Apparatus."
18. RCA Catalogue "Radio Apparatus," p. 22.

Chapter 17

The Early Days of Broadcasting,
1920-1930: *United States (Independents)*

The tremendous demand for vacuum tubes brought on by the rapid increase in the number of broadcasting stations is indicated by the sales records of RCA. In 1922 RCA sold about 1.25 million receiving tubes; in 1923 their sales topped 4.26 million; in 1924 sales reached 11.35 million. Amateur operators had returned to the air in 1919, the Department of Commerce records list 253 broadcasting stations in 1922, and millions were clamoring for radio sets. RCA was hard pressed to supply this incredible demand, and RCA controlled the market.

During the years before the formation of RCA in 1919, only two "independents" of note produced tubes—Cunningham and Moorhead. They had become entangled in pseudo-agreements with de Forest and Marconi (Chapter 9). When RCA was formed, the ownership of pertinent patents and patent rights was clearly defined. Shortly thereafter, both Cunningham and Moorhead became legitimate tube dealers, licensed by RCA under very generous terms.

In the radio boom of the 1920s, it was inevitable that some unauthorized persons would attempt to cash in on quick profits. Independent manufacturers materialized overnight. Their factories dotted New York, New Jersey, Chicago, and San Francisco. They were called independents because they made tubes without being licensed. Some eventually became licensed; others remained "bootleggers" (a term which originated with the custom of concealing and transporting contraband, usually liquor, in the leg of a high boot).

Tube bootleggers, always on the run to elude legal authorities, continually changed their company names, location of business, and brand names of tubes—sometimes all three simultaneously. They developed an efficient system of business management for migrants. Ever on the alert for spies, if they suspected a spurious customer, they went into action: they could dismantle their equipment, move to a new spot, reassemble the machinery, notify their employees where to report for work, and be back in tube production under a new name in forty-eight hours. They covered their tracks so well that tracing their wanderings and origins in some cases is impossible. (See the list of brand names at the end of this chapter.)

The bootleggers flooded the market with marked and unmarked tubes. RCA spent a fortune pursuing these infringers for prosecution and personal injunctions. This was only partially successful, and the bootleggers' games of hide-and-seek persisted until the de Forest and Fleming patents expired. The voluminous court records of litigation pertaining to this activity suggest that the radio industry generated as many jobs for the legal profession as for the electronics business. These published records are the only sources of information available to supply some historical links.

Independents initiated their enterprises in various ways. Some opened shops and advertised as "tube hospitals" where they repaired burnt-out tubes. Their service of replacing filaments and evacuating tubes was highly successful. Having the skill and equipment, their next step seemed expedient. They made new tubes, advertised them for less than half the RCA list price, and sold them under enticing brand names. A few went into business openly, claiming to be privately licensed. Radio Audion Company of Jersey City, New Jersey (originally Radio Lamp Corporation of New York), was the first prominent independent to appear after the formation of RCA. It is covered in some detail, because it presents a composite of the modus operandi of the infringers.

Elman B. Myers, one of the directors and chief engineer, designed and marketed the RAC3 Audion, aiming for the business of the amateur operator rather than the broadcast trade. Fig. 17-1 is the RAC3 Audion in its mounting bracket. This tube was first advertised in December 1920.[1] Myers had an interesting career before joining this group. The following information is taken in part from his testimony before the Federal Trade Commission in 1927.[2] The portions in quotes are direct quotations from his testimony.

According to Myers' story, he worked for the Poulsen Wireless Telephone and Telegraph Company of San Francisco for about two years beginning in 1908. In 1912 he went to work for the De Forest Company at High Bridge, New York, and "did tube development work until 1915." Then he went back to the Pacific Coast "to take charge of the Pacific Coast division of the De Forest Co. in the introduction and installation of commercial ship apparatus." He left de Forest in the fall of 1915 and manufactured and sold a tube he called a "radiotron." Then de Forest notified him that he was infringing the triode patent and brought suit against him. Myers did not defend, and de Forest obtained a personal injunction against Myers, prohibiting further infringement. Myers stopped making tubes, returned to the east, and early in 1916 went back to work for the De Forest Company. Shortly thereafter, in the line of duty, he broke into the Marconi Company station at Belmar, New Jer-

Fig. 17-1. Front and side views of RAC3 Audion in mounting socket.

sey, to get evidence that Marconi was using triodes for commercial purposes. He took samples of the tubes being so used and also an operator's logbook showing a record of their use in commercial work. The Marconi Company had him indicted and arrested for this action. He was convicted, fined $150, and put on probation for one year. He remained with the De Forest Company until early in 1918 and then went to work for the General Electric Company, where he did "tube development work at the Harrison, N.J. factory." In 1919 he went to work for the Western Electric Company, at 463 West Street, in New York. He was employed as "an expert on tube manufacture who took charge of their production and shrinkage. . . . At this time they were making 150 tubes per day. I was with them

seven months and by the introduction of efficient methods in shrink-
ing tubes and modern methods of manufacture we were at the end
of that time turning out tubes at the rate of 5700 per day."

As the testimony continues, dates conflict. He said that he was
chief engineer for the Radio Lamp Corporation of New York City,
manufacturing tubes for the Government under Government patent
protection at the end of World War I (1918). This company decided to continue making tubes after the patent protection ceased.
Since Myers was under personal injunction against infringement,
Radio Lamp signed an agreement with the De Forest Radio Telephone and Telegraph Company on November 25, 1919. According
to this covenant the De Forest Company agreed not to sue Radio
Lamp for making and selling Audions, provided de Forest received
a royalty of $1 per tube. Armed with this pledge of immunity, which
they claimed was a license, Radio Lamp manufactured tubes, including the RAC3, in Verona, New Jersey.

The RAC3 was a well-constructed unit of good design. The anode
and positive filament lead were at one end, which had a red
molded cap. The grid and negative filament lead wire were at
the other end, which had a black molded cap. A molded mounting
block was supplied with the tube. The filament operated with 0.8
ampere at 4 volts. The anode voltage was 2–22 volts. The wide
separation of the grid and anode leads tended to provide low direct
capacitance between these elements, which made the tube usable
at higher frequencies than conventional single-ended tubes.

RCA did not take kindly to the introduction of the RAC3, and
on May 4, 1920, notified both Myers and the Radio Lamp Corporation that they were infringing the Fleming patent on the diode.
This RCA could do, since the triode had been held to be an infringement on the diode by the U.S. Circuit Court of Appeals, and RCA
owned the Fleming patent. They threatened suit and demanded
compensation for acts of infringement. Radio Lamp continued manufacture of tubes and reincorporated as the Radio Audion Company,
Inc., on September 4, 1920, in Delaware to escape New York juris-
diction, "following the law of self-preservation," and opened a factory at 90 Oakland Avenue, Jersey City.

The A.T.&T. Company then filed suit against the Radio Audion
Company for infringement of the de Forest triode patents, claiming
that de Forest could not grant them immunity from prosecution for
infringement, having sold to A.T.&T. exclusive rights to the triode,
except for the retention of a personal, nontransferable right to make
and sell directly to the consumer for certain restricted purposes.
Radio Audion was adjudged an infringer, and A.T.&T. obtained an
injunction against further infringement. This injunction was issued
by the District Court in May 1922[3] and sustained by the Circuit

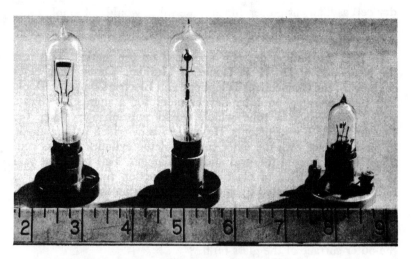

Fig. 17-2. Two views of the Electrad diode (left and middle), and the Margo detector (right).

Court of Appeals.[4] Shortly thereafter the Radio Audion Company went into bankruptcy.

Myers moved to Montreal and obtained new backing. His backers set up a Canadian company, E. B. Myers, Ltd., and proceeded to advertise "Myers" tubes in United States magazines, the tubes to be delivered by mail. This continued until the expiration of the de Forest triode patent. E. B. Myers, Ltd. then moved to Cleveland, Ohio, but Myers did not go with them. While in Cleveland they advertised Myers 201A and 201X tubes, equipped with UV and UX bases respectively. RCA sued them for back royalties, and they went bankrupt.[5]

The next independent tube to appear on the market, the Electro-dyne, was a rectifier, announced in February 1920, and pictured in an advertisement in October 1920.[6] This was a half-wave power rectifier which could presumably be marketed since it did not infringe the Fleming patent. It had a spherical bulb, a cylindrical anode mounted with its axis vertical, and a UV-type base.

With the expiration of the Fleming diode patent in November 1922, a number of diodes appeared on the market in the United States. Fig. 17-2 shows two such tubes. The tube at the left, of which two views are shown, was the Electrad Diode, made by the Electrad Corporation of America.[7] These bulbs were clear, but later production tubes were flashed with magnesium. This tube continued to be advertised for about a year. The tube at the right, the Margo Detector, was sold by Modell's.[8] It operated with a single dry cell as filament power. Since these tubes would not amplify and would not function in regenerative circuits, they had a short commercial life.

In 1923 the Sodion detector appeared on the market. This was the brainchild of Dr. H. P. Donle, of Meriden, Connecticut, chief engineer of the Connecticut Telephone and Electric Company. Donle had been working on tube development for a number of years trying to produce a tube which would not infringe either the Fleming or de Forest patents. He made a tube which had an anode in close contact with the outer surface of the cylindrical glass container which housed the grid and the filament. This tube was said to operate by virtue of electrolytic conduction through the glass bulb when it was heated by energy radiated from the filament. This arrangement was the subject of a patent,[9] from which Fig. 17-3 is taken. Donle also devised another form of this "valve" (Fig. 17-4). In this latter patent both the anode and control electrode were on the outer surface of the glass bulb.[10]

A tube fashioned along the lines of that shown in Fig. 17-3 was described in an article by Donle and identified as the Type C Donle Electron Tube.[11] Mention is made in this article of a Type A, and a photograph is given, but there appears to be no difference between the types except possibly size (see Fig. 17-5). The purpose of the outer enclosing tube was to aid in stabilizing the temperature of the wall of the inner tube. Apparently this was later found to be unnecessary. The Donle sample in Fig. 17-6 does not have an enclosing tube and has a UV base.

Donle's next attempt to make a new and different tube resulted in the Connecticut J117, shown in Fig. 17-7. The original form of this tube and its method of operation in a detector unit of which it

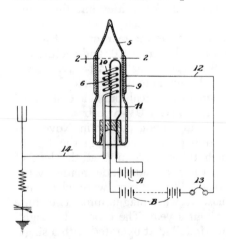

Fig. 17-3. Drawing of the Donle electron valve. (Reproduced from U.S. Patent No. 1,291,441.)

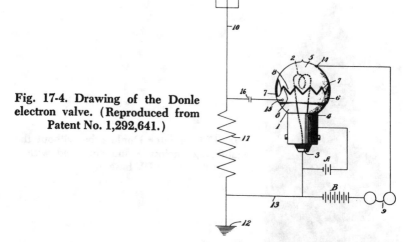

Fig. 17-4. Drawing of the Donle
electron valve. (Reproduced from
Patent No. 1,292,641.)

formed a part is described in an article in *QST* for October 1921.[12]
The circuit in which it was used is shown in Fig. 17-8. The filament
operated directly from a 6-volt storage battery and was insensitive
to voltage changes. In the detector the tube was surrounded by a
coil through which direct current flowed, setting up a magnetic
field parallel to the axis of the tube. The statement is made that the
tube "must be tuned to the desired signal." This was accomplished

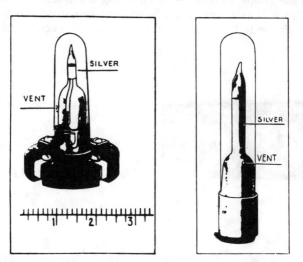

Fig. 17-5. Drawing of the Donle Type A (left) and Type C (right)
valves. (Reproduced from *Radio Amat. News*, 1919.)

Fig. 17-6. A later Donle tube without the stabilizing enclosure and equipped with a UV base.

by varying the dc field intensity produced by the field winding, by varying the anode voltage, or by changing the position of the tube within the field coil. Donle is said to have explained the operation of the device as follows: "Inside the tube there is a certain phenome-

Fig. 17-7. Connecticut J117 tube.

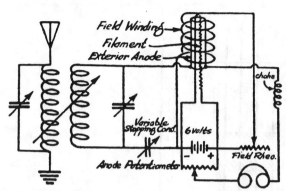

**Fig. 17-8. Circuit in which the Connecticut J117 tube was used.
(Reproduced from *QST*, Oct. 1921.)**

non going on continually which gives a sinusoidal variation of the
internal impedance."[13] Apparently this arrangement was difficult
for the amateur to operate, and most of the sets sold were returned
as unusable, according to a few "who were there."

Dr. Donle decided on a new method of attack on the detector
problem. On December 20, 1922, he presented a paper, "New Non-
Interfering Detector," before the Institute of Radio Engineers.[14] His
new tube, a diagram of which is given in Fig. 17-9 and a photograph
in Fig. 17-10, was used in the circuit shown in Fig. 17-11. The anode
was of liquid sodium; hence the tube had to be mounted base up
in the receiver (Fig. 17-12). No designation for this tube was given
in the paper referred to previously.

On October 10, 1923, Donle presented another paper before the
I.R.E. entitled "New Applications of the Sodion Detector."[15] In
this he described an improved form of Sodion detector designated
S13 which had been preceded by a less improved form designated
S11. Both the S11 and S13 are shown in Fig. 17-13. The S11 had
a standard UV base, but the S13 had a nonstandard base and required a special socket, or alternatively an adapter to mount it in
a UV socket. The S13 required a filament current of 0.24 ampere
at a voltage of about 3.8 volts. Part of this filament power was used
to heat the inner glass container in which the elements were in-
installed.

The S13 was followed by the S14, which was superseded by D-21.
Both had UV bases and are shown in Fig. 17-14. Like its predecessors, the D-21 operated with 0.25 ampere at 5 volts on the filament
circuit, which included the heater applied to the outer surface of the
inner glass bulb. Unlike the S13, the D-21 could be made to oscillate.[16] It had a tantalum filament instead of the tungsten filament
previously used. The D-21 had a mutual conductance of about 260

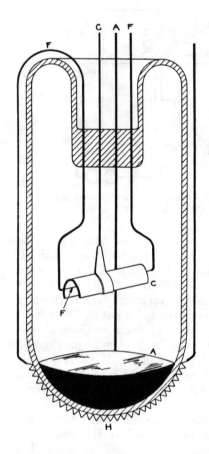

Fig. 17-9. Diagram of an early Sodion detector. (Reproduced from
Proc. I.R.E., Apr. 1923.)

micromhos, an anode impedance of 51,000 ohms, and an amplification factor of 22.

In 1925 Donle left the Connecticut Telephone and Electric Company and set up the Donle-Bristol Corporation of Meriden, Connecticut. By May 1926 he had developed and advertised a new tube
designated B6.[17] It was described in the instruction sheet as having
"the usual elements of filament, grid and plate but instead of these
being enclosed in an evacuated bulb, the bulb contains a rare atmosphere, gas, which is directly responsible for the extraordinary
sensitivity of the tubes." Unlike the Sodion tubes the B6 had only
one bulb. The required warming resistor was wrapped around the
lower end of the bulb, which was inserted into the base. The element assembly had a cylindrical anode and spiral grid. Donle described the proper method of using this tube in an article in *Radio
News* for May 1926.[18] The B6 was advertised until June 1927. Other

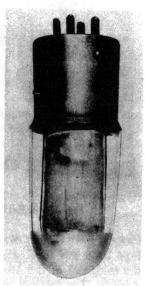

Fig. 17-10. Photograph of an early Sodion detector tube. (Reproduced from *Proc. I.R.E.*, Apr., 1923.)

Donle tubes which appeared on the market late in 1927 were the DR-1V, DP-10, DP-11, and B8.[19]

The Arcturus Radio Company first advertised tubes in November 1927.[20] The name was changed to the Arcturus Radio Tube Company in February 1929. The first series of tubes they produced had indirectly heated cathodes with carbon heaters operating at 15 volts. (This voltage was probably chosen because 15-volt trans-

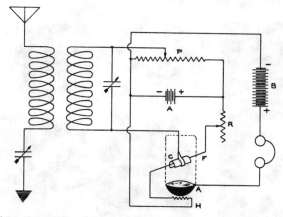

Fig. 17-11. Circuit in which early Sodion tube was used as a detector. (Reproduced from *Proc. I.R.E.*, Apr., 1923.)

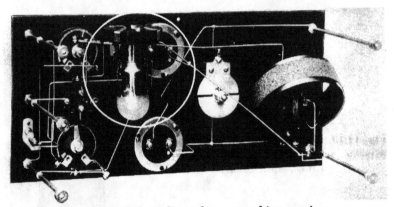

Fig. 17-12. Early Sodion tube mounted in a receiver.

formers were readily available for electrically driven toys.) The UV-type base was used, and the cathode was connected internally to the midpoint of the heater. Only four terminals were required for a triode. The original series consisted of the AC-22, AC-26, AC-28, AC-30, AC-31, AC-32, AC-40, AC-46, AC-48, and the AF, which was a full-wave power rectifier. The AC-30 was a power output tube. The AC-26 and AC-30 are shown in Fig. 17-15.

Arcturus apparently wanted to use blue glass to make "Arcturus Blue" a sort of trademark. When the supply periodically ran out they were forced to adopt makeshifts. The author has samples of Arcturus tubes which are made of clear glass to which a coating of dull blue lacquer has been applied. Other samples of the Arcturus 147 made of clear glass have the word BLUE stamped in bright blue on the clear glass bulbs.

Fig. 17-13. Sodions S11 and S13.

Fig. 17-14. Sodions S14 and D-21.

By late 1928 the trend was away from the home-made receivers. Factory-made receivers were usually set up to use 2.5-volt heater-type tubes (such as the UY224 and the UY227) and 5-volt output tubes. The whole assembly was enclosed in a cabinet. Radio sets became pieces of furniture as well as sources of entertainment. Arcturus had to produce tubes which could be used as replacements for those supplied by manufacturers, and the 15-volt tubes went into oblivion. By November 1928 Arcturus was advertising tubes for every socket in the home broadcast receiver,[21] in some cases offering a choice of filament type or indirectly heated cathode type—for example, 126 or 126H—for the same socket. The Arcturus ads in 1930 made no mention of new designs but were concerned

Fig. 17-15. Arcturus AC-30 and
AC-26 tubes.

with "7 second heating" and "humless" operation. Arcturus continued in business until its owner died in 1952, at which time manufacture practically ceased. In 1959 the rights to the name Arcturus were bought by two men who formed the Arcturus Electronics Company. They became jobbers of electronics equipment and the tubes they sold were mostly of foreign manufacture.

The C.E. Manufacturing Company (Ce Co), of Providence, Rhode Island, entered the vacuum tube field in 1925, and their first ad appeared in July 1925.[22] They offered three tubes for sale, designated as types A, B, and C: A was of the 201A type, B of the 199 type, and C the 199 type but with standard UV base. In February 1926 the bases were changed to the UX type. By October 1926 the line had been expanded to include types D, E, F, G, H, AX, BX, and J71.[23] The D was a rectifier, E was the 120 type, F was the 112 type, G was the high-mu type for resistance-coupled circuits, H was similar to the 200A, J71 was the 171 type. In May 1927 a special radio-frequency triode amplifier designated K was introduced. In August 1927 came their gas-filled cold-cathode rectifier, rated at 85 milliamperes output, designated D-G for use in B-eliminators.

About this time Ce Co began to use tube designations which closely resembled those used by RCA. In September 1927 they announced two new tubes, M26 and N27, equivalents respectively to the RCA 226 and 227.[24] In October 1927 they announced a cold-cathode gas-filled rectifier.[25] In March 1928 they offered the R80 and R81,[26] equivalent to the RCA 280 and RCA 281. In May 1928 they brought out the RF22 with characteristics similar to the UX222.[27] In June 1928 the AC-24 and L50, equivalent to the UY224 and UX250, were placed on the market. From then on, Ce Co tube designations followed RCA codification step by step, the similarity implying like characteristics.

In Chapter 16 the development of the UY227, the first indirectly heated cathode tube made for RCA, was covered. This, however, was not the first such tube to appear on the U.S. market. In the July 1925 issue of *Radio News* there appeared an article describing a new vacuum tube of the indirectly heated cathode type which had just come on the market.[28] In the same month, in two other magazines, there appeared advertisements by the McCullough Sales Company offering these tubes for sale.[29]

The designer of these tubes was Frederick S. McCullough, an engineer who had worked for Westinghouse on indirectly heated cathode tubes.[30] He left Westinghouse and under the name of McCullough Sales Company began advertising the McCullough AC Tube. Since he had no manufacturing facilities, the question concerning who made the first of these tubes remains unresolved. In January 1926 the McCullough's ad states that "McCullough tubes

Fig. 17-16. McCullough tubes. The one in the middle is the earliest embodiment.

are now being made by Kellogg Switchboard and Supply Co. of Chicago."[31] By June 1929 the McCullough tubes were being made by the A.C. Neon Corporation of New York City.

Three variants of the McCullough tube are shown in Fig. 17-16. The one in the middle is the earliest type with a UV brass base. The bulb is of black glass so the elements are not visible. The connector block at the top carries the heater terminals. The one on the right has a molded UV base, and the McCullough emblem is etched on the glass. The tube at the left has a UX molded base with steel-stamped markings which identify the tube as a McCullough Type 401. The heater of the McCullough tube operated at 3 volts and 1 ampere. It had an amplification factor of 8–9, an anode impedance of about 9500 ohms, and a mutual conductance of about 870 micromhos. With 90 volts on the anode and −4.5 volts on the grid, the anode current was about 4 milliamperes.

Marathon tubes, made by Northern Manufacturing Company, were first advertised in August 1925,[32] but Marathon did not enter the ac tube field until early 1927.[33] Their tubes were of the indirectly heated cathode type, and the heaters operated at 5.5 volts with 1 ampere. Marathon used designation numbers 605, 608, 615, and 630. Samples of the 608 are shown in Fig. 17-17. The 605 was a low-gain, low-impedance tube. It had an amplification factor of 4.5, anode impedance of 4400 ohms, and mutual conductance of 1000 micromhos. The 608 had an amplification factor of 7.3, anode impedance of 9500 ohms, and mutual conductance of 775 micromhos. Corresponding figures for the 615 type were 12.0, 19,000 ohms, and 635 micromhos, and for the 630 type 28.0, 40,000 ohms, and 680 micromhos. These Marathon tubes were usually sold with a Marathon A.C. Kit, which consisted of a cable with the necessary clips to connect to the heater terminals on the side of the tube base. Northern Manufacturing Company also made Marathon conven-

Fig. 17-17. Marathon ac tubes.

tional tubes. Northern ceased separate operations when it merged with other companies to form the National Union Radio Corporation, which was announced on August 24, 1929.

The Sovereign AC tube came on the market about the middle of 1927. This tube (Fig. 17-18) apparently had a short commercial life. The last advertisement to offer it appeared in March 1928. No designation was given in the ads, but one in the author's collection has "Type 501" marked on its shipping carton. It is a double-ended tube but requires no special top-connector, as did the McCullough and Kellogg tubes. The top-cap was equipped with binding posts to which ordinary wires could be connected. The Sovereign tube took

Fig. 17-18. Sovereign 501 ac tube, with carton.

Fig. 17-19. The Apco Twin tube.
The base with the switching mechanism is shown at the right.

1.1 amperes at 3.0 volts for the heater. When operated with 90 volts
on the anode and grid bias of −4.5 volts the anode current was 4.6
milliamperes. Under these conditions it had an amplification factor
of 8.5. The anode resistance was 9100 ohms, and the mutual conductance was 935 micromhos.

In addition to what might be called regular or conventional tubes,
there appeared on the market during this period a number of un-
usual tubes which are of interest to collectors. Because of limitation of space only a few significant tubes are mentioned.

The Apco Twin Tube, two views of which are shown in Fig. 17-
19, was made by the Apco Manufacturing Company of Providence,
Rhode Island, in the period 1925–1926. It contained two complete
sets of 201A-type elements. These were connected in parallel except for one end of each filament. When the first filament failed, the
second one could be brought into service by slightly unscrewing
one of the filament prongs so that a switch arm could be moved
from one contact to another. This brought the second filament into
the circuit. Each filament took 0.25 ampere at 5 volts. The base
was of the UX type and the only identification on the tube was an
oval black paper label on the glass bulb with the words "Apco Twin
Tube." At the left of the trade name "5 volt" and to the right ".25-
amp" were printed—all in dark red on the black label.

The Emerson Multivalve, marketed by Emerson Radval Corporation of 25 West 43rd Street, New York, was first advertised in
Radio News for March 1927.[34] The use of the Multivalve in a receiver was described in an article in the February issue of the
same magazine.[35] Fig. 17-20 is a drawing of the tube and its external connections, reproduced from this article. The Emerson Multivalve had three sets of triode elements with a common three-section
filament which operated with 0.25 ampere at 5.0 volts. In the article
describing the receiver, the parts list indicates that the manufacturer

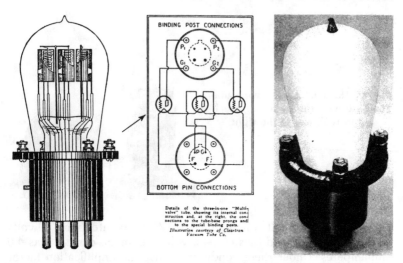

BINDING POST CONNECTIONS

BOTTOM PIN CONNECTIONS

Details of the three-in-one "Multi-valve" tube, showing its internal con-struction and, at the right, the con-nections to the tube-base prongs and to the special binding posts.
Illustration courtesy of Cleartron Vacuum Tube Co.

Fig. 17-20. The Emerson Multivalve. Note that the drawing was supplied by Cleartron Vacuum Tube Co.

of the Multivalve was the Cleartron Vacuum Tube Company. The drawing is credited to the same company. Cleartron was doing business at 28 West 44th Street, meaning that the backyards of Emerson and Cleartron were adjoining. Records do not show which side of this common backyard originated the idea for the Emerson Multivalve, but both companies participated in its manufacture and promotion. It had a short commercial life. *Radio News* carried its last ad for the Emerson Multivalve in September 1927.[36]

The Quadratron, produced by the Baker-Smith Company of San Francisco, was described in an article in *Radio News*, July 1926.[37] According to this article, the fourth element, which was termed an "auxiliary grid," "is always to be connected so that its polarity is opposite to that of the normal grid. In this way both halves of the input voltage will be utilized as control factors." The article further states, "When the usual grid is charged with a negative potential no electrons should reach the plate. Those that do leave the filament are absorbed by the fourth element, called the auxiliary grid. During the other half of the cycle, the auxiliary grid is charged negatively and accelerates the flow of electrons to the plate."[38] The only marking on the author's specimen of this tube is a small sticker with the word "Quadratron" typed on it.

Demands of the set manufacturers and public for an ac-operated radio began in the early 1920s and grew more persistent year by year. Here and abroad intensive research was being carried on in laboratories to develop an ac tube. This urgent activity in that period makes one other independent tube particularly interesting. This tube was a Canadian product made by Edward Samuels Rogers, who in 1924, at the age of twenty-four, formed the Rogers Radio Company, Ltd. of Toronto, for the manufacture of radio receivers. While on a trip to the United States in that same year, Rogers visited an American laboratory where he saw a small tube designed to be operated from ordinary household alternating current. When he went back to Toronto he took with him the Canadian patent rights to this tube.[39]

The tube he saw—the invention of Frederick S. McCullough—was far from perfect, being prone to produce excessive hum. During the fall of 1924 Rogers succeeded in developing a better insulator for the heater, and presumably redesigned the heater so that the ac hum was greatly reduced. His first commercially practical ac tube was produced on August 26, 1925.

Rogers established the Standard Radio Manufacturing Corporation in 1925 to manufacture a radio set using his ac tubes. Then, having his patent rights, improvements, production facilities, and ready market, he launched the Rogers Batteryless Radio Receiving Set. This three-tube receiver had a detector using regeneration and a two-stage amplifier. It was equipped with Rogers Type 32 tubes. An external B-eliminator was used to supply plate voltage. Accompanying each such set was an instruction card stating that the set was "made by the Standard Radio Mfg. Corp. Ltd., Toronto (owners of the Canadian De Forest patents)—under the patents of Canadian De Forest, Edward S. Rogers and F. S. McCullough."

Fig. 17-21. Rogers Types 30 and 32 tubes. Left to right: Type 32 with markings etched on bulb, Type 32 with paper label, Type 30 with markings etched on bulb, and Type 30 with markings stamped on base.

Fig. 17-22. Rogers Types 227 and 224 tubes. Left to right: Type 227 with paper label, Type 224 with paper label, Type 227S with spray shield and markings on base, and Type 224S with spray shield and markings on base.

By 1928 Rogers was apparently concentrating on the manufacture of tubes rather than radio receivers. The name of his company was changed to Rogers Radio Tube Company, Ltd. He was making ac-operated triodes of the single-ended type and ac-operated tetrodes. After a short time this company became the Rogers-Majestic Corporation and continued in business until it was taken over in 1946 by the Philips organization. Philips continued to turn out commercial tubes under the Rogers-Majestic label.

Representative Rogers tubes are shown in Figs. 17-21, 17-22, and 17-23. The middle tube in Fig. 17-23 was Rogers' answer to the "metal tubes" developed in the U.S. and first marketed in the mid-1930s. Published information pertaining to Rogers' dates of manu-

Fig. 17-23. Rogers Types 88S, 88M, and Rogers-Majestic Type 27 with carton. Left to right: 88S with spray shield, 88M with black "metallized" coating, and Rogers Majestic Type 27 with carton.

facture and establishment of companies is limited and conflicting. For example, the brochure "Edward Samuel Rogers Collection" is a disservice to Rogers because of inaccuracies. His contributions to the industry and Canadian radio history need no embellishment.

The following is a partial list of brand names of thermionic tubes offered for sale in the period 1920–1930, together with manufacturer's or vendor's names and addresses (when known to author) and dates on which brands were first advertised (when known). Many brand names were never advertised but were shipped only to retail outlets for over-the-counter sale.

Brand Name	Date	Notes
ACTRON	1929	Advertised by The Actron Corp., 123 North Sangamon Street, Chicago.
ADVANCE	1930	Advertised by Advance Battery Corp., Tube Division, Brooklyn.
AIRLINE		No information available.
AIRTRON	1924	Advertised by H. & H. Radio Co., Cl. Hill Sta., Box 22, Newark.
ALADDIN	1925	Advertised in 1925 by Continental Sales Co., 77 West Washington Street, Chicago. Address given in 1926 was 179 West Washington Street.
ALLAN A		Made by Allan Manufacturing and Electric Corp., Lawrence, Mass.
ALLTRON	1926	Advertised by Allan Manufacturing Co., 117 Windsor Street, Arlington, N.J. This concern also advertised Vogue Nonpareil tubes in 1927.
ALPHA	1923	Maker unknown, but he also made Murdon tubes, and the manufacture of both brands was stopped by court injunction in 1923.
AMERICA	1926	Advertised by Elite Radio Tube Company, 409 South 8th Street, Newark. These tubes had blue glass envelopes.
AMERICAN	1926	Advertised by H. C. Roberts Radio Co., 112 Trinity Place, New York.
AMERTRON	1924	Advertised by Bryant Radio Electric Co., 203 Park Row Building, New York, and by Corona Electric Co., 157 East 47th Street, New York.
AMPLION		Sold by Export Radio Products Co. Address unknown.
AMPLITRON	1925	Advertised by Pennant Radio Laboratories, 23 Central Avenue, Newark.
ANODYNE	1930	Advertised by Anodyne Engineering Corp., Newark.

Brand Name	Date	Notes
A-P TWO-IN-ONE		Advertised by A-P Radio Labs., San Francisco.
APCO TWIN TUBE	1925	Made by Apco Manufacturing Co., Providence, R.I.
APEX AUDIOTRON	1924	Advertised by Radio Tube Corporation, 70 Halsey Street, Newark. This concern also made Cleartron and Dillion tubes.
ARCHATRON	1927	Made by KenRad Corp., Owensboro, Ky.
ARCO	1928	Advertised by Arco Radio Laboratory, New York.
ARCTURUS	1927	Made by Arcturus Radio Co., 253 Sherman Avenue, Newark. Later became Arcturus Radio Tube Co., 220 Elizabeth Avenue, Newark. This company was licensed by RCA in 1929. For several years it used blue glass envelopes on its tubes.
ARION	1925	Advertised by Electric Sales Co., 140 Halsey Street, Newark.
ARMOR	1926	Made by Armstrong Electric & Manufacturing Co., 351 Halsey Street, Newark. Later address is given as 187–193 Sylvan Avenue, Newark.
ATLAS	1925	Made by the RSK Co., for which three addresses are given: 310 Caxton Building, Cleveland, Ohio; 771 Ellicott Square Building, Buffalo, N.Y.; 609 Chamber of Commerce Building, Pittsburgh, Pa.
AUBURN		No information available.
AUREX		No information available.
BEACON	1925	Beacon Radio Company, address unknown. Used blue glass envelopes.
BELLTONE	1924	Advertised by Radio Tube Laboratory, 296 Broadway, New York. This manufacturer also made Cleartron tubes.
BESTONE	1925	Advertised by W. H. Bryant, 453 Washington Street, Boston.
BLACKSTONE		Made by Blackstone Radio Tube Manufacturing Co., Pawtucket, R.I.
BLUE BELL	1925	Advertised by Branford Manufacturing Co., 1145 Fox Street, New York.
BLUEBIRD	1925	Advertised by Bluebird Tube Co., 200 Broadway, New York.
B-M	1924	Advertised by Birk-Morton Vacuum Products, Owensboro, Ky.
BOEHM	1925	Sold by Boehm Radio Company, 264 Canal Street, New York.
BOND		Made by Bond Electric Corp., Jersey City, N.J.

Brand Name	Date	Notes
BREMCO	1925	Made by Bennington Radio & Electric Manufacturing Co., Bennington, Vt.
BRENDONNE	1924	Advertised by Brendonne Corp., Orange, N.J.
BRIGHTSON TRUE BLUE	1925	Made by Brightson Laboratories, Inc., 16 West 34th Street, New York. This concern used blue glass envelopes and sold "matched sets" of three tubes, packed in a plush-lined box.
BRUNSWICK		No information available.
BUCK	1927	Advertised by National Electric Lamp and Universal Electric Lamp Co., both of Newark.
BULL DOG	1926	Advertised by Radiotive Corp., 5317 21st Avenue, Brooklyn.
CARDON	1930	Made by Cardon Phonocraft Corp., Jackson, Mich.
CECILIAN	1926	Made by Esetroc Manufacturing Co., 28 Longworth Street, Newark.
CE CO	1925	Made by C. E. Manufacturing Co., 702 Eddy Street, Providence, R.I.
CETRON	1927	Made by Continental Electric Co., 6 North Michigan Avenue, Chicago.
CHAMPION	1927	Made by Champion Radio Works, Danvers, Mass.
CLARITRON	1924	Made by Superior Radio Company, 176 Shepard Avenue, Newark.
CLEARTONE	1924	Made by Radio Tube Laboratory, 296 Broadway, New York. This company also made Belltone tubes.
CLEARTRON	1925	Made by Cleartron Vacuum Tube Co., West New York, N.J. Office was at 28 West 44th Street, New York.
COLUMBIATRON	1925	Made by Columbia Radio Laboratories, Inc., 5 Columbus Avenue, New York.
CONCERT MASTER	1928	Made by Continental Corporation, 179 West Washington Street, Chicago. This corporation also made Continental tubes.
CONNECTICUT DETECTOR	1921	Made by Connecticut Telephone & Electric Co., Meriden, Conn. This is the first of the Donle-designed tubes.
CONTINENTAL	1928	Made by Continental Corporation, 179 West Washington Street, Chicago. This concern also marketed Concert Master tubes.
CORONADO		No information available.
CROSSLEY		Made by KenRad Corporation.
CROYDEN		No information available.

Brand Name	Date	Notes
CROYDON		Made by Gold Seal Electric Co., 259 Park Avenue, New York.
CRUSADER	1926	Made by The Sunlight Lamp Co. In 1926 address was Newton Falls, Ohio. In 1930 it was Irvington, N.J.
DAVEN	1925	Made by Daven Corporation, 170 Summit Street, Newark.
DELATONE		Sold by Wright & Wright, no address available.
DEXTRON	1925	Made by Dextron Radio Laboratory, 74 Sterling Street, East Orange, N.J.
DIAMOND		Made by Diamond Electric Corp., 780 Freylinghousen Avenue, Newark.
DIATRON	1926	Made by Diamond Vacuum Products Co., 4053 Diversey Avenue, Chicago.
DIETZEN	1923	Dietzen Inc., 71 Cortlandt Street, New York, were the manufacturers.
DILCO	1929	Made by Dilco Radio Tube Corp., Harrison, N.J.
DILLION		Marketed by Radio Tube Laboratories, Irvington, N.J. This concern also marketed the Apex Audiotron.
DISTATRON		Made by DX Electric Products Corp., 28 Church Street, New York.
DIS X TRON	1925	Made by Justrite Sales Co., 250 Market Street, Newark.
DONLE	1926	Donle-Bristol Corp., Tremont Street, Meriden, Conn. In 1927 the address was 54 Cambridge Street, Meriden. In 1928 it became the Donle Electrical Products Corp., Meriden.
DRY CELL		No information available.
DUOVAC	1929	Made by Duovac Radio Corp., 360 Furman Street, Brooklyn.
DURACO	1925	Made by Duratron Products Corp., 539 Lewis Street, Union City, N.J. This concern also made Permatron tubes.
DURATRON	1925	No information available, but probably made by the makers of Duraco tubes.
DURO		No information available.
DUROTRON		Made by Electrical Products Corp., 199 Livingston Street, Newark.
DXTRON		No information available.
DYN-A-BLUE	1925	Made by Magnite Laboratories, P.O. Box 472, Newark.
DYNETRON		Made by Magnite Laboratories, P.O. Box 472, Newark. Both Dyn-A-Blue and Dynetron tubes used blue glass envelopes.
ECLIPSE		No information available.

Brand Name	Date	Notes
ECONOTRON	1925	Made by Nulite Electric Co., 220 West 42nd Street, New York. This concern also made Mizpah and La France tubes.
ELECTRAD DIODE	1923	Made by Electrad Corp. of America, 428 Broadway, New York. Some tubes were flashed with magnesium, others not.
ELECTRODYNE	1920	This was a rectifier tube marketed by Wireless Equipment Co., 188–190 Greenwich Street, New York.
ELECTRON	1925	This was marketed by Macksound Radio Labs., 84 Washington Street, New York.
ELECTRON	1925	This was made by Radio Products Co., 15 Moore Street, New York. They were sued for infringement by RCA in 1925.
ELECTRONATOR		No information available.
ELEKTRON	1925	Made by Lectrodio Corp., Lynn, Mass.
EMERSON MULTIVALVE	1927	Made by Emerson Radval Corp., 25 West 43rd Street, New York.
EMPIRETRON	1925	In 1925 this tube was being made by American International Trading Co., 26 Stone Street, New York. In 1926 it was being made by Empire Electrical Products Corp., Kearny, N.J. In 1930 it was advertised by Empire Electrical Products Corp., 141 Wooster Street, New York.
E.R.C.	1926	Made by Eastern Radio Company, 36 Devereux Street, Arlington, Mass.
ERGON		Made by Ergon Electric Corp., Brooklyn.
ERLA	1926	Advertised by Electrical Research Laboratories, 2500 Cottage Grove Avenue, Chicago.
EVEREDY	1925	Advertised by Nussbaum & Silver, 175 Fifth Avenue, New York.
EVEREST WORLD TOP	1926	Made by Everest Manufacturing Co., address unknown.
FALCK		Made by Advance Electric Co., 1260 West 2nd Street, Los Angeles.
FASTRON	1930	Made by F. A. Schiller, Inc., Irvington, N.J. Claims to be licensed under all patents.
FEDERAL	1925	Made by Federal Telegraph Co., 200 Mt. Pleasant Avenue, Newark.
FEDERAL DRY CELL	1924	Made by Federal Electric and Radio Co., 112–114 Trinity Place, New York.
FRESHMAN		No information available.
FRISCO	1924	Made by Western Radio Co., 2922 Fulton Street, Brooklyn.
GEM	1925	Made by Gem Tube Co. Address in 1925

Brand Name	Date	Notes
		was 200 Broadway, New York. Address in 1926 was 16 Hudson Street, New York.
GIBRALTAR	1929	Made by Gibraltar Radio Supply Co., 87 Sylvan Avenue, Newark. Office address was 5 Union Square, New York.
GOLD LABEL	1923	Advertised by W. Guild, 38–40 Clinton Street, Newark.
GOLD SEAL	1925	Advertised by Gold Seal Products Co., Inc., 250 Park Avenue, New York. Name in 1928 was Gold Seal Electrical Products Co.
GOLDENTONE	1925	Made by United Radio & Electric Corp., 418 Central Avenue, Newark. This concern also made Ureco tubes.
GOLDTONE	1926	Sold by Goldtone Radio Co., 5 Columbus Circle, New York.
GOODE TWO-O-ONE-A	1925	Made by Goode Tube Corp., Evansville, Ind.
GOULD		Sold by Manhattan Electrical Supply Co.
GRANDTONE		Sold by F. & W. Grand (5–10–25-cent stores).
GRANGER		No information available.
HARP	1924	Made by Royal Manufacturing Co., 206 Broadway, New York. This company also made Royaltron tubes. Harp tubes had straight-sided bulbs, and in some cases the base was nickel plated.
HELIOTRON	1925	Made by Helios Electric Co., West New York, N.J.
HERCULES	1925	Made by Lincoln Radio Tube Co., 37 Walker Street, New York.
HI-CONSTRON	1925	Made by Cleartron Vacuum Tube Co., 28 West 44th Street, New York. Factory was at West New York, N.J. This concern also made Cleartron tubes.
HYGRADE	1931	Made by Hygrade Lamp Co., Salem, Mass.
HYGRADE-SYLVANIA	1931	These tubes made by Hygrade-Sylvania Corp., of Emporium, Pa. This concern was a merger of Sylvania Products Corp., Hygrade Lamp Co., and Nilco Lamp Works. This merger was announced in July 1931. In 1932 it established offices at 500 Fifth Avenue, New York. The address of the tube factory was Electronics Division, 64 Lakeview Avenue, Clifton, N.J. It was licensed by RCA.

Brand Name	Date	Notes
HYTRON	1926	Made by Hytron Corp., 19 Oakland Street, Salem, Mass. It was licensed by RCA.
HYVAC	1929	Made by Hyvac Radio Tube Corp., Newark. At first it was located at 38 Spring Street, but soon moved to 86 Shipman Street. This corporation was an amalgamation of several manufacturers which had been operating in the Newark area.
IMPERIALTRON		No information available.
INDEPENDENT		Made by Independent Lamp Works, Weehawken, N.J.
INTERNATIONAL		Manufacturer's name not available, but they made rectifier tubes.
J. & A.		Jenkins & Adair, 3333 Belmont Avenue, Chicago, were the manufacturers.
JAEGER	1926	Made by Jaeger Research Laboratories, 270–280 Park Avenue, Weehawken, N.J.
JRC		Made by Johnsonburg Radio Corp., Johnsonburg, Pa.
KEENTONE	1927	Made by K. T. Products Co., 68 William Street, New York.
KELLOGG		Kellogg Switchboard & Supply Co., 1066 West Adams Street, Chicago. This concern started out by making ac tubes for F. S. McCullough and later put out the same tubes under their own name.
KELLY	1929	Made by Kelly Tube Co., 57 Dey Street, New York.
KELVIN	1927	Made by Eureka Tube Manufacturing Co., 42 Walnut Street, Newark.
KEN RAD	1933	Made by KenRad Corp. (later KenRad Tube & Lamp Corp.), Owensboro, Ky. They were licensed by RCA. This concern had previously made Archatron tubes.
KEYSTONE	1924	Made by Keystone Electric & Radio Co., 110–116 Nassau Street, New York.
KLEERTONE	1927	Made by Globe Electric Co., 341 Halsey Street, Newark.
LA FRANCE	1923	Sold by La France Import & Sales Co. Inc., 280 Madison Avenue, New York. Made by Nulite Electric Co., 220 West 42nd Street, New York. This latter company also made Mizpah and Econotron tubes.
LA SALLE	1928	Made by La Salle Radio Corp., 149 West Austin Avenue, Chicago. Also sold by

Brand Name	Date	Notes
		Matchless Electric Co. of 143 West Austin Avenue, Chicago.
LECO	1926	Made by Lynn Electric Corp., 412 Broad Street, Lynn, Mass.
LECTRON	1925	Made by Lectron Radio Co., 1270 Broadway, New York.
LERADION		Made by Chicago Lamp Co.
LEWIS		Sold by Lewis Radio Jobbers, Inc., 2326 Columbia Avenue, Philadelphia. These tubes had blue glass envelopes.
LIVETONE	1926	Made by Royal Electric Co., 186 Third Street, Boston.
LORD BALTIMORE		Made by Diana Radio Tube Corp., 250 Park Avenue, New York.
LOUDSPEAKER	1925	Made by James H. Konkle, 192 Market Street, Newark.
LYRIC		Manufacturer unknown, but tubes used blue glass envelopes.
McCULLOUGH	1925	Sold by McCullough Sales Co. Address in 1925 was given as 963 Liberty Avenue, Pittsburgh. In February 1926 McCullough Sales Co. had offices at 25 West Broadway, New York, and 533 Wabash Avenue, Chicago. In September 1926 office address was 20 Grand Avenue, Brooklyn. An advertisement in February 1926 says that McCullough tubes are now being made by Kellogg Switchboard & Supply Co. of Chicago. Note on page 82 of June 1929 issue of *Radio Engineering* says McCullough tubes are now being made by A. C. Neon Corp., 122 Greenwich Street, New York.
MAGICTRON	1925	Made by F & C Corporation, 206 Broadway, New York.
MAGNATRON	1923	Made by Connewey Electric Laboratories, Magnatron Building, Hoboken, N.J.
MAGNAVOX	1924	Made by the Magnavox Company, 2723 East 14th Street, Oakland, Calif. For detailed information on the construction of this tube see article by Herbert E. Metcalf, "The New Magnavox Tube," in *QST*, March 1925, 9:24–25.
MAJESTIC	1927	Made by Grigsby-Grunow-Hinds, 4560 Armitage Avenue, Chicago.
MARATHON	1925	Made by Northern Manufacturing Co., Hoboken, N.J.
MARGO	1923	Sold by Modell's, 191 Fulton Street, New York.

Brand Name	Date	Notes
MARVIN	1929	Made by Marvin Radio Tube Corp.,
MASTER BUILT		Irvington, N.J.
MASTERTONE	1923	Made by Mastertone Radio Co., 903 Broad Street, Newark.
MECO	1925	Made by Metropolitan Electric Co., Des Moines, Iowa.
MELOPHONIC		No information available.
MICROTUBE		No information available.
MILO		No information available.
MINUET		Made by the National Radio & Television Corp., Fort Wayne, Ind., and Chicago.
MIZPAH	1925	Made by Nulite Electric Co., 220 West 42nd Street, New York. This company also made La France and Econotron tubes.
MODERN	1925	Made by Modern Radio Tube Mfg. Co., 57–59 Branford Street, Newark.
MONOTRON		No information available.
MURDON	1923	Maker unknown, but he also made Alpha tubes, and the manufacture of both brands was stopped by court injunction in 1923.
MUSIKTRON	1926	Made by K & H Electric Co., 43 Commercial Street, Newark.
MUSSELMAN	1925	Made by A. J. Musselman—The Van Horne Co., Franklin, Ohio.
MUZADA	1926	Made by Mazda Radio Mfg. Co., 3405 Perkins Avenue, Cleveland.
MYERS	1926	Made by Myers Radio Tube Corp., Cleveland.
NATIONAL UNION	1929	Made by National Union Radio Corp., 350 Scotland Road, Orange, N.J. This corporation was formed in 1929 by the merger of Sonatron, Magnatron, Marathon, and Televocal. It was licensed by RCA.
NATTANS		No information available on this manufacturer, but he made Type 200 tubes.
NOVOTRON	1924	Made by Radio Electric Laboratories, 152 West 42nd Street, New York.
NU TRO	1924	Made by C.A.W. Laboratories, 608 Chestnut Street, Philadelphia.
NUTRON	1924	Made by Nutron Manufacturing Co., 715 Main Street, Passaic, N.J. This company also made Solodyne tubes.
ODEON	1932	Made by Odeon Manufacturing Co., 30 Clinton Street, Newark.
O.K.		Sold by S. S. Kresge & Co.

Brand Name	Date	Notes
OSCILLECTOR	1925	Made by St. James Laboratories, 845 West Washington Boulevard, Chicago.
OSCILLOTRON		Made by G & M Specialty Co., Cleveland.
O-T	1923	Made by O & T Electric Corp., 1818 Broadway, New York. Tubes made by this company bore the legend on the base "Made by De Forest Tel. & Tel. Co. Exclusively for O & T Electric Corporation." This statement was false, and de Forest sued O & T for damages on account of it.
PACKARD	1926	Made by Martin Radio & Electric Co., 130 North(?) 52nd Street, New York.
PARAMOUNT		No information available.
PEERLESS		Made by Alfred Lopacker—Titan Miniature Lamp Co.
PEERTRON	1926	Made by Artee Radio Sales & Mfg. Co., 16 Hudson Street, New York. Preliminary injunction obtained by RCA in 1923.
PERFECTRON	1926	Made by Pacific Radio Laboratory, 256 South Los Angeles Street, Los Angeles.
PERMATRON	1926	Made by Duratron Products Corp., 531 Lewis Street, Union City, N.J. This concern also made Duraco tubes.
PERRYMAN	1927	Made by Perryman Electric Co., 13th Street and Hudson Boulevard, North Bergen, N.J. Their New York office was at 33 West 60th Street.
PHILCO	1928	Made by Lansdale Tube Co., Division of Philco Corp., Church Road, Lansdale, Pa.
PHILOTRON	1926	Made by Philadelphia Radio Mfg. Co., 3040 West Stiles Street, Philadelphia.
PHONOTRON	1926	Made by Vacuum Products Co., P. O. Box 220, Weehawken, N.J. This company later combined with Schultz Machine Co. to form Radio Products Corporation.
PILOTRON	1930	Made by Pilot Radio & Tube Corp., 323 Berry Street, Brooklyn.
PINGREE	1926	Made by Pingree Radio Service, Inc., 170 Summer Street, Boston.
PLAYTRON	1926	Made by Commercial Enclosed Fuse Co., 1817 Willow Avenue, Hoboken, N.J.
POWERTONE	1925	Made by Barfield Electrical Laboratories, 206 Broadway, New York.
PREMIER		Made by Premier Vacuum Tube Co., Chicago.

Brand Name	Date	Notes
PURATRON	1926	Made by Ideal Products Corp., 78 Mechanic Street, Newark.
QRS RED TOP	1927	Made by QRS Music Co., 75 East Jackson Boulevard, Chicago. These were gaudy tubes: the tops were coated with red lacquer, and the emblem was of gilt-faced paper, attached to the bulb with adhesive.
QUADROTRON	1926	This tube was designed especially for use in neutrodyne receivers, and is described by its designer, H. K. Huppert, in an article in the July 1926 issue of Radio News, on pages 50–51. It was made by Baker-Smith Co., New Call Building, San Francisco, who also made Sylfan tubes.
QUALITRON	1926	Made by Qualitron Mfg. Co., 521 Morgan Avenue, Newark.
RADEX	1924	Made by S. P. Hankins & Co., 1411 Castro Street, Oakland, Calif.
RADIO KNIGHT	1925	Made by Chisholm-Barfield Corp., 206 Broadway, New York.
RAY-O-VAC		Made by French Battery Co., Madison, Wis.
RAYTHEON		Made by Raytheon Mfg. Co., Cambridge, Mass. (later Raytheon Production Corp., Newton, Mass.). These tubes were licensed by RCA.
REAL TONE		Made by Real Tone Tube Co., Pawtucket, R.I.
RECTOBULB	1928	Made by National Radio Tube Co., 3420 18th Street, San Francisco. This company made only rectifier tubes.
RECTUBE		Made by Specialty Appliance Co., 6611 Euclid Avenue, Cleveland. This company made only rectifier tubes.
RELIABLE	1931?	Made by Reliable Radio Co., 143 West 45th Street, New York.
REXTRON		No information available.
ROICE	1925	Made by Roice Tube Co., 21 Norwood Street, Newark.
ROLLS ROYCE	1924	Made by Rolls-Royce Tube Co., 21 Norwood Street, Newark.
ROXY	1930	Manufacturer unknown.
ROY	1925	Made by Tectron Radio Corp., 1270 Broadway, New York.
ROYAL BLUE	1926	Made by Royal Blue Tube Laboratories, Newark.
ROYALFONE	1926	Made by Royal Electrical Laboratories, 104 Tichenor Street, Newark.

Brand Name	Date	Notes
ROYALTRON	1924	Made by Royal Manufacturing Co., 206 Broadway, New York. This company also made Harp tubes.
RRA		These tubes were marketed by Radio Retailers Assn. They were made by Munder Electrical Co., 97 Orleans Street, Springfield, Mass., who also made Vox tubes.
SAMSON	1924	Made by Phoenix Tube Co., 28 East 26th Street, New York.
SAVOY		Made by Savoy Radio Co., New York.
SCHICKERLING	1924	Originally made by TVT Co., Newark; later by Schickerling Products Manufacturing Co., 313 Halsey Street, Newark; still later by Schickerling Radio Tube Corp., address unknown. These tubes had an unusual construction and were alleged to be nonmicrophonic.
SEA GULL	1925	Made by Aberdeen Specialty Co., Inc., 1641 North Hutchinson Street, Philadelphia. These tubes used letter designations rather than the usual numbers; e.g., type E was the equivalent of the usual 201A.
SHEPHERD	1926	Made by W. C. Braun & Co., 32 South Clinton Street, Chicago.
SHERATON		No information available.
SHIELDPLATE	1928	Made by Shieldplate Tube Corp., 208 South La Salle Street, Chicago.
SILVERTONE		No information available.
SILVERTRON	1924	Made by New York Radio Co. Address in 1924 was 71 West Broadway, New York. In 1926 address was 275 Greenwich Street, New York.
SIMPLEX	1925	Made by Titania Manufacturing Co., 236 West 55th Street, New York.
SINGER	1925	Made by Singer Radio Corp., Times Building, New York. This firm was originally in the tube repair business.
SJ1 DETECTOR		No information available.
SKY SWEEPER	1926	Made by Charles R. Ablett Co., 22 Reade Street, New York.
SODION	1923	Made by Connecticut Telephone & Electric Co., Meriden, Conn.
SODIUM		Made by Electro Chemical Laboratories, New York and San Francisco.
SOLODYNE	1926	Made by Nutron Mfg. Co., 715 Main Street, Passaic, N.J. This company also made Nutron tubes. Solodyne is a tet-

Brand Name	Date	Notes
		rode, with outer grid connected to base shell.
SONATRON	1926	Made by Sonatron Tube Co. Two addresses are given for this firm: 220 South State Street, Chicago, and, in 1928, 16 Hudson Street, New York.
SONGBIRD		No information available.
SONORA	1924	Made by Sonora Tube Co., 220 South State Street, Chicago.
SOVEREIGN A.C.	1927	Made by Sovereign Electric & Mfg. Co., 123 North Sagamon Street, Chicago.
SPARTON		Made by Sparks Withington Co., Jackson, Mich. This firm was licensed by RCA.
SPEED	1926	Made by Cable Supply Co., Inc. (later Cable Radio Tube Corp.). Address in 1926 was 907 Broadway, New York; in 1927, 31 Union Square, New York.
STANDARD	1924	Made by Standard Radio Tube Co., 270 Plane Street, Newark.
STAR		Made by Star Radio Laboratories, New York.
STRONGSON COPPER PLATED	1926	Made by Moulded Products Corp., 549–551 West 52nd Street, New York.
STURDY	1927	Made by Sturdy Engineering Corp., 422 South Clark Street, Chicago. Later address 1323 South Michigan Avenue, Chicago.
SUNLIGHT	1926	Made by Sunlight Lamp Co., Newton Falls, Ohio.
SUPER AIRLINE		No information available.
SUPERTHEON		No information available.
SUPERTRON	1925	Made by Supertron Mfg. Co., 222–228 Washington Street, Hoboken, N.J.
SYLFAN	1925	Made by Baker-Smith Co., New Call Building, San Francisco. Tubes used blue glass envelopes. This company also made Quadrotron.
SYLVANIA	1925	Made by Sylvania Products Co., Emporium, Pa.
SYNTRON		Made by Syntron Co., Homer City, Pa.
TAYLOR	1931	Made by Taylor Vacuum Products Co., 1500 Ogden Avenue, Chicago. In 1936 this concern was Taylor Tubes Inc., 2341 Wabanasia Avenue, Chicago.
TECTRON	1926	Tectron Tubes were made by makers of Roy tubes; i.e., Tectron Radio Corp. They were also made by Farad Corporation.

Brand Name	Date	Notes
TELETRON	1925	Made by Champion Electric Co., Detroit. Teletron tubes had cylindrical envelopes.
TELEVOCAL	1927	Made by Televocal Corporation, 588 12th Street, West New York, N.J. This company became a part of National Union.
THERMATRON	1924	Made by Emko Radio Mfg. Co., 97 Springfield Avenue, Newark.
THERMIONIC	1926	Made by Radio Requirements Co., 5th and Market Streets, Philadelphia.
THORIO	1924	Made by Hayden Sales Co., Jersey City, N.J.
TRAV LER		No information available.
TRIAD	1929	Made by Triad Television & Mfg. Co., Pawtucket, R.I. This manufacturer was licensed by RCA.
TRIPLETONE	1925	Made by Radio Tube Mfg. Co., 154 Nassau Street, New York.
TROY		No information available.
TRUE BLUE		Made by Brightson "True Blue" Labs, 16 West 34th Street, New York.
TUNG SOL	1929	Made by Tung Sol Lamp Works, 95 Eighth Avenue, Newark. This firm entered the radio tube field in September 1929 and was licensed by RCA.
ULTRA	1925	No information as to manufacturer available.
URECO	1924	Made by United Radio & Electric Corp., 418 Central Avenue, Newark. Ureco Mfg. is a subsidiary. This concern was sued by RCA on de Forest patents, settled for $1500 damages; final decree was issued September 6, 1925.
UNITRON NOBEE		No information available.
UNIVERSAL		No information available.
VAC-O-BUB		Made by Standard Radio Light Co., Newark.
VAN DYCK		Sold by S. S. Kresge Co. Made by Van Dyck Laboratories, address unknown.
VAN DYKE		No information available.
VAN HORNE	1926	Made by the Van Horne Company, 1004 Center Street, Franklin, Ohio.
VEBY	1926	Made by Veby Radio Corp., 47–51 Morris Avenue, Newark.
VESTA	1926	No information on manufacturer available.
VITAVOX	1925	Made by Imp Radio Corp., 6 East Lake Street, Chicago. In 1926 made by Imperial Radio Corp., 1945 Wabanasia Avenue, Chicago.

Brand Name	Date	Notes
VOGUE NONPAREIL	1927	Made by Allan Mfg. Co., Arlington, N.J. In 1928 address was 102 North Fifth Street, Harrison, N.J. This company also made Alltron tubes.
VOLTRON	1926	Made by MacLaren Mfg. Co., 26 Park Place, New York.
VOLUTRON		No information available.
VOX	1929	Made by the Munder Electrical Co., 97 Orleans Street, Springfield, Mass. This company also made RRA tubes.
WARD WEAR		No information available.
WELSH	1923	Made by Welsh Electric Lamp Corp., 72 Boylan Street, Newark. Later 38–40 Clinton Street, Newark. Tubes sold by Radio Research Guild, 9–15 Clinton Street, Newark.
WESTERN		No information available.
WESTRON		Made by Westron Products Co., New York. These tubes had blue glass envelopes.
WIZARD		No information available.
WORLD RADIO TUBE		Made by World Battery Co., Chicago.
WRC	1923	Made by Conway Electrical Laboratories, 123 East 34th Street, New York.
WUNDERLICH	1932	Made by Arcturus Radio Tube Co., Newark.
YANKEE	1925	Made by Yankee Tube Corp., 6 Church Street, New York.
ZENITH		No information available.
ZETKA PROCESS (Z-P)	1927	Made by Zetka Laboratories, 67–73 Winthrop Street, Newark. Later (1929) became Radio Utilities Corp.

REFERENCES

1. Advertisement in *Sci. & Invent.*, Dec. 1920, p. 896.
2. *Federal Trade Commission vs. General Electric Co. et al. Transcript of Record*, Vol. 8, pp. 3708–3800.
3. 281 Fed 200, Apr. 22, 1922.
4. 284 Fed 1020, Dec. 15, 1922.
5. *Transcript* (No. 2 above), pp. 3768–3769.
6. Advertisement by Wireless Equipment Co., *Radio News*, Feb. 1920, *1*:494, and in *QST*, Oct. 1920, *4*:92.
7. Advertisement in *Radio News*, Jul. 1923, 5:103.
8. Advertisement in *Radio News*, Aug. 1923, 5:206.
9. U.S. Patent No. 1,291,441 on an "Electron Valve," application date Aug. 8, 1918, issued Jan. 14, 1919.

10. U.S. Patent No. 1,291,641 on "Radio Communication," application date Mar. 23, 1918, issued Jan. 14, 1919.
11. H. P. Donle, "A New Electron Tube," *Radio Amat. News,* Jul. 1919, *1:* 14–15. See also "The Connecticut Tube," *QST,* Oct. 1919, 3:22–24.
12. "Some New Apparatus at the Conventions," *QST,* Oct. 1921, 5:22–24.
13. *Ibid.,* p. 24.
14. H. P. Donle, "A New Non-Interfering Detector," *Proc. I.R.E.,* Apr. 1923, pp. 97–110.
15. H. P. Donle, "New Applications of the Sodion Detector," *Proc. I.R.E.,* Apr. 1924, pp. 159–175.
16. "The New Sodion D-21 Detector," *QST,* Dec. 1924, 8:23–26.
17. Advertisement of Donle-Bristol Corp., *Radio News,* May 1926, 7:1605.
18. H. P. Donle, "The New B-6 Donle Detector," *Radio News,* May 1926, 7: 1548, 1549, 1594, 1595, 1597.
19. Advertisement of Warford Electric Co., *Pop. Radio,* Sept. 1927, p. 173.
20. Advertisements in *QST,* Nov. 1927, *13*:1; *Radio News,* Nov. 1927, 9:447; *Radio Broadcast,* Nov. 1927, *12*:5.
21. Advertisements in *QST,* Nov. 1928, *12*:93; *Radio News,* Oct. 1928, *10*:390.
22. Advertisement of Providence Distributing Co., *Radio News,* Jul. 1925, 7: 125.
23. Advertisement in *Radio News,* Oct. 1926, 8:391.
24. *Radio World,* Sept. 3, 1927, *11*:18.
25. Advertisement in *Radio Broadcast,* Oct. 1927, *11*:386.
26. Advertisement in *Radio News,* Mar. 1928, 9:1085.
27. Advertisement in *Radio News,* May 1928, 9:1279.
28. G. C. B. Rowe, "New 110-Volt Vacuum Tube," *Radio News,* Jul. 1925, 7:25.
29. Advertisement in *Radio Broadcast,* Jul. 1925, 7:422; *Pop. Radio,* June 1925, 7:1 and back cover.
30. F. S. McCullough, "Thermionic Tubes," *Proc. I.R.E.,* Dec. 1922, *10:* 468–485.
31. Advertisement in *Pop. Radio,* Jan. 1926, 8:89.
32. Advertisement of Northern Manufacturing Co., *Radio Broadcast,* Aug. 1925, 7:555.
33. H. E. Rhodes, "Constructing a Five-Tube Neutrodyne," *Radio Broadcast,* Aug. 1927, *11*:232–234.
34. Advertisement by Emerson-Radval Corp., *Radio News,* Mar. 1927, 8:1081.
35. A. J. Haynes, "The Haynes D-X Multivalve Receiver," *Radio News,* Feb. 1927, 8:976–979.
36. Advertisement of Emerson-Radval Corp., *Radio News,* Sept. 1927, 9:270.
37. H. K. Huppert, "A Departure in Radio Tube Design," *Radio News,* Jul. 1926, 8:50–51.
38. *Ibid.,* p. 51.
39. Obituary notices of E. S. Rogers, *Toronto Telegraph,* May 6, 1939, and *Toronto Star,* May 6, 1939.

Chapter 18

The Early Days of Broadcasting, 1920-1930: *Great Britain*

The telephone network in Great Britain (see Chapter 11) continued to grow. By 1926 there were twenty-six repeater stations with a total of 670 repeaters in service.[1] One of the standard amplifying valves used in such repeaters, designated by the Post Office as "Valve, Thermionic, No. 25," is illustrated Fig. 18-1. It was made by the General Electric Company, Ltd., of London (not affiliated with GE in the United States) and was a further development of the R valve used in radio applications. It was used in radio receivers as an output valve under the designation LS5. In telephone equipment it operated with a filament current of 0.82 ampere at 4.5 volts, had a life of 1000–2000 hours,[2] and was used in both two-wire and four-wire repeaters. A two-wire repeater, designated Repeater No. 10, is shown in Fig. 18-2.

Another type of repeater (Fig. 18-3) of the same vintage was installed on a London-Glasgow cable which was placed in service about 1926.[3] The repeater equipment of this cable was made and installed by Standard Telephones and Cables Ltd. (S.T.&C.). The valves used were S.T.&C. types 4101D and 4102D, designated by the Post Office as V.T. No. 31 and V.T. No. 32, respectively. These were essentially the same as the Western Electric (U.S.) 101D and 102D vacuum tubes. This similarity came about because S.T.&C. Ltd. had originally been the Western Electric Co. Ltd., a subsidiary of International Western Electric Co., which in turn was a subsidiary of the Western Electric Co. Inc. of the United States. Development of early S.T.&C. valves had thus closely paralleled that of American Western Electric tubes.

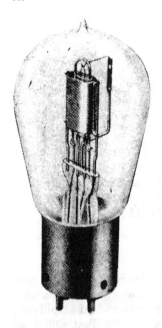

Fig. 18-1. Valve, Thermionic, No. 25. Made by General Electric Company, Ltd. (Reproduced from J. A. Fleming, *The Thermionic Valve and Its Developments in Radio Telegraphy and Telephony*, 2nd ed., London, 1924.)

The chief difference in the tubes and valves mentioned above was the base. The American Western Electric base shell was formed from sheet nickel silver and had a vertical seam. The British Western Electric manufactured approximately 6000 4101D valves with

Fig. 18-2. Two-wire repeater using V.T. No. 25 valves. (Reproduced from Paper No. 99, *Inst. P.O.E.E.*, 1924.)

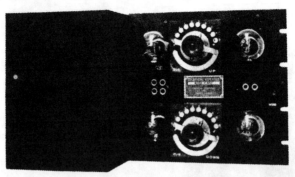

Fig. 18-3. Standard Telephones and Cables Type 4202F telephone repeater (four-wire type) using 4101D (V.T. No. 31) and 4102D (V.T. No. 32) valves. (Reproduced from *P.O.E.E.J.*, 1926.)

a similar base before changing to a seamless nickel silver shell, which was also used by S.T.&C.

Subsequently S.T.&C. developed repeater valves which operated at lower filament currents.[4] A group of these quarter-ampere repeater valves is shown in Fig. 18-4. All except the 4020A had oxide-coated filaments operating with 0.25 ampere at 4 volts. The 4020A operated with 0.25 ampere at 2 volts. The 4019A had anode characteristics similar in general to those of the 4101D and could be used to replace it in existing equipment—with a slight increase in gain. The 4020A was intended to replace the 4102D. The 4021A replaced the 4104D, also with some increase in gain. The 4022A was a higher-gain 4101D. The 4019A, 4020A, and 4022A had a life exceeding 10,000 hours. The life of the 4021A was in excess of 3000 hours.

The axis of the element assembly was at an angle to the vertical axis of these valves and was so designed to solve problems of manufacture. These valves were made by a vapor process in which barium

Fig. 18-4. S.T.&C. quarter-ampere repeater valves. Left to right: 4019A, 4020A, 4021A, 4022A. (Reproduced from *Elect. Commun.*, Oct. 1932.)

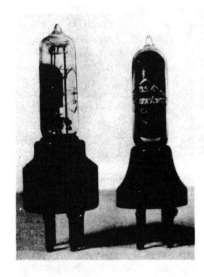

Fig. 18-5. S.T.& C. 4215A with adapter for use in British socket (left) and the 4215AB, with base to fit British socket.

Fig. 18-6. S.T.& C. Micromesh 9A. 1 valve.

vapor was distilled into the bulb from a supply in the electrode assembly. If the electrode system were vertical, trouble might occur as a result of condensation of the barium on the press, leading to electrical leakage. If the axis of the electrical assembly were horizontal, its length would require a wider opening in the bulb neck, making the sealing-in process more difficult. The compromise of putting the element assembly at an angle solved the two problems and decreased the overall height of the bulb.

Two S.T.&C. valves of interest to the collector are pictured in Fig. 18-5. They are modifications of the Western Electric (U.S.) 215A. The 4215A has the same base as the 215A, but an adapter could be obtained to enable it to be inserted in a British four-pin socket. The 4215AB was electrically the same as the 215A, but the base was of the British type. The 4215A was also made by the British Thomson-Houston Company (B.T.H.)[5] and by Mullard,[6] and was sold by them under the name Wecovalve. S.T.&C. also made a line of tubes for use in broadcast receivers. These carried the brand name Micromesh and were made up to about 1935. A Micromesh 9A.1 is shown in Fig. 18-6.

Identification of valves and manufacturers of the post World War I era in England requires analysis of the growth of the valve industry as it developed along protective nationalistic lines. In 1922 there were six major and several smaller manufacturers of valves in the United Kingdom. The major companies were as follows:

Manufacturer	Brand Name
British Thomson-Houston Co. Ltd.	B.T.H. and Mazda
A. C. Cossor Ltd.	Cossor
Edison Swan Electric Co. Ltd.	Ediswan
Metropolitan-Vickers Electrical Co. Ltd.	Cosmos
The M. O. Valve Co. Ltd.	Osram and Marconi-Osram
Mullard Radio Valve Co. Ltd.	Mullard

In 1924, when production reached 2.5 million, a Valve Manufacturers Association was formed. This was superseded two years later by the British Radio Valve Manufacturers Association (BVA), which comprised all members of the Valve Manufacturers Association plus one new member, Cleartron Radio Ltd. At its founding as a trade union in July 1926, BVA thus had the following membership:

British Thomson-Houston Co. Ltd. (B.T.H.)
Burndept Wireless Ltd.
Cleartron Radio Ltd.

A. C. Cossor Ltd.
Edison Swan Electric Co. Ltd. (Ediswan)
Electron Co. Ltd.
General Electric Co. Ltd. (GE Co. Ltd.)
Marconi's Wireless Telegraph Co. Ltd. and Marconiphone Co. Ltd.
Mullard Radio Valve Co. Ltd. (Mullard)
Standard Telephones and Cables Ltd. (S.T.&C.)

BVA was formed "to promote, encourage, foster, develop and protect the interests of the public, the trade, and the manufacturers of British-made valves," and on its way to becoming a monopoly the interests were protected in reverse order to that stated. Limitation of imports was a major feature of the BVA policy. Valves from some European countries and the United States could be sold at "uneconomical" prices and were a constant threat to the stability of the home industry. Throughout its history BVA regulated the prices, terms, and conditions of sale of valves by its members and made restrictive agreements with retailers, thus insuring handling of valves made exclusively by BVA members.

The maneuvers within BVA and the resulting changes which took place in corporation set-ups make it difficult to determine who was making what brand valves at any given time. In some cases records show that Company X introduced or placed on the market a particular type of valve but give no evidence that Company X actually made the product.

The Edison Swan Electric Co. Ltd., which in 1916 replaced the Edison and Swan United Electric Light Co. Ltd., made valves during World War I for the British armed services. They made valves both before and after the war for Marconi's Wireless Telegraph Co. Ltd., and manufactured Marconi valves up to the founding of the Marconi-Osram Valve Co. Ltd. in 1919 (name changed to M.O. Valve Co. Ltd. one year later). It cannot be emphasized too strongly that despite the markings on valves used by them, Marconi Co. never made valves.

In 1921 Edison Swan Electric Co. (Ediswan) brought out the ES2 and ES4 valves. These differed only in the extent to which they were exhausted. The ES4 (Fig. 18-7) was a hard valve. In receiving circuits it was operated with 0.75 ampere at about 4 volts on the filament. The recommended anode voltage was 30–80 volts. If the filament current was increased to 1 ampere at 6 volts, it could be used as a transmitter up to about 30 watts. The anode potential under these conditions could be raised as high as 1000 volts. The ES2 had a lower vacuum but could be operated satisfactorily in a receiver with a filament current of 0.75 ampere at anode voltage in the range of 15–60 volts.

Fig. 18-7 (Left). Ediswan
ES4 valve.

Fig. 18-8 (Right). Ediswan
AR.06 valve.

In 1922 Ediswan brought out the AR, and followed in 1923 with the AR.06[7] (Fig. 18-8), ARDE, ARDE(HF), ARDE(LF), and DE2.[8] They announced no new valves in 1924, but in 1925 they introduced the GP2, GP4, PV4, PV5(DE), PV6(DE) and PV8(DE). Characteristics of the ARDE(HF), ARDE(LF), PV5 (DE), and PV6(DE) are described in *Experimental Wireless & The Wireless Engineer*.[9] The design of the PV6(DE) was changed late in 1925 and its characteristics are given in the December issue of the same journal.[10] The Ediswan HF210, PV2, and RC came out in 1926, and the M in 1927.

The Metropolitan-Vickers Electrical Co. Ltd. (Metrovick) was an outgrowth of the British Westinghouse Electrical and Manufacturing Co. Ltd., which was established in 1899. They engaged in quantity production of valves during World War I and continued manufacture into the postwar era. Their brand name was Cosmos. Metrovick in 1923 secured the services of E. Brian Munt, who held a number of patents on valves. Through his efforts and know-how they began to produce valves of entirely new design. The first was the DE11, which appeared in 1924.[11] This was followed in 1925 by the A45, SP18/G (Fig. 18-9), SP18/R,[12] and SP18/RR. In 1926 they produced the SP55/B (Fig. 18-10) and the SP55/R. In these designations the G, R, and B indicated green, red, and blue identification marks. SP indicated "short path," a distinguishing feature of the construction. In 1927 twelve more valves were added to the Metrovick line. Nine valves, including the AC/S (Fig. 18-11), were introduced by Metrovick in 1928.

The valve activities of Metrovick, B.T.H., and Ediswan were combined in 1928 in a new company called Associated Electrical Industries (AEI). All valve production was taken over by Ediswan, the valves carrying the brand names Ediswan, Ediswan-Mazda, or Mazda. The name Cosmos disappeared.

Fig. 18-9. Metrovick   Fig. 18-10. Metrovick   Fig. 18-11. Metrovick
SP18/G valve.   SP55/B valve.   AC/S valve.

The Cossor company had its origin in the family business established by A. C. Cossor in Clerkenwell in the early 1890s. They made scientific glassware, including Crookes tubes, X-ray tubes, spinthariscopes, and a wide range of incandescent lamps for medical and surgical apparatus. They claim to have made the first Fleming valves. In 1908 the family business became A. C. Cossor Ltd.—a private company. During World War I they made wireless apparatus for the Royal Navy and Royal Flying Corps.

After the war Cossor moved to Highbury, where they continued their intensive work on valve development. In 1922, in time for the premiere of the British Broadcasting Corporation service, they put on the market two new types of receiving valves designated P1 (with plain top) and P2 (with red top). The P1 was intended for use as a detector and low-frequency amplifier, the P2 for high-frequency amplification.[13] Both valves operated with nominal filament current of 0.7 ampere at 3.5–4.0 volts. The P1 was rated at 20–80 volts on the anode. The nominal amplification factor was 6.6, and internal impedance was 20,000 ohms. The P2 used 60–80 volts on the anode, had an amplification factor of 11 and internal impedance of 40,000 ohms (Fig. 18-12).

The P1 and P2 were followed in 1924 by their "dull-emitter" equivalents, the P3 (green top) and P4 (blue top) respectively. They operated with a filament current of 0.22 ampere at 0.8–1.1 volts. The other characteristics were the same as those of their "bright-emitter" predecessors. The P3 and P4 carried the name WUNCELL. Later, in May 1925, Cossor brought out the WUNCELL series. As originally announced this consisted of the W1, WR, WR1, and WR2.[14] A "loudspeaker" valve, the W3, was added in July 1925.[15] The WR1 and WR2 (Fig. 18-13) are of particular interest to collectors. These were designed to be used with filament batteries of from 2 to 6 volts. They were provided with two threaded holes in the base and a thumbscrew which could be inserted into

Fig. 18-12. Cossor P2 valve.

Fig. 18-13. Cossor WR2 valve with view of the base.

either hole. When the thumbscrew is inserted in the hole marked "4–6 V," an 8-ohm resistor (wound in a slot in the base) is connected in series with the filament; when inserted in the hole marked "2 V," the resistor is short circuited. Fine adjustment of the filament current was made by using the filament rheostat incorporated in the receiving set.[16]

Late in 1926 Cossor introduced their new Kalenised filament.[17] Exactly what the Kalenising process was they did not state, making only the modest claim that it "gives off a torrent of electrons practically without heat." This filament was used in the Cossor Point One, 210D, and 210H valves, and also in a power valve denoted only as the Stentor Two, to which the number 215P was later assigned.

In February 1928 Cossor announced a new series of 2-volt, double-ended screen-grid valves.[18] One of these pictured in the announcement appears to have been patterned after the S625 designed by H. J. Round and made by M. O. Valve. Apparently the double-ended construction did not appeal to set designers and constructors, and its commercial life was short. By September 1928 Cossor was offering a full line of 2-, 4-, and 6-volt triode valves, two pentodes (which they termed Quintodes), three tetrodes of single-ended construction, and four directly heated ac valves. Available records indicate that Cossor produced indirectly heated valves in 1931.

Cossor valves had identification markings on a paper label which was stuck onto the glass bulb. If this label is missing, it is impossible to determine who made the valve or what the designation was. The Mullard Radio Valve Co. Ltd. was founded in 1920 by Stanley R. Mullard, whose exceptional background is worthy of note. His first employment in the electrical engineering field was with a manufacturer of incandescent lamps and X-ray tubes. At age twenty-one he was manager of a lamp works and soon became head of the Ediswan lamp laboratories. When World War I was declared, he enlisted in the Engineers Battalion of the Royal Naval Division. The Admiralty assigned him to remain at Ediswan and continue his development work on radio valves because his knowledge of vacuum technique was invaluable. In 1916, commissioned as a lieutenant, he was put in charge of a laboratory at the Imperial College of Sciences. In 1918 he was a captain in the newly formed RAF. After military discharge in 1919 he became a director of the Z Electric Lamp Co. Ltd. at Southfield, where he developed transmitting valves for the Royal Navy with envelopes of fused silica instead of glass. In September of the following year he formed his own company, occupying space rented from the Z Electric Lamp Co. Initially Mullard produced high-power silica-envelope valves, but he soon abandoned this limited field and produced smaller valves for radio reception and low-power transmission.

Interest in radio increased sharply about this time. There was no public broadcasting organization in Britain, but there were isolated stations, and reception of continental European stations was possible. Amateurs began to build radio receivers and low-power transmitters. Many of them used war-surplus valves such as the TM type, imported from France, but these were tungsten-filament valves of uncertain life. British R valves were available but cost twice as much as the French TM. This upsurge of interest in radio created a shortage of reliable receiving valves.

Mullard began to produce valves in quantity for this market. He used the trade name ORA—the initials of the three main functions of the valve: "Oscillates, Rectifies, Amplifies."[19] Two samples of the ORA are shown in Fig. 18-14. The original ORA operated at a filament voltage of 3.6–4 volts, with a filament current of 0.7 ampere. It used 30–90 volts on the anode, had an amplification factor of about 8.5, and an anode impedance of 30,000 ohms. The demand for these valves soon outstripped the production capacity of his space at the Z Electric Lamp Co., and in 1922 Mullard found larger quarters at Hammersmith. He moved again in 1924 to still larger quarters in Balham.

Like other manufacturers Mullard also produced the R-type bright-emitter valve during this period. Toward the end of 1923 he

Fig. 18-14. Mullard ORA valves. Left: with British base. Right: with American UV base.

introduced the RA type, which was the R with minor modifications. The amplification factor was slightly lower, but the other constants were about the same as for the standard R type.

The One-Volt ORA was introduced early in 1924.[20] This had the same filament as the Wecovalve. A further modification of the original ORA was the DF ORA, which appeared a short time later.[21] This took a filament current of 0.06 ampere at 2.5–3.0 volts. It operated with an anode voltage of 20–100 volts, had an amplification factor of 5.5 and anode resistance of 20,000 ohms.

Late in 1923 Mullard had brought out two more valves. The LF, a general-purpose low-filament-current valve, was the first. The filament of it could be powered by a single storage cell. The second was the PA and was intended for driving a loudspeaker.[22] By August 1924 the LF had been replaced by the LF (Green Ring) for low-frequency applications (Fig. 18-15), and a corresponding high-frequency amplifier, the HF (Red Ring), was being offered.[23] Late in 1924 Mullard announced a four-electrode valve of the space-charge-grid type, designated DG. This used a four-pin base and had the inner grid lead brought out to the metal base shell.[24] By July 1925 this series had grown to include valves with the following designations: HF Double Red Ring D3, HF Double Red Ring D.06, LF Double Green Ring D3 (Fig. 18-15), LF Double Green Ring D.06, DFA0, and DFA1.[25] Data on some of these valves is given in the article "Six New Mullard Valves."[26]

While his valve business flourished, Mullard was harassed by patent suits. In 1922 the Marconi Company filed suit against Mullard claiming infringement of two of their patents. Mullard filed countersuits claiming the patents did not apply to his product and

Fig. 18-15. Left: Mullard LF green ring valve. Middle: Mullard LF double green ring D3. Right: Philips-Mullard PM6.

charged that the patents were invalid. In the two years of litigation which followed, the first court held that the patents were not infringed but were valid. Both parties appealed. The higher court ruled that the validity of the patents was not in question, but that they had not been infringed. The case was finally settled by the House of Lords in 1924 with the decision that the patents were not valid.

In 1924 Mullard sold half of his stock in the Mullard Radio Valve Co. Ltd. to N. V. Philips Gloeilampenfabrieken of Holland. In 1927 Philips bought the remainder of Mullard's stock, and the Mullard Radio Valve Co. Ltd. became a wholly owned subsidiary of N. V. Philips. Even before the new owners were in complete control, Philips' simplification of valve nomenclature could be noted in designations assigned to new valves. In 1926 the PM1, PM2, PM3, PM4, and others were introduced.[27] (See Figs. 18-15 and 18-16.) The PM indicated Philips-Mullard, and the marking "PHILIPS-MULLARD" is shown on the valve in one advertisement.[28] This nomenclature was continued into the 1930s.

In 1919 the Marconi-Osram Valve Co. Ltd. was formed. This was a joint venture of Marconi's Wireless Telegraph Co. Ltd. and General Electric Co. Ltd. (brand name Osram), each owning half the stock in the new company. About a year later the name was changed to The M.O. Valve Co. Ltd. "The inception of the present company . . . is due to a combination of the experience of Marconi's Wireless Telegraph Co. Ltd. and the General Electric Co.

Fig. 18-16. Mullard PM4 valve.

Ltd., who have combined together the valve business and manufacture under the title of the M.O. Valve Co. Ltd."[29] Since the Marconi company never made any valves, we must conclude that their contribution was largely the use of their valve patents and their experience in the applications of valves. The GE Co. had manufactured valves for the British armed services during World War I at their factory in Hammersmith. This location became the place of manufacture for Marconi-Osram (later M.O.) valves.

By 1922 M.O. Valve had a large number of receiving and transmitting valves on the market. The receiving types included the R, R4B (Fig. 18-17), RAC, DE3 (first M.O. dull emitter), LT3 (Fig. 18-18), LT1, and F.E.1 (see Chapter 11). Transmitting triodes in-

Fig. 18-17. Marconi-Osram R4B valve.

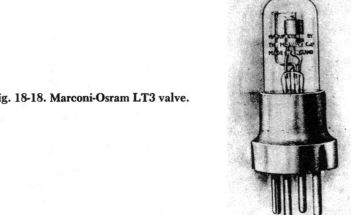

Fig. 18-18. Marconi-Osram LT3 valve.

cluded AT25, AT40, T30, and T250 (Fig. 18-19), MT1 (Fig. 18-20), and larger valves. Transmitting rectifiers included ERECT (Fig. 18-21), MR1 (Fig. 18-22), MR4, and others.

In 1923 Marconi's Wireless Telegraph Co. discontinued the manufacture and sale of receiving sets to the general public. They formed a subsidiary company, the Marconiphone Co. Ltd., to take over this work and sold to it the good will of Marconi's Wireless Telegraph Co.'s set-making business and the right to use the Marconi trademark. This included the right to sell Marconi-brand valves. Marconiphone sold valves branded "Marconi," which were made by M.O. Valve; identical valves branded "Osram," also made by

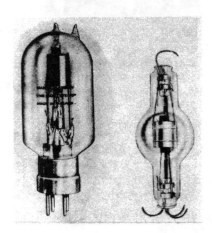

Fig. 18-19. Marconi-Osram T30 and T250 valves.

Fig. 18-20. Marconi-Osram MT1 valve.

M.O. Valve, were being sold by GE. Marconiphone was a founding member of BVA. By 1925 M.O. Valve was offering for sale the DER, R5V, DE2HF, DE2LF, DE3B, DE4, DE5, DE5B, DE6, DE7, DE8HF, DE8LF, LS1, LS2, LS3, LS5, QX, DEQ, DEV, and F.E.3 (tetrode) valves. Some of these are shown in Figs. 18-23 through 18-26.

The F.E.3 and DE7, lineal descendants of the F.E.1 and F.E.2

Fig. 18-21. Marconi-Osram ERECT diode.

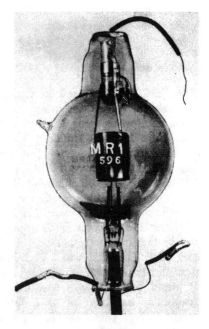

Fig. 18-22. Marconi-Osram MR1
transmitting valve.

space-charge-grid tetrode types, were fitted with British standard
four–pin bases. The base shell was the connection for the inner
grid. The F.E.3 had a bright-emitter filament operating with 0.7
ampere at 4 volts on the filament. The anode and inner grid operated over the range 6–15 volts. The amplification factor was 4.5,
and the anode impedance was 8000–20,000 ohms, depending on the
anode voltage. The DE7, similar to the F.E.3, had a dull-emitter
filament operating with a current of 0.4 ampere at 1.8–2.0 volts.

In 1927 M.O. Valve placed on the market the S625 (Fig. 18-27),
a double-ended tetrode designed by H. J. Round. This valve is
described in a book by Round but is referred to as the D.E.S.625.[30]
The filament was the dull-emitter type, similar to that used in the
DE3 valve but operated with a current of 0.25 ampere at 6 volts.

Fig. 18-23. Marconi-Osram DEV valve.

Fig. 18-24. Marconi-Osram
DEQ valve.

The "D.E." prefix used in Round's book did not appear in the commercial valve designation.

The following year another M.O. tetrode, S215, was marketed. This tube had the standard British four-pin base with a top-cap for the inner grid connection (Fig. 18-28). A screen grid was brought out on the grid terminal of the base. It operated with 0.15 ampere at 2 volts filament. The S215 had an amplification factor of 170 and an anode impedance of 200,000 ohms. The corresponding constants of the S625 were 110 and 175,000 ohms.

About the time the S625 appeared, the M.O. Valve Co. brought out its first indirectly heated cathode triode valves, designated KH1 and KL1. The KH1 was a high-gain, high-impedance valve with an amplification factor of 40 and anode impedance of 30,000 ohms. It could be used as a resistance-coupled high-frequency or low-frequency amplifier or as a detector. The maximum permissible anode voltage was 150. The KL1 was a general-purpose valve with

Fig. 18-25. Marconi-Osram R5V valve.

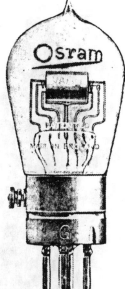

Fig. 18-26. Marconi-Osram F.E.3 tetrode.

an amplification factor of 7.5 and an anode impedance of 5500 ohms. The maximum permissible anode voltage was 100 volts. It was well suited for use as a low-frequency amplifier using transformer coupling. The heater voltage of each valve was 3.5 volts and the current was 2.0 amperes. Both valves required at least a minute to become operative after being switched on.

In 1929 the Marconi Company's share of M.O. Valve Co. was

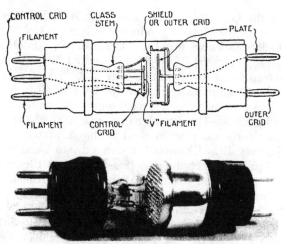

Fig. 18-27. Marconi-Osram S625 valve.

Fig. 18-28. Marconi-Osram S215.   Fig. 18-29. Marconi-Osram S410.

acquired by the Gramaphone Co. Ltd., but M.O. Valve continued to be a source for the Marconi's Wireless Telegraph Co.

Late in 1929 M.O. Valve introduced the S410 (Fig. 18-29) and S610 screen-grid valves and the PT240, PT425, and PT625 pentodes.

The Electron Co. Ltd. was registered in 1923 as a valve manufacturer and was a founding member of BVA in 1926. At first the brand name Amrex was used. Two samples of Amrex valves are shown in Fig. 18-30. The brand name was soon changed to Six-Sixty, and an early valve so marked is shown at the left in Fig. 18-31. In January 1926 Electron Co. entered into a ten-year agreement with Mullard. According to this agreement Electron would be supplied with valves by Mullard exclusively, and Electron ceased to make valves in commercial quantities. The Electron SS4 Detector, supplied by Mullard, is shown at the right in Fig. 18-31. In 1928 Mullard bought all shares of Electron Co. and changed the name to The Six-Sixty Radio Co. Ltd. because of the established name.

Another early producer of valves was Economic Electric Ltd.

Fig. 18-30. Electron Company
Amrex valves.

In 1922 they advertised the Xtraudion (Fig. 18-32).[31] As originally advertised it had a 0.5-ampere 4-volt filament and operated with 60–100 volts on the anode. It was a general-purpose tube. There was a later version intended for use as a high-frequency amplifier, which also took a filament current of 0.5 ampere at 4 volts, but the internal structure was changed to improve high frequency operation. By 1924 the Xtraudion was supplanted by the Dextraudion, which looked like its predecessor but had a dull-emitting filament.[32]

Fig. 18-31. Six-Sixty valves. Left: early design with no specific designation. Right: SS4 Det. A.C., made by Mullard.

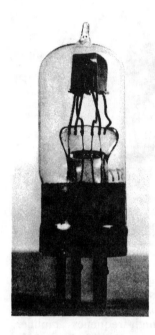

Fig. 18-32. Economic Electric Xtraudion.

The Dextraudion was made in eight types, differing chiefly in filament rating. These were designated Dex235 (2-v, 0.35 amp), Dex240 (2-v, 0.4-amp), Dex376 (3-v, 0.06-amp), Dex312 (3-v, 0.12-amp), Dex406 (4-v, 0.06-amp), Dex412 (4-v, 0.12-amp), Dex440 (4-v, 0.4-amp), and Dex530 (5-v, 0.3-amp).[33] Economic Electric ceased advertising in 1926.

The Thorpe Radio Valve Co. of London made two valves of interest to collectors—the K1 and K4. Both had helically wound wire for the anode and grid. The K1 was a triode which operated with a filament current of 0.42 ampere at 5 volts. The anode voltage rating was 50–100 volts. This valve appeared on the market early in 1924[34] and was distributed exclusively by Bower Electric Ltd. of London. The Thorpe K4 (Fig. 18-33) was a tetrode of the space-charge-grid type. It was intended primarily for use in the Unidyne or Solodyne circuits which were popular at that time.[35] The advantage which this valve offered was that no separate anode voltage supply was required, as both anode and inner grid were fed from the 6-volt filament battery. In the period 1925–1927 the K4 valve was offered for sale by at least three vendors in London, but it was not advertised by Bower Electric.

British Thomson-Houston Co. (B.T.H.) continued to make valves in the postwar era. At first they made the R-type valve, pictured in Fig. 18-34. It differed from their wartime production by

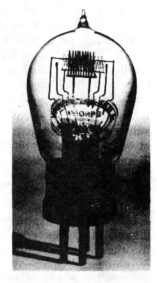

Fig. 18-33. Thorpe K4 valve.

having a nickel-plated base and was offered for sale as late as 1924.[36]

After the advent of BBC broadcasting, B.T.H. developed and produced valves for use in broadcast receivers. Their valves, the B2, B3, B4, B4H, B5, and B5H were introduced in 1923. The B2 was a bright-emitter general-purpose valve. The filament took 0.7 ampere at 5.0 volts. The anode voltage was 40–120 volts, and the amplification factor was about 10. The anode impedance was about 37,000 ohms. The B3, a general-purpose valve, operated at a filament voltage of 1.8 volts with 0.3–0.4 ampere. Recommended anode voltage was 20–80 volts. The amplification factor was about 7.5, and the anode resistance about 27,000 ohms.

Fig. 18-34. B.T.H. R valve.

The B4 was a power-output valve. The filament took 0.25 ampere at 6 volts. Recommended anode voltage was 40–100 volts. The amplification factor was 4.5, and anode impedance was 7500 ohms. The B4H was intended for high-frequency amplifier or detector use. Its filament was the same as that of the B4. The amplification factor was 20, and anode impedance was 28,000 ohms. The B5 was basically a detector valve, and its modification designated B5H was intended for high-frequency amplifier use. The filaments of these valves took 0.06 ampere at 2.8 volts. The B5 operated as a detector at an anode voltage of 20–80 volts, had an amplification factor of 7 and anode impedance of 17,000 ohms. The B5H operated with 40–120 volts on the anode. The amplification factor was 17.5, and the anode resistance was 55,000 ohms.[37] Samples of the B3, B4, and B5 are shown in Fig. 18-35.

In 1924 B.T.H. introduced the B6, B7, and B8. The B6 had a 2.8-volt, 0.12-ampere dull-emitter filament. The amplification factor was about 8, and the anode impedance about 12,000 ohms. The recommended anode voltage was 40–120 volts.[38] The B7 was a dull-emitter power valve with a 6-volt, 0.06-ampere filament. The amplification factor was about 6.3, and the anode impedance about 9000 ohms. The recommended anode voltage was 50–150 volts. The B8 had a 2.8-volt filament taking 0.12 ampere, with an amplification factor of 50 and anode impedance of 180,000 ohms.[39] The B6, B7, and B8 are shown in Fig. 18-36.

In 1927 B.T.H. brought out the B11, B12, B21, B22, B23, and TS215 valves, among others. The filament of the B12 took 1.25 amperes at 7.5 volts. The amplification factor was 2.85, and anode impedance was 2900 ohms.[40] The maximum permissible anode voltage was 425 volts. The B21, B22, and B23 valves, all 2-volt filaments,

Fig. 18-35. B.T.H. B3, B4, and B5 valves (left to right).

Fig. 18-36. B.T.H. B6, B7, and B8 valves (left to right).

were announced in July 1927 in an ad in the *Wireless World and Radio Review*.[41]

In 1928 B.T.H., Ediswan, and Metrovick were merged to form Associated Electrical Industries Ltd. (AEI). B.T.H. took over set manufacture for the merged companies and thereafter made only the special valves required for its production of nondomestic electronic equipment. Valves labeled Mazda continued to be made by Ediswan and in general carried the same designations as Marconi and Osram valves. For a few months in the latter part of 1926 Benjamin Electric Ltd. advertised Benjamin Shortpath valves. Their valve designations were almost identical with those used by Metrovick, and the valves may have been made by Metrovick to be sold under the Benjamin label.

British Tungsram assembled valves, but since they used parts imported from Hungary, their product cannot be classified as British.

BSA Radio Products sold valves made by Standard Telephones and Cables bearing the trademark BSA-Standard. They advertised various valves in the *South African Wireless Weekly* beginning with the April 27, 1927, issue (front cover). The first ad promoted BSA Peanut Type valves.

Burndept Wireless Ltd., originally Burnham & Co. of Deptford, used Burndept as a trademark.[42] They manufactured scientific research apparatus and were among the earliest wireless set makers. In 1925 they sold Burndept Valves (Fig. 18-37). In 1926 Burndept became a founding member of the BVA. They went into receivership in 1927[43] and later emerged as Burndept Wireless (1928) Ltd. Subsequently this company became Burndept Electronics Ltd.

Cleartron Radio Ltd. was a founding member of BVA in 1926. The name was later changed to Cleartron (1927) Ltd. They used the

Fig. 18-37. Burndept HL-512 valve.

brand name C.T. for both the American and British types of valves which they made.[44]

Ever Ready Radio Valve Co. Ltd. never manufactured valves. They obtained all their valves from Mullard.

Louden valves were marketed by Fellows Magneto Co. Ltd. in 1924 and 1925. Some Louden designations used were FE1 and FE2 for bright emitters; FER1, FER2, and 0.06 designated dull emitters having thoriated filaments.

Ferranti Ltd. was incorporated in 1905 and manufactured electrical equipment. They started making valves and receiving sets in 1930.

Dario valves were sold in Great Britain by Impex Electrical Ltd., beginning in July 1929.[45] They were made in the Netherlands by N.V. Philips.

Lissen Ltd. valves were listed in the valve table on page 188 of the October 1930 issue of *Wireless Magazine*. Lissen Ltd. applied for membership in BVA late in 1934, indicating that it was embarking on large-scale production of receiving valves, and was admitted to full membership. Soon thereafter trouble arose over the brand names Lissen was proposing to use, and it appeared that Lissen intended to buy valves from Ever Ready, a nonmanufacturing member supplied by Mullard. The BVA ruled that the arrangements of these three members concerning the brand names to be put on valves were a breach of the BVA constitution. Lissen did not proceed with its proposal to make valves, and its membership was merged with that of Ever Ready. The valves sold in 1930 were obtained from Ever Ready, which, in turn, was supplied by Mullard.

Fig. 18-38. Neutron H406 valve.

Lustrolux Ltd. made valves in 1926 and 1927. Their brand names were Lustrolux and Ensign.

Nelson Multivalves were offered for sale by Nelson Electric Co. Ltd. in 1926. These valves had three filaments controlled by a "scissors switch" in the base of the valve. With this switch closed, any one of the three filaments could be used. Opening the switch put two of the filaments in parallel, thus making it a power valve. This valve was made in four types, designated A, DEA, DE2, and DE.06.[46]

Neutron valves were advertised in Great Britain in 1926 by Neutron Distributors. No maker's name appeared on the valve or on the carton in which it was packed (Fig. 18-38).

Penton valves were offered for sale by the Penton Engineering Co. at the Olympia Radio Show in 1924. They had a spirally wound wire as anode. The standard R type and two dull emitters, HE4 and HE6, were advertised.[47]

The Radio Communications Co. Ltd. started advertising radio apparatus, including valves, in 1919.[48] In 1923 they advertised the Polar Peanut Valve,[49] a duplicate of the Wecovalve produced by Mullard and others, including the same type of socket and adapter as offered by Mullard, S.T.&C., and BSA Radio Sales. They also marketed the Polar R in Fig. 18-39.

Radions Ltd. entered the valve manufacturing field via the valve repair business. In May 1925 they advertised valve repairs but stated, "We are actual makers of valves. . . ."[50] In 1926 their advertisements were alternately for repairs and new valves. Their new valves included types A (Fig. 18-40), GP, A2, D4, DE34, DE34HF, DE.06, DE.06HF, 525B, 525C, 525H. The 525B had a British base, the 525C an American base.

Fig. 18-39. Radio Communications Company Polar R valve.

Fig. 18-40. Radion Type A valve.

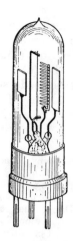

Fig. 18-41. Scott-Taggart Negatron.

The S.T. Co. Ltd. was founded and operated by John Scott-Taggart. The formation of this company was announced in an advertisement on October 20, 1926.[51] The valves they sold were marked ST, followed by significant numbers; the first digit indicated the filament voltage. Valves ST21, ST22, and ST23 had 2-volt filaments; ST41, ST42, ST43 had 4-volt filaments; ST61A, ST61B, ST62, and ST63 had 6-volt filaments. These valves were advertised on February 26, 1927.[52]

The S.T. Co. Ltd. advertised for a comparatively short time, but Scott-Taggart was a dynamic force in bringing wireless into the home. This engineer had a distinguished career as wireless officer to various military units in World War I. He knew the needs and limitations of the wireless enthusiasts and foresaw the impact of their trade on the British economy. Early in his postwar career he worked for Ediswan; for three years he was departmental manager and research engineer for Radio Communication Co. Ltd., and in 1924 was consultant to this company and advisor to others. He was the designer of the Ediswan ES2 and ES4[53] and developed rectifying and transmitting valves.[54] He worked on double-grid valves and the circuits in which they were used[55] and in 1921 devised a negative resistance arrangement, a Biotron, using two triode valves.[56] In January 1922 he announced his Negatron, a single valve which could be operated so as to give a negative resistance characteristic. This valve had been developed in 1919, but information concerning it had been withheld until the patent which had been applied for was issued.[57] Fig. 18-41 shows a drawing of a Negatron.

Scott-Taggart crowded a lifetime of achievement into the 1920s. He developed his ST series of valves, founded his own company, and designed the popular ST series of broadcast receiver kits, thousands of which were bought and assembled for home use. He was granted innumerable patents pertaining to wireless, was director of Radio Press Ltd., editor of *Modern Wireless* and *Wireless Weekly*, and the author of numerous books for home constructors.[58] Year after year he made signal contributions to the technology, literature, and industry of radio.

REFERENCES

1. F. R. Manning, "Recent Repeater Station Installations," Paper No. 151, *Inst. P.O.E.E.*

2. J. A. Fleming, *The Thermionic Valve and Its Developments in Radio Telegraphy and Telephony* (2nd ed., London: Iliffe, 1924), p. 383.

3. A. B. Hart, "The London-Glasgow Trunk Telephone Cable and Its Repeater Installations," *P.O.E.E. J.*, Jul. 1926, *19*(2):105–148. See also *Elect. Commun.*, Oct. 1926, *5*:119–155.

4. W. E. Benham, J. S. Lyall, and A. R. A. Rendall, "The New Quarter-Ampere Repeater Tube and Its Applications," *Elect. Commun.*, Oct. 1932, *11*:74–78.

5. "New Types of Valves," *Wireless World*, Nov. 14, 1923, *13*:211.

6. Advertisement of Mullard Radio Valve Co. Ltd., *Wireless World*, Dec. 14, 1923, *13*:xxix.

7. Ediswan advertisement, *Wireless World*, Nov. 21, 1923, *13*:xxix. W. E. M. Ayres, "Low Consumption Dull-Emitter Valves," *Exp. Wireless*, May 1924, pp. 457 ff.

8. Ayres, "Low Consumption . . . Valves."

9. "Some More Valves Tested," *Exp. Wireless*, Jul. 1925, pp. 642–644.

10. "Some Valves Tested," *Exp. Wireless*, Dec. 1925, pp. 967–968.

11. "More Valves Tested," *Exp. Wireless*, May 1925, p. 509.

12. *Ibid.*, pp. 509–510.

13. Advertisement in *Wireless World*, Oct. 31, 1923, *13*:xxxv.

14. Advertisement in *Mod. Wireless*, May 1925, *4*:456; also *Wireless Constr.*, June 1925, *7*:744.

15. Advertisement in *Amat. Wireless*, Jul. 11, 1925, *7*:40.

16. See *Exp. Wireless*, Mar. 1925, p. 368.

17. Advertisement in *Pop. Wireless*, Dec. 25, 1926, *10*:1030.

18. Advertisement in *Mod. Wireless*, Feb. 1928, *9*:114.

19. Mullard advertisement, *Wireless World*, Mar. 24, 1923, p. xxiii.

20. Mullard advertisement, *Wireless World*, Jan. 23, 1924, p. x.

21. Mullard advertisement, *Wireless World*, Jan. 30, 1924. See also Ayres, "Low Consumption . . . Valves."

22. Mullard advertisement, *Wireless World*, Nov. 14, 1923, p. xxix.

23. Mullard advertisement, *Amat. Wireless*, Aug. 30, 1924, p. 255.

24. See *Exp. Wireless*, Nov. 1924, pp. 116–117.

25. Mullard advertisement, *Wireless Constr.*, June 1925, *1*:inside front cover.

26. "Six New Mullard Valves," *Exp. Wireless*, Feb. 1925, pp. 278–280.

27. Mullard advertisement, *Pop. Wireless*, Oct. 9, 1926, *10*:back cover.

28. Mullard Wireless Service Co. advertisement, *Wireless World*, Jan. 6, 1926.

29. "Valve Manufacture—A Brief Description of the Simpler Processes Adopted in the Manufacture of M.O. Valves," *Wireless World*, Aug. 19, 1922, *10*:641–647 and continued Aug. 26, 1922, *10*:683–688; see p. 641.

30. H. J. Round, *The Shielded Four-Electrode Valve—Theory and Practice* (London: Cassell, 1927). See also *Riv. Ital. Rad. Tec.*, Mar. 1928, *1*:67.

31. Advertisement of Economic Electric Ltd., *Wireless World*, Aug. 26, 1922, p. xxxiv.
32. Advertisement of Economic Electric Ltd., *Amat. Wireless*, Aug. 30, 1924, 10:inside cover.
33. Advertisement of Economic Electric Ltd., *Exp. Wireless*, May 1926, p. iv.
34. Advertisement of Bower Electric Ltd., *Wireless World*, Feb. 13, 1924, p. xxvi. "The Thorpe Valve," *Wireless World*, Mar. 12, 1924, p. 745.
35. T. H. Nakken, "Multiple Grid Vacuum Tubes and Their Advantages," *Radio News*, Dec. 1925, 7:804–805, 826. Norman Edwards, "Circuits Favored by British Listeners," *Radio News*, May 1927, 8:1334–1335, 1402.
36. B.T.H. advertisement, *Wireless World*, Jan. 9, 1924, p. xxvi.
37. B.T.H. advertisement, *Pop. Wireless*, Feb. 19, 1927, p. 1459.
38. *Ibid.*
39. *Wireless Mag.*, Sept. 1928, 8:84.
40. *Ibid.*
41. B.T.H. advertisement, *Wireless World*, Jul. 13, 1927, p. 5 (advts.).
42. John Scott-Taggart, *Elementary Text-Book on Wireless Vacuum Tubes* (3rd ed., London: Radio Press, Ltd., 1922). See p. 3 of advertisements.
43. See p. 90 of Jul. 20, 1927, *Wireless World*, for note concerning the appointment by the court of a "Receiver and Manager" for Burndept Wireless, Ltd.
44. Cleartron Radio, Ltd. advertisement, *Wireless World*, Jan. 6, 1926, p. 19 (advts.).
45. Impex Electrical Ltd. advertisement, *Wireless Mag.*, Jul. 1929, 9:505.
46. Nelson Electric Co. Ltd. advertisement, *Wireless World*, Jan. 6, 1926, p. 27 (advts.).
47. Penton Engineering advertisement, *Wireless World*, Mar. 19, 1924, p. vi.
48. Radio Communications Co. advertisement, *Radio Rev.*, Oct. 1919, 1:v.
49. Radio Communications Co. advertisement, *Wireless World*, Oct. 3, 1923, 13:xxxi.
50. Radions, Ltd. advertisement, *Mod. Wireless*, 1925, 4:499. Also *Wireless Constr.*, June 1925, 1:777.
51. S.T. Ltd. advertisement, *Wireless World*, Oct. 20, 1926, p. 10 (advts.).
52. S.T. Ltd. advertisement, *Pop. Wireless*, Feb. 26, 1927, p. 1545.
53. Discussion of L. A. T. Broadwood's paper "Harmonics in C.W. Transmission" by John Scott-Taggart, *Wireless World*, May 15, 1920, 8:125.
54. *Wireless World*, Dec. 1919, pp. 524–525.
55. John Scott-Taggart, "Some New Circuits for Radio Telegraphy Employing a Double-Grid Vacuum Tube," *Radio News*, May 1921, 2:774. See also *Electrician*, Jan. 21, 1921, 86:97–98.
56. John Scott-Taggart, "The Biotron—A New Device Having Negative Resistance Characteristics," *Electr. Rev. Lond.*, Sept. 20, 1921, 89:450. See also *Wireless Age*, Sept. 1921, 8:21–22.
57. John Scott-Taggart, "The Negatron—A New Negative Resistance Vacuum Tube," *Wireless Age*, Jan. 1922, 9:22–24. See also *Elect. Rev. Lond.*, Sept. 30, 1921, 89:449, and Scott-Taggart, *Elementary Text-Book on Wireless Vacuum Tubes*, pp. 191–199.
58. *The Yearbook of Wireless Telegraphy and Telephony, 1924* (London: Wireless Press, Ltd.), p. 905.

Chapter 19

The Early Days of Broadcasting, 1920-1930: *France*[1]

At the end of World War I there were only two companies engaged in tube production in France—Compagnie des Lampes (Lampe Métal),and E.C.&A. Grammont (Fotos). In 1919 two other companies started to manufacture tubes. Société Independante de T.S.F. (SIF) made receiving tubes in 1919, produced transmitting tubes up to 1925, and telephone repeater tubes up to 1931. Samples of SIF tubes are shown in Figs. 19-1 and 19-2. Société La Radiotechnique was founded in 1919 and was bought in 1921 by Société Française Radioélectrique (SFR), which was an associate of Compagnie Générale de Télégraphie sans Fil (CSF). La Radiotechnique at first used the trademark R superimposed on the outline of a transmitting tube. In 1923 with the advent of the thoriated filament, the R was changed to RT (Fig. 19-3). In 1927 the trademark became Dario, and some tubes had both RT and Dario markings.

All these companies started out on a small scale making TM-type tubes. The electrodes were degassed during the pumping process by heating the grid to cause emission and by applying a high positive voltage to the anode to cause heating by bombardment. The nickel used for the anode was of doubtful purity and sometimes volatilized excessively, producing a dark deposit on the interior of the bulb. This made the tube suspect to customers who had noted that tubes became blackened in use and did not want to buy a used tube. To disguise the blackened appearance, some manufacturers, notably Fotos, adopted dark blue glass for the envelopes of their tubes.

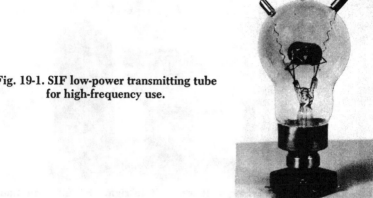

Fig. 19-1. SIF low-power transmitting tube
for high-frequency use.

At first no getters were used. In 1922 Métal began using a phosphorus getter which resulted in an iridescent appearance. Other manufacturers followed suit.

The TM-type tube was improved about 1923. A closer-spaced grid of finer wire was used in an attempt to improve its characteristics, but the grid was not rigid enough to insure holding the required shape. A bracing wire of 8-mils diameter was added and soon thereafter a second one. This construction precluded the use of the grid as an electron source for bombardment; hence, high-frequency induction heating had to be used.

The high power consumption of the filament of the TM tube, about 2.8 watts per tube, which had to be supplied by a storage battery, led to a demand for lower-powered thoriated filament tubes. These tubes were produced by La Radiotechnique late in 1923 and

Fig. 19-2. SIF receiving tubes.
Left: TM. Right: TM15.

Fig. 19-3. La Radiotechnique tubes. Left to right: R3, R5, and Radio Ampli R5. The RT marking on the Radio Ampli R5 was adopted in 1923 with the change to a thoriated filament.

by other manufacturers soon afterward. La Radiotechnique tubes were degassed by induction heating during evacuation. The lower filament operating temperature (about 1800 K) resulted in a longer life while still giving an emission of about ten times that of a tungsten filament. The necessity for the extremely high vacuum required for operation of the thoriated filaments led to the introduction of a magnesium getter.

In 1924 La Radiotechnique marketed tubes having both a name and a number. One of these dull-emitter types was Radio Micro R36. At the same time Métal offered the 6/100 Micro-Métal (Fig.

Fig. 19-4. Variants of 6/100 Micro-Métal. The tube at the extreme right, "MICRO-METAL 6/100 AMP. R.M.," was intended for operation with ac on the filament. Note G·D·E·R· markings.

Fig. 19-5. La Radiotechnique tubes. Left to right: Radio Micro, Micro-Bigril, and Radio Micro Special.

19-4), and Grammont advertised the Micro-Triode and Radiofotos. Note "G·D·E·R·" etched on tubes in Fig. 19-4. This stands for Groupement pour le Développement des Émissions Radiophoniques (Group for the development of broadcasting), which existed from 1924 to 1929. This organization was formed to give financial assistance to broadcasting stations before they had income from advertising. Funds were raised by a tax on all tubes sold in France—whether domestic or foreign. Supporting manufacturers could brand their tubes with this mark. All the foregoing tubes were general-purpose

Fig. 19-6. Fotos (Grammont) tubes with blue glass envelopes. Left to right: V.O., Bigrille-Ampli, Bigrille-Oscillatrice, 209 Marine. Note difference in spelling as compared with La Radiotechnique tubes shown in Fig. 19-5.

types. In 1924–1925 manufacturers began to produce tubes for specific applications.

Double-grid tubes came on the French market in 1924. At first they had tungsten filaments. By 1925 they were superseded by the dull-emitter version, space-charge rather than shield-grid tubes, and were first used in receivers at low anode voltage. Later they were used as frequency changers in superheterodynes. Examples of these are Métal's DG and RM (Fig. 19-4), La Radiotechnique's Micro-Bigril R43 (Fig. 19-5), and Grammont's Bigrille-Ampli (Fig. 19-6) and Bigrille BF.

Specialized tubes of the high-mu type for resistance-coupled radio-frequency and audio-frequency applications then appeared. Such tubes were the Super Micro R15 and Super Micro R24 of La Radiotechnique, the CL64B and CL172 of Métal, and the Fotos HF and MF of Grammont. At this time, audio power output tubes were introduced. La Radiotechnique brought out Super Ampli R29, Super Ampli 41, and Radio Watt R31 (Fig. 19-7). Métal advertised the CL104 and CL124 (Fig. 19-8). Fotos offered the BF1 and BF2.

In 1926 a new process of filament manufacture was introduced by La Radiotechnique and soon adopted by other makers. This was known as the "azide" or "nitride" process. The basic filament was pure tungsten wire, copper plated, then oxidized by heating in air at 800 °C. After mounting, a small quantity of an aqueous solution of barium nitride was painted on the anode and dried. During pumping, the tube was baked at 500 °C. The barium nitride decomposed, producing nitrogen, which was removed by the pumping process,

Fig. 19-7. La Radiotechnique tubes. Left to right: Radio Watt R31 (radio output tube), Super Ampli, E27 (output tube).

Fig. 19-8. Métal output tubes.
Left: CL104. Right: CL124.

and barium, which adhered to the anode. After pumping, the tubes were induction heated, and simultaneously the filament was heated to 1200 °C. The barium vapor which evolved from the anode coating reacted with the copper oxide on the surface of the filament to form barium oxide with an excess of barium. The result was a filament with very high emission. From 1926 to 1928, tubes with this type of cathode were made by a number of manufacturers. These included La Radiotechnique (Dario), Métal, Fotos, and J. Visseaux, a lamp maker who began to produce radio tubes in 1928.

In the area of general-purpose tubes were the Dario R42 and R75, Métal DZ813 and DZ908, Fotos B9 and C9, and Visseaux RO4010. Detector triodes offered were R76 by Dario, Métal DZ1508, Fotos D15, and Visseaux RO4215 (Fig. 19-9). Audio output triode tubes included Dario R56, R77, and R85 (Fig. 19-10), Métal DX502, DY604, DX804, Fotos D5 and D9, Visseaux RO4305 and RO4309. These manufacturers also made tubes for specific purposes such as resistance-coupled amplifiers, audio power pentodes, and radio-frequency tetrodes. The Dario R81 tetrode is shown in Fig. 19-11.

Up to 1929 practically all French broadcast receivers operated on battery power and required the operator of the set to perform

Fig. 19-9. Visseaux RO4215. Note
difference in length of base pins.

**Fig. 19-10. Dario R85 audio
output tube.**

**Fig. 19-11. Dario R81 radio-
frequency tetrode amplifier.**

numerous odd jobs. Small battery chargers were available, so it was
not necessary to haul the filament storage battery (no light weight)
to a garage or electrical shop for recharging periodically, but the
batteries tended to develop acid leakage. Even if this was overcome,
the space in the vicinity of the radio somehow became cluttered
with unsightly wires, and the living room soon looked like a
workshop.

For a number of years half-hearted attempts had been made to
produce radio receiving tubes which could be operated from the
ac lighting circuit. The first attempt had been made in 1922 by
Métal, who produced a tube called Radio Secteur (Fig. 19-12).
This had a short, thick filament which took 2 amperes at 2.3 volts
and could be ac heated. It was unsatisfactory because of the ac hum
which resulted. A second attempt was made in 1927 by La Radiotechnique, and they marketed a series of tubes which heated at
0.6 volt and 1.3 amperes. The cathodes were made of six nickel-

Fig. 19-12. Métal's first ac tube,
the Radio Secteur, 1922.

chromium alloy wires in parallel. These filaments were coated with
barium-strontium carbonates by a spraying process. Examples of
these tubes are the R636, R656 (Fig. 19-13), R655, and R643. Because of the low filament voltage and the high thermal inertia,
these tubes were an improvement over the Radio Secteur. The ac
hum was considerably reduced but not completely suppressed.

The brand name Dario was used for the first time on these tubes.
Uniformity is lacking in the use of R and RT in their identification.
In catalogues advertising these tubes which are marked R the desig-
nation RT is frequently found.

The problem of the ac hum was solved in 1929 with indirectly
heated tubes having equipotential, oxide-coated cathodes. The great-
est difficulty in this development in France, as in other countries,
had arisen from the heater. The step-by-step evolution of a satisfactory heater construction followed the same path in France and
ended with the same construction as that found in other countries.

In the continuing research at La Radiotechnique attempts were
made to use a stretched tungsten wire in the axis of a nickel tube
to which the emitting surface was applied. Hence the cathode was
radiation heated. This was not only an inefficient process but also
resulted in an unconscionably long delay in bringing the cathode
to emission temperature. Placement of a silica tube between the
tungsten heater wire and the oxide-coated sleeve was tried, but the

Fig. 19-13. Dario multiple-filament cathode tubes. Left: R636. Right: R656. The filament leads of the R656 were brought out on binding post terminals on the back of the tube and are not shown in this photograph.

tungsten was rapidly attacked by the silica. The next step was the use of two-hole alumina insulators and hairpin filaments; this arrangement sufficed for several years. The need for reducing the warm-up time finally resulted in the use of heaters coated with alumina by a "dip and dry" procedure.

The four leading French manufacturers then marketed a series of indirectly heated tubes having this construction. The all-purpose triodes were I4075 (Dario), DW704 (Métal), T425 (Fotos), and RS4324 (Visseaux). Detector triodes were I4076 (Dario), DW1508 (Métal), S415N (Fotos), and RS4215 (Visseaux). The radio-frequency and intermediate frequency amplifier triodes were I4077 and I4078 (Dario), DW3020 and DW3559 (Métal), T425 and S440N (Fotos), and RS4230 (Visseaux). Tetrode frequency converters were I4043 and I4053 (Dario), DW1 (Métal), TM4 (Fotos), and RS4141 (Visseaux). Radio-frequency amplifier tetrodes were I4081, I4091, and I4092 (Dario), DW2 and DW6 (Métal), S4150 (Fotos), and RS4142 (Visseaux).

Audio-frequency power amplifier triodes were DW1003 (Métal) and T410 (Fotos). Dario and Visseaux made none. Audio-frequency power pentodes and rectifier tubes continued to be made with filamentary cathodes and operated on raw alternating current. The filaments were made by the nitride process. The R89 audio-frequency power output pentode by Dario is shown in Fig. 19-14. Métal made the DW3, Fotos marketed the F100, and Visseaux sold the RS4343.

There were in France, as in other countries, independent manu-

Fig. 19-14. Dario R89 pentode output tube.

facturers who made tubes, and dealers who had tubes made especially for them by the larger manufacturers. There were also firms importing tubes from foreign countries and selling the imports under the original maker's name or under their own brand names. Detailed information about some of these independents is elusive, and few samples of their work have survived.

The following companies were active in the 1920s:

Compagnie Générale de Radiologie (CGR) started life as Caiffe-Callot et Rochefort. The original company made TM tubes. In 1923 they absorbed Établissement H. Pilon, a maker of power tubes. Shortly thereafter the combination changed its name to Compagnie Générale de Radiologie. Little information is available concerning what they produced in the 1920s. One of their tubes, PA68, is shown in Fig. 19-15. This is not a radio tube but is a half-wave mercury-vapor rectifier tube used in X-ray equipment.

Société Française Radioélectrique (SFRE, also SFR) was a subsidiary of CSF and was originally a supplier of marine and shore station radio equipment, buying all tubes from Marconi. About 1922–1923, SFR began to make some of its own tubes and at this

Fig. 19-15. CGR PA68 rectifier.

time was obtaining the bulk of supply from its subsidiary, La Radiotechnique. This arrangement continued until La Radiotechnique left the CSF group and joined the Philips group. SFR then made their own tubes at Levallois-Perret (Seine). SFR tubes are shown in Figs. 19-16, 19-17, and 19-18.

An explanation of La Radiotechnique's joining the Philips group is pertinent to this history. Manufacturers of tubes in France became

Fig. 19-16. SFR tubes. Left to right: R5, E52, E.

**Fig. 19-17. SFR E253B
transmitting tube.**

**Fig. 19-18. SFR P150
transmitting tube.**

involved in patent litigation just as they did in England and America. In the late 1920s La Radiotechnique and Philips instituted a series of actions against each other claiming patent infringement. When these suits were finally settled in 1930, Philips lost and was ordered to pay damages. Philips proposed to pay this debt with equipment, but because of the economic crisis and business depression, this was not acceptable to La Radiotechnique. In 1931 Philips negotiated the purchase of La Radiotechnique. The research laboratory and manufacture of transmitting tubes reverted to SFR. From then on La Radiotechnique made only receiving tubes of Philips types, and Philips used the brand name Dario.

A. Bertrand, 1, rue de Metz, Paris, marketed tubes under the brand names Microlux and Mercure from 1924 to 1928. These were double-filament tubes with filaments operating with 0.06 ampere at 3.5 volts. The Microlux had a short, cylindrical bulb, shorter than the height of the base, and was made by Microlux S.A. of the same address, which later marketed a series of tubes. The Microlux C2, sold by Bertrand, had not only two filaments but also two complete sets of elements which could be used in succession or in parallel to get more power output. Microlux also made a single-filament tube, Type A1, with characteristics similar to the American 199 type, and a low-power output tube, C3, with a 3.8-volt, 0.10-ampere filament. This tube operated with 80–120 volts on the anode. It had an amplification factor of 9 and anode impedance of 10,000 ohms.

Radio Celsior, 17, rue des Tournelles, Paris, made receiving tubes bearing the brand name Celsior. By 1930 they were producing a wide variety of tubes, including indirectly heated cathode amplifiers of the triode and tetrode types, as well as rectifiers. All of these tubes operated with 4 volts on the filament or heater, including both oxide-coated and thoriated filament types. Among them were the CB510 (frequency changer), E200/300 (tetrode), ME1520 (high- and intermediate-frequency amplifier), and D.12 08 (detector and audio-frequency amplifier). For final stages of audio-frequency amplifiers they offered HP604, PU10.02 and PV801. Their double-grid frequency changer (BS1212), tetrode amplifier (ES 300–200), and detector and low-frequency amplifier (DS1610) were indirectly heated cathode tubes. Celsior also made directly heated thoriated filament tubes, and half-wave and full-wave rectifiers.

Établissements M.C.B., 27, rue d'Orleans, Neuilly-sur-Seine, sold tubes bearing the brand name Cyrnos, beginning with the TM type in the early 1920s. In 1927 they were still making the TM type and were also marketing tubes with thoriated filaments designated Micro

Fig. 19-19. Micro Eclipse 306.

0.06, Ampli, Bigrille, and Trigrille, the last for use in driving a loudspeaker. They made the Micro-Alternatif, which had an ac filament operating at 2.1-volts ac with 0.7 ampere, and they produced several rectifier tubes (both half-wave and full-wave types) for use in anode power supplies.

In 1928 M.C.B. brought out two series of tubes designated Standard and Labo and also a series of rectifiers. The Standard series was composed of the A2403 (high-mu triode), A1404 (general-purpose triode), B1209 (detector and audio-frequency voltage amplifier), B712 (audio-power output tube), and Bigrille (frequency changer). All of these tubes operated with 3.8–4 volts dc on the filament. The Labo series was made up of Trigrilles in which the third grid was placed between the filament and the control grid and was used to accelerate the electron stream. The filament voltage was the same as that of the Standard series. The Labo series consisted of the Trigrille 29 (frequency changer) and Trigrille B5008 and B3510 (amplifiers).

In the M.C.B. series of rectifier tubes for use in anode voltage supplies were two half-wave and three full-wave rectifier tubes. In addition, M.C.B. made two general-purpose tubes. TM1003, a TM-type triode, had a tungsten filament. The triode AL1203 was designed for operation with a filament current of 0.5 ampere at 1.5–2 volts ac.

J. Besson et Cie., 9, avenue Jean Jaurès, Issy-les-Moulineaux (Seine), were originally makers of incandescent lamps. They produced vacuum tubes in the period 1923–1927, and their brand name was Eclipse. They made rectifiers, triodes, and tetrodes. One of their triodes, the Micro Eclipse 306, is shown in Fig. 19-19. Its thoriated filament operated with a current of 0.06 ampere at 3.5–3.8

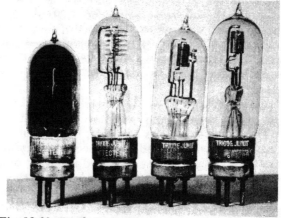

Fig. 19-20. Triode Junot Detecteurs and Amplificateurs.

Fig. 19-21. Tela N tube.

volts. This was a general-purpose tube with an amplification factor of 9–15. The anode voltage was 40–100 volts. It may be noted from the photograph that the base pins are somewhat shorter than those commonly used.

Société Française des Lampes Luxor, 10, rue Edouard Vaillant, Levallois (Seine), produced ac filament tubes from about 1925 to 1928 with the brand name Euréka. The Lampe Euréka operated with a filament current of 1.4 amperes at 1.6 volts ac, had an amplification factor of 9–12, and anode impedance of 20,000–35,000 ohms. It could be obtained with either the standard four-pin base for sets constructed especially for its use or with a base having two binding posts. The latter type was made for existing sets and was provided with binding posts to which the low-voltage ac supply was connected.

Lutèce-Lumière S.A., 32, rue d'Hauteville, Paris, was another incandescent lamp manufacturer who made tubes in the years 1925–1929. The lamp factory was at Reims, but the tubes carrying the brand name Lutèce were made in a special factory at Issy-les-Moulineaux (Seine). In 1928 they produced receiving tubes of the filamentary type, the filaments being made by the barium process.

Lutèce-Lumière made the following tubes for direct-current–operated sets with 4-volt filament supply: G112 (general purpose), H430 (high-frequency and/or resistance-coupled amplifier), L408

Fig. 19-22. Vatea DGP3 tube.

low-frequency voltage amplifier), P405 (audio output tube), and 2G412 (double-grid frequency changer). For operation with 2–2.5 volts on the filament they listed S215 (general purpose), S205 (audio power output), and 2GS (double-grid frequency changer). For higher-power output with dc filaments operating at 4–6 volts they made the P403 (medium power), Ph515A, and Ph515B. They produced the type M73 half-wave power rectifiers and the B507 and B515 full-wave rectifiers.

Fig. 19-23. Orion tubes.
Left: ND4. Right: L43.

Fig. 19-24. Sator tubes. Left: S4. Right: NSS4.

J. Visseaux, 88, quai Pierre-Seize, Lyons (Rhone), began to manufacture tubes in 1928. In 1929 he advertised a series of ten tubes
with four-digit designation numbers preceded by either RH or RO.
The RHs had thoriated filaments, and the ROs had oxide-coated
filaments. All were 4-volt filaments. The RH4010 was a general-
purpose tube, RH4041 and RH4141 were bigrilles for use as
frequency changers, high-frequency amplifiers, or detectors. The
RO4206 was a triode audio output tube, and the RO4243 a trigrille
audio output tube. The RO4125 was an intermediate-frequency amplifier, RO4109 a detector, the RO4215 a "super-detector," and
RO4142 a screen-grid tube for high-frequency amplification.

Tubes bearing the brand name Iris were made by Métal for export only. They were sold in England by Anglo-Franconia, Ltd.
of London.

Établissements G.M.R., 8, Boulevard de Vaugirard, Paris, was a
merchandiser of tubes. He sold Junot Detecteurs and Amplificateurs
(Fig. 19-20). He also sold Tela tubes (Fig. 19-21), which were
made in Austria.

Établissement H. Palicot, 51, rue de Paradis, Paris, was a merchandiser who sold Vatea tubes (Fig. 19-22), which he imported from
Hungary.

Radio-Vicco (C. J. Soulam), 40, rue Denfert-Rocherau, Paris,
imported Orion (Fig. 19-23) and Sator (Fig. 19-24) tubes from
Hungary for sale in France. In some cases these were re-marked
Radio-Vicco. (Both Orion and Vatea tubes are discussed in some
detail in Chapter 22.)

In 1930 tubes made by Compagnie des Lampes (Métal) bore
the trademark Métal-Mazda.

REFERENCES

1. Little can be cited in the way of references for the material presented in this chapter. The facts are drawn from confidential memoranda made available in the author's visits to Gabrielle Pelletier (former associate of Professor Edouard Branly), M. J. Nenot (former design engineer with Compagnie des Lampes and La Radiotechnique), M. Nozières of La Radiotechnique, M. Larragaldie (who worked on the Holweck demountable tube), and others.

The major portion of the information comes from Dr. Ing. Robert Champeix, formerly with Compagnie Générale de Télégraphie sans Fil and now a consulting engineer in Paris. Dr. Champeix, who shares the author's penchant for collecting tubes and tube information, has written numerous articles on tube and radio history for periodicals. He is the author of a two-volume work, *Physique et technique des tubes électroniques* (Paris: Dunod, 1958–1960), and *Savants méconnus, inventions oubliées* (Paris: Dunod, 1966). He has written a popular book, *Radio, T.S.F., télévision: Simple histoire* (Paris: Editions L'indispensables, 1969), and is the co-author of other books on radio subjects.

Chapter 20

The Early Days of Broadcasting, 1920-1930: *The Netherlands*[1]

N. V. Philips was impressed by the sales of the Ideezet and its companion transmitting tube, the Zendlampe (described in Chapter 13), and embarked on an intensive program of tube development. By April 1922 they were offering two varieties of the Ideezet which had been rechristened the C type. The C I (Fig. 20-1) was a soft tube like the original Ideezet Model C for operation with 25–30 volts on the anode. The C II was the same structure but pumped to a high vacuum and was intended for operation with 30–75 volts on the anode. Both tubes had the same filament, taking 0.5 ampere at 3–3.5 volts.

With these they offered the B I, B II, and B III. These tubes had cylindrical bulbs with cylindrical element assemblies positioned horizontally, and were equipped with four-pin bases. They were electrically similar except for the filaments; the remaining parameters were like those of the C type. These tubes were made with both the French-type four-pin base with 3-millimeter pin diameter, and the Telefunken-type four-pin base with shorter pins 4 millimeters in diameter, disposed at the corners of a square, the diagonal of which was 17 millimeters long. The latter base had a projecting lug to insure its proper location in a Telefunken socket. Fig. 20-2 shows a D2 of later construction with a tipless bulb.

At this time Philips also offered a Type E power tube (Fig. 20-3) for use in the last audio stage. This tube had a spherical envelope about 55 millimeters in diameter. The filament current was 0.68 ampere at 4 volts, and the anode operated at 60–100 volts. In the field of transmitting tubes, they had produced the Type F having

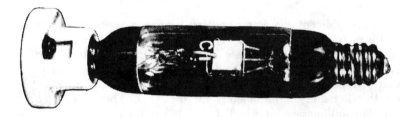

Fig. 20-1. Philips C I tube.

a spherical envelope 50 millimeters in diameter and a four-pin base. The rated output was 2.5 watts with 250 volts on the anode. The filament current was 1.4 amperes at 4 volts.

Next in their line was the G I, a slightly larger tube of the same general appearance as the original Zendlampe sold in 1919. Like the Zendlampe it was double ended. The filament took 2.25 amperes at 6 volts; it was rated at 500-volts anode, the output being 10–20 watts. The G II, also designated the 302, was a single-ended, pear-shaped tube with a four-pin base and had the same operating parameters as the G I, and the same output. Types H and I were double ended with an Ediswan bayonet base on each end. The bulb was similar to that used for the early American UV204, with a center spherical section 105 millimeters in diameter for the H and 125-millimeters diameter for the I. The H had a filament which took 5 amperes at 9 volts and operated at 1000–5000 volts anode to give an output of 100–200 watts. The I had a 14-volt 0.8-ampere filament, took 2000–2500 volts on the anode, and was rated 250–500 watts output.

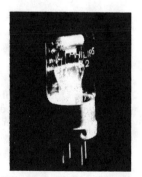

Fig. 20-2. Philips D2 tube.

Fig. 20-3. Philips E power tube.

To complement these transmitting triodes, a series of half-wave rectifiers was offered, T I, T II, and T III. The T I and T II had an Edison medium screw base for the filament connections and an Ediswan base for the anode end. The bulb was similar in shape to that of types H and I with a maximum diameter of 65 millimeters for the T I and 75 millimeters for the T II. The overall length was 175 millimeters for the T I and 195 millimeters for the T II. The permissible anode currents were 50 and 100 milliamperes respectively, and the corresponding internal voltage drops were 100 and 150 volts. The T III had a cylindrical bulb of 60 millimeters maximum diameter, and the total length of the tube was 225 millimeters. The filament took 11 amperes at 6 volts. The maximum anode current was 150 milliamperes, and the corresponding voltage drop was 150 volts. Later this tube was assigned the designation 7985.

The B II was soon changed to employ a dull-emitter filament and a pear-shaped bulb with a maximum diameter of about 30 millimeters. The new filament operated at 1.6–1.8 volts with a current of 0.15 ampere.

The D series of tubes was brought out about the same time. The D I and D IV were similar except for the bases. The D I had a European (French) base (Fig. 20-4) and the D IV an American UV base. They had tungsten filaments operating at 3.5 volts and 0.5 ampere and were soft tubes intended for detector application. The D IV had a pear-shaped bulb, approximately 45 millimeters maximum diameter; the D I had a cylindrical bulb 30 millimeters in diameter. They operated at anode voltages 25–30 volts. The D II and D V were hard tubes intended for both detector and amplifier applications. Both had filaments operating at 3.5 volts

Fig. 20-4. Philips D I tube. Tube at left, with tip, is an early product; that at right, tipless, is later.

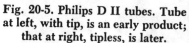

Fig. 20-5. Philips D II tubes. Tube at left, with tip, is an early product; that at right, tipless, is later.

with 0.5 ampere. The recommended anode voltage was 30–75 volts. Two samples of the D II are shown in Fig. 20-5; the one with the tip is the earlier version.

The D III was a hard tube equipped with a Telefunken base, had a cylindrical bulb like the D II, and the same operating parameters. The type D VI was a space-charge tetrode which had originally been marketed under the designation Q in 1921. The tungsten filament operated at 3.5 volts with 0.5 ampere. The anode and space-charge-grid voltage was 2–10 volts. Both tubes (Q and D VI) had spherical bulbs about 55 millimeters in diameter. (See Fig. 20-6.) The inner (space-charge) grid was connected to the base shell.

The B VI (Fig. 20-7) was also a tetrode of the space-charge-grid type. It had a dull-emitter filament which took 0.15 ampere at 1.6–1.8 volts, and the anode (and space-charge grid) operated at 2–10 volts. The space-charge grid was connected to the base shell, as it was in the D VI. With the exception of the B II and B VI (the first of the Miniwatt tubes), all these tubes were popularly known as *helgloeienderadiolampen*, "hell-glowing radio lamps," because of the brilliancy of the tungsten filaments while in operation.

In 1924 the Philips system of nomenclature was changed and the term *radiolampen* was replaced by *radiobuzien* (radio tubes). The new system was used until 1934. In the system adopted in 1924 each tube was designated by a letter followed by a three- or four-digit number. The letter indicated the approximate filament cur-

Fig. 20-6. Philips Q and D VI tubes. Tubes are the same but bear
different markings. The Q is the earlier marking.

rent: A = 0.06–0.10 ampere; B = 0.10–0.20 ampere; C = 0.20–0.40
ampere; D = 0.40–0.70 ampere; E = 0.70–1.25 amperes; F = 1.25
amperes and higher. The filament voltage was indicated by the first
digit of a three-digit number or the first two digits of a four-digit

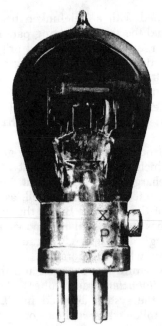

Fig. 20-7. Philips B VI tube.

number. The last two digits indicated the amplification factor if the tube was a triode.

In the case of other kinds of tubes the numbers have the following meanings:

41, 51, . . ., tetrodes of the space-charge-grid types
42, 52, . . ., high-frequency screen-grid tubes
43, 53, . . ., pentode output tubes
44, 54, . . ., binodes
45, 55, . . ., high-frequency tetrode selectodes
46, 56, . . ., high-frequency pentodes
47, 57, . . ., high-frequency pentode selectodes
48, 58, . . ., mixed hexodes
49, 59, . . ., hexode selectodes

In Dutch terminology "binode" indicated a tube which contains two separate element assemblies (e.g., diode and triode or two separate triodes) in the same bulb. A "selectode" is a remote-cut-off tetrode or pentode, which in American parlance would be called a "variable-mu" tube.

In 1924 the Miniwatt series (starting with the B II and B VI) was greatly extended. The dull-emitter filaments were of the azide or nitride type described in Chapter 19. The series initially included the A106, A109, A141, A209, A241, A409, A410, A441, B403, and B406. Shortly after this the A415, A425, and B405 were added. Fig. 20-8 shows the A410 and B406.

In 1927 the first Philips tube having an indirectly heated cathode was marketed. This was the F215, intended for use as a detector. Accompanying this were the C142 (high-frequency tetrode), D143 (output pentode), and B443 (output pentode). These last three

Fig. 20-8. Philips A410 and B406 tubes.

Fig. 20-9. Philips F215 and B443 tubes. Markings are applied to tops of tubes instead of on sides, which facilitates identification of tubes when assembled in apparatus.

tubes had filaments for operation on low-voltage ac. The F215 and B443 are shown in Fig. 20-9.

The E series of indirectly heated cathode tubes appeared in 1928, and with them came the change from metal shell bases to molded plastic bases. The molded base material was known as Philite, and these bases soon appeared on all Philips receiving tubes. The first E tubes were E415, E435, and E442, and had 4-volt heaters. The E415 is shown in Fig. 20-10. The next Philips tube development of importance was the E445 selectode, a variable-mu tube, which was introduced in 1931.

It is interesting to note that a given Philips tube could bear different designations depending on where it was marketed. At the left in Fig. 20-11 is an illustration used in a Philips advertising pamphlet to portray the Type-T II rectifier. At the right is a reproduction taken from a catalogue issued by a South American radio dealer showing the same tube bearing the marking ZG II.

In the Netherlands there were a number of independent manufacturers of tubes in the period 1920–1930.

Metaaldraadlampenfabriek Holland has already been mentioned in connection with its work for the Netherlands navy late in World

Fig. 20-10. Variants of the Philips E415 tube. Left to right: five-pin base, four-pin base and side connection, top marking.

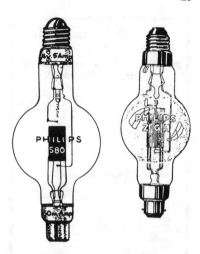

Fig. 20-11. Left: drawing of Philips T II (also designated 580) tube taken from advertising literature put out for European use. Right: drawing from South American catalogue showing designation for South American trade, ZG II.

War I. After the war, production of tubes was continued for sales to the general public. They used the brand names Stangold and Radispar and possibly others. Fig. 20-12 shows one of their advertisements which appeared in 1926. This company ceased operations in 1928.

Gloeilampenfabriek M. Heussen & Co., of Arnhem, began to manufacture tubes late in 1921. A double-grid tube of their production was advertised by various Dutch radio-parts dealers during the first half of 1922.[2] In July 1922 Heussen & Co. began to advertise, and its first full-page ad, in October, is reproduced in Fig. 20-13.[3] One of the tubes offered in this ad, the double-grid V.E. (Fig.

Fig. 20-12. 1926 advertisement for Radispar tubes.

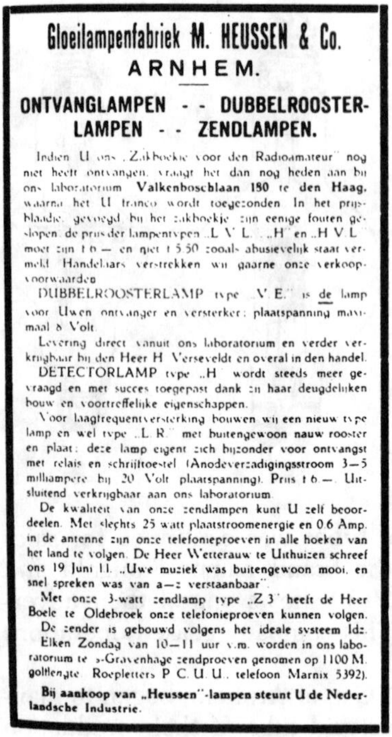
Gloeilampenfabriek M. HEUSSEN & Co.

ARNHEM.

ONTVANGLAMPEN - - DUBBELROOSTER-LAMPEN - - ZENDLAMPEN.

Indien U ons „Zakboekje voor den Radioamateur" nog niet heeft ontvangen, vraagt het dan nog heden aan bij ons laboratorium **Valkenboschlaan 180 te den Haag**, waarna het U franco wordt toegezonden. In het prijsblaadje, gevoegd bij het zakboekje zijn eenige fouten geslopen: de prijs der lampentypen „L V L", „H" en „H V L" moet zijn f 6.— en niet f 5.50 zooals abusievelijk staat vermeld. Handelaars verstrekken wij gaarne onze verkoopvoorwaarden.

DUBBELROOSTERLAMP type „V. E." is de lamp voor Uwen ontvanger en versterker; plaatspanning maximaal 8 Volt.

Levering direct vanuit ons laboratorium en verder verkrijgbaar bij den Heer H. Verseveldt en overal in den handel.

DETECTORLAMP type „H" wordt steeds meer gevraagd en met succes toegepast dank zij haar deugdelijken bouw en voortreffelijke eigenschappen.

Voor laagfrequentversterking bouwen wij een nieuw type lamp en wel type „L. R." met buitengewoon nauw rooster en plaat; deze lamp eigent zich bijzonder voor ontvangst met relais en schrijftoestel (Anodeverzadigingsstroom 3—5 milliampère bij 20 Volt plaatspanning). Prijs f 6.—. Uitsluitend verkrijgbaar aan ons laboratorium.

De kwaliteit van onze zendlampen kunt U zelf beoordeelen. Met slechts 25 watt plaatstroomenergie en 0.6 Amp. in de antenne zijn onze telefonieproeven in alle hoeken van het land te volgen. De Heer Wetterauw te Uithuizen schreef ons 19 Juni l.l. „Uwe muziek was buitengewoon mooi, en snel spreken was van a—z verstaanbaar".

Met onze 3-watt zendlamp type „Z 3" heeft de Heer Boele te Oldebroek onze telefonieproeven kunnen volgen.

De zender is gebouwd volgens het ideale systeem Idz.

Elken Zondag van 10—11 uur v.m. worden in ons laboratorium te 's-Gravenhage zendproeven genomen op 1100 M. golflengte. Roepletters P. C. U. U., telefoon Marnix 5392).

Bij aankoop van „Heussen"-lampen steunt U de Nederlandsche Industrie.

Fig. 20-13. 1922 advertisement for Heussen tubes.

20-14) was a space-charge-grid tetrode which operated at 3.8-volts filament and 8-volts anode.

In a subsequent ad Heussen offered the tubular detector L.V.B. (Fig. 20-15). This tube was similar in construction to the original "Holland" tube and operated at 3.7-volts filament and 20–24-volts anode. It could be used as a local oscillator. Fig. 20-16, a composite reproduced from Heussen advertising of 1922, shows other early Heussen tubes. By 1927 Heussen tubes were being marketed under the brand names Fairy, Farma, Splendid, Champion, Aurore, Frelat, and Neutral. Many of these tubes were made for export. Frelat valves were offered for sale by several British importers in 1926 and 1927.[4] Famar Dutch Valves (Famar = Farma?) were sold by another British importer in 1925.[5]

N.V. Gloeilampenfabriek "Elektra," of Tilburg, began advertising tubes for sale in 1924[6] and continued production until at least sometime in 1930. They used the brand names Electra and Mars and in 1930 advertised receiving tubes, transmitting tubes, and rectifiers.

N.V. Gloeilampenfabriek Nijmegen was incorporated in November 1919 as an incandescent lamp manufacturing company in Nijmegen. In 1927 the name was changed to N.V. Splendor Gloei-

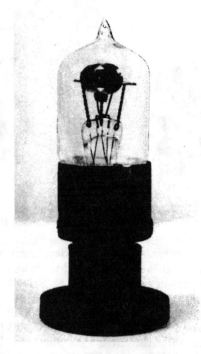

Fig. 20-14. Heussen Type V.E.
tetrode (1922).

Fig. 20-15. Heussen Type L.V.B.
triode (1922).

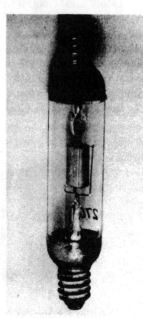

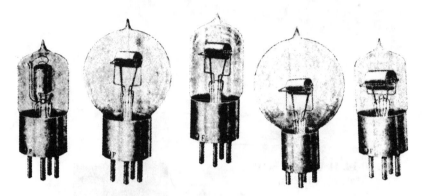

Fig. 20-16. Composite of advertising leaflets offering other Heussen
tubes (1922).

lampenfabrieken, and they began to make radio tubes. Operating
through a subsidiary sales company in France, they sold Splendor
tubes in Paris in 1928. The Splendor line that year included the following tubes: high-frequency amplifiers VH40 and VH300, detector
and low-frequency amplifier V1508, detector and resistance-coupled
amplifier V3030, and output tube V62. These tubes all had 4-volt filaments. Also listed were the G335 (half-wave high-voltage rectifier),
the G450 and G650 (full-wave high-voltage rectifiers), and two
low-voltage rectifiers, L13 and L14, for battery chargers. The V1508
and G450 are shown in Fig. 20-17. In November 1929 this company
entered into an agreement with Philips, and in 1930 the company
name was changed to N.V. Splendor Radio-Nijmegen.

N.V. Gloeilampenfabriek Radium started in the business of repairing tubes in 1922 in Amsterdam. Later they moved to Tilburg
to take advantage of the skilled labor which was available there.

Fig. 20-17. Splendor tubes. Left to right: V1508, G450, and HF.

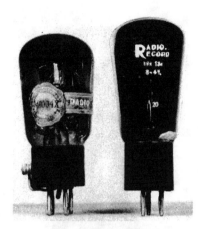

Fig. 20-18. Radio Record tubes.
Left: M1004X. Right: RRR134.

In 1927 they began to manufacture tubes, adopting the brand name
Radio Record. Two of their tubes are shown in Fig. 20-18—the
RRR134 is a half-wave rectifier and M1004X is an output amplifier.

N.V. Vereenigde Industrieen (N.V.V.I.), of Rotterdam, was originally a maker of textiles from which it graduated into gas mantles
(Welsbach burner mantles) and then switched to the making of
incandescent lamps. Shortly after Radio Röhrenfabrik of Hamburg
was formed in 1924 it became a subsidiary of N.V.V.I. In 1926
N.V.V.I. started to manufacture radio tubes, with the trade name
VIR. Their first production consisted of four types: VIRAA, VIRAB,
VIRAC, and VIRAD. The earliest samples had metal bases; later
tubes had molded bases and tipless bulbs. The early samples of
the VIRAA, a general-purpose tube, had the designation and operating parameters printed on a white paper label on the base. The
label on the VIRAC, a low-frequency amplifier, was of pink paper.

Fig. 20-19. VIR tubes. Two samples each of VIRAA, VIRAC, and
VIRAD, showing variations in markings.

Fig. 20-20. "Star Tube 201A Made in Holland." Left: front view.
Right: back view.

The VIRAD was a detector. Samples of these tubes are shown in
Fig 20-19.

The mystery 201A tube (Fig. 20-20) indicates that there may have
been other manufacturers in Holland whose records have been destroyed. This tube is marked "STAR TUBE 201A MADE IN HOL-
LAND" on one side of the bulb and "5V–0.25 amp, 20–120V" on
the other. The lettering is typically Philips, but according to their
Patents and Trademarks Department this mark was never registered
by Philips. Research of early records discloses an intriguing story
of a "star tube" and reveals that Holland was not immune to the epi-
demic of international litigation brought on by the vacuum tube
in the 1920s.

In the case of Philips, history was repeating itself. The original
N.V. Philips Gloeilampenfabrieken was organized for the manufacture and sale of incandescent lamps. About 1913 Philips exported
and sold in the United States lamps which infringed a General
Electric patent, and GE brought suit. Philips paid damages and
ceased selling lamps in the United States. In 1920 these companies
agreed to cooperate on a friendly basis, and each acquired an
interest in the other's company. As part of the agreement GE supplied Philips with machines to manufacture more efficiently a better quality of lamps and tubes.

With the rise of interest in radio, Philips organized the N.V.
Philips Radio Company, which was owned by the N.V. Philips

Gloeilampenfabrieken, to manufacture radio tubes. In the early 1920s Philips began to execute plans for worldwide distribution of its tubes. The first Philips tubes trickled into the U.S. market in the fall of 1923. These were called "star tubes" and were marked "Model [8 pointed star] 201A" and "Model [8 pointed star] 199." They had standard UV bases and sold for $1.75. The quantity of tubes was small, but there were rumors that large shipments of "star tubes" were about to be delivered for the U.S. market.

Since the major part of RCA's tube business at that time was the sale of UV201A and UV199 tubes, which retailed at $3 each, RCA purchased some "star tubes" for examination. Tests showed them to be exact duplicates of RCA tubes and also showed that they were made on machines supplied to Philips by GE as part of the 1920 agreement. The tubes infringed RCA patents and bore simulating markings which were misleading to the public. RCA took effective steps "to protect the American public" and prevent the importation of Philips tubes. GE filed four patent infringement suits against importers of Philips "star tubes," and U.S. Customs prohibited the importation of vacuum tubes bearing simulations of trademarks and designations of RCA.

Both companies realized the disadvantages of years of pending litigation. RCA knew that in the interim Philips could flood the RCA market with its "star tubes," and Philips regarded American technical know-how as the only thing of value RCA had to offer in making any trade to protect the American market. After months of negotiations over territories and patents, an agreement was reached in July 1925: RCA and Philips would share vacuum-tube patent rights and Philips would stay out of RCA territory.

On the "Star Tube 201A Made in Holland", (Fig. 20-20) there is no trace of an eight-pointed star, and the question persists: Who made it?

REFERENCES

1. Information on N. V. Philips developments has been compiled through the cooperation of Drs. D. Boer of the Philips Bureau of Archives, who made early Philips records available, supplied copies of Philips advertising pamphlets dating back to July 1, 1919, and documented his answers to the author's searching questions. Additional details of early Dutch tube inventors and makers have come from Jacob Verwer of the Technical University of Delft, and from the unpublished "History of Radio Tubes," by Harry de Weijer of the Technical University of Eindhoven.
2. See advertisements in *Radio Nieuws*, Jan. 1922, 5, and Mar. 1922, 5, advertising sections (pp. unnumbered) by Radio Technisch Bureau Herm. Verseveldt, The Hague; and Fa. Ch. Velthuisen, 'sGravenhage, in *Radio Nieuws*, Feb. 1922, 5.
3. Advertisement in *Radio Nieuws*, Oct. 1922, 5 (advertising section).

4. Advertisement of Continental Radio Import Co. Ltd., *Pop. Wireless,* Dec. 25, 1926, *10*:1070; and that of J. H. Taylor & Co. in the same issue. Also Continental Radio Import Co. Ltd. advertisement in *Pop. Wireless,* Feb. 26, 1927, *11*:1542, and Dec. 31, 1927, *12*:938.

5. Advertisement of H. D. Zealander & Co. in *Wireless Constr.,* June 1925, *1*:762.

6. Advertisement in *Radioélectricité,* Nov. 25, 1924, p. xxiv (advertising section).

Chapter 21

The Early Days of Broadcasting, 1920-1930: *Germany*

During this period, the development work done by the major companies, Siemens & Halske and AEG-Telefunken, was divided according to the use to be made of their product. In general, Siemens & Halske concentrated its effort on tubes and equipment for wire telephony; Telefunken intensified research on tubes for radio application.

Siemens & Halske's earliest developments were based on the results attained with some special double-grid tubes which had been evolved during World War I. The VS27 (Fig. 21-1) was the progenitor of the tubes developed for telephone use in the postwar era. The intricate glass structure used to position and support the electrode system in this tube is a tribute to German glassworkers. It provides the ultimate in stable electrode systems.

Siemens & Halske attempted to capitalize on their experience with tetrodes of the Schottky design during the war and developed a line of tetrodes for repeater applications. The first of these was the R type (Fig. 21-2) for the new multiplex telegraphy system.[1] The grid structure of this tube followed the Schottky design, a punched-out structure with angular bars as shown in Fig. 21-3. The development series of this tube is shown in Fig. 21-4. The R type was soon superseded by the OR pictured in Fig. 21-5 in the multiplex telegraph systems. The chief difference was that in the OR the cathode was oxide coated. The tungsten filament of the R tube took 2.1 amperes at 4.3 volts; the OR took 1.1 amperes at 2.5 volts, or about one-third the filament power. The amplification factor for both tubes was 4. The OR was also made by Telefunken as the RE87.

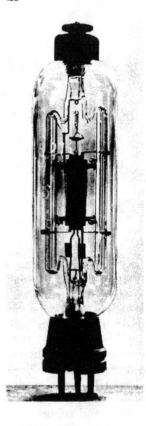

Fig. 21-1. Siemens & Halske VS27 tube.

It should be noted that in Germany the terms "amplification factor" and "mutual conductance" are not used. For amplification factor the Germans substitute *Durchgriff*, which is the reciprocal of the amplification factor expressed as a percent. Thus a tube with an amplification factor of 25 has a *Durchgriff* of 4 percent. For mutual conductance (in micromhos) they use "slope," and express slope in terms of milliamperes per volt. Thus a slope of 1 milliampere/volt is equivalent to a mutual conductance of 1000 micromhos.

Triodes were preferable for application in the German telephone network. The BF tube (Fig. 21-6) was introduced in 1920 and was used until 1925 by the German Reichspost in all amplifiers. This tube was made by Siemens & Halske. Electrically equivalent tubes were made by AEG, Süddeutsche Telefon-Apparate-, Kabel-, und Drahtwerke of Nürnberg, C. Lorenz A.G., and Dr. Erich F. Huth, GmbH. With the exception of the Huth tubes, which had plane-parallel electrodes,[2] they all had a cylindrical electrode assembly.

The Siemens & Halske BE tube (Fig. 21-7) was used in multi-

Fig. 21-2. Siemens & Halske R tube.

Fig. 21-3. Grid structure of Siemens & Halske R tube. (Reproduced from Veröff. NachrTech., 1935, 5.)

Fig. 21-4. Development series of the R tube. (Reproduced from Veröff. NachrTech., 1935, 5.)

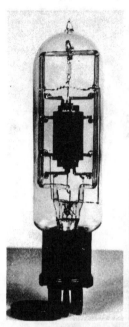

Fig. 21-5. Siemens &
Halske OR tube.

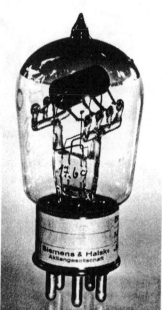

Fig. 21-6. Siemens &
Halske BF tube.

Fig. 21-7. Siemens &
Halske BE tube.
(Reproduced from
Siemens-Z., 1922.)

plex telephony in 1922.[3] It had a tungsten filament requiring 2.1
amperes at 4.8 volts. The anode voltage was 220–400 volts, the amplification factor was 11, and the mutual conductance was 800 micromhos. The BF tube had a tungsten filament which required 1.1

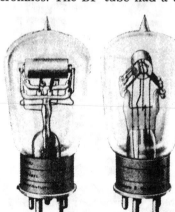

Fig. 21-8. Siemens & Halske Type
BO. (Reproduced from *Elekt.
NachrTech.*, Mar. 1925.)

Fig. 21-9. Siemens & Halske OCK
tube. Left: OCK of 1925. Right:
OCK of 1930. (Reproduced from
Veröff. NachrTech., 1935, 5.)

amperes at 3.5 volts. The anode voltage was 220 volts, the amplification factor was about 14, and anode resistance was 25,000 to
30,000 ohms.[4] The mutual conductance was about 500 micromhos.
The useful life was 2500 hours.[5] The BO tube (Fig. 21-8), which
replaced the BF, had an oxide-coated cathode which took 1.1 amperes at 1.8 volts, about one half the power required for the BF.
Its emission was about two and one half times that of the BF.[6]
The BO had a service life of 7500 hours.[7]

About the time of the introduction of the BO tube (1926), there
arose a demand for tubes with about four times the output of the
BO for undersea cable use. To meet this need, the OCK tube in
Fig. 21-9 was designed. The amplification factor was about 7 and
the anode impedance 5000 ohms. The mutual conductance (slope)
was about 1400 micromhos. The grid of this tube had a new construction (Fig. 21-10) which made possible the use of very thin
(50-microns diameter) grid laterals, too thin to be welded. They
were made of tungsten wire mechanically pressed into nickel sup-

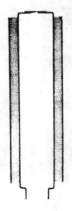

Fig. 21-10. Grid of OCK tube. (Reproduced
from *Veröff. NachrTech.*, 1935, 5.)

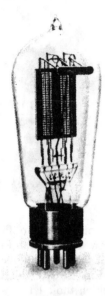

Fig. 21-11. Siemens & Halske CO tube. (Reproduced from *Veröff. NachrTech.*, 1935, 5.)

ports. The result was increased uniformity in the product. The anode was made of wire netting, blackened to facilitate heat radiation.

The CO tube (Fig. 21-11) was the next in this series. It was basically intended for the operation of telegraph sounders. In telephony it was only used when the incoming transmission was at an extremely low level. It was similar in construction to the OCK, but had an output of 1 watt.

Fig. 21-12. Siemens & Halske Types Da and Aa tubes.

Fig. 21-13. Siemens & Halske
Types Ba and Bas tubes.

Late in the 1920s the system of nomenclature was changed to comply with a request from the Reichspost Ministerium. In this changed system each new type of tube was designated by a capital letter which indicated the output of the tube. This capital letter was followed by one or more lower-case letters which delineated the specific characteristics.[8] The first group included tubes having the lowest output. The Aa tube at the right in Fig. 21-12 was the first tube in the A series. It had an amplification factor of about 30 and a mutual conductance of 1000 micromhos. The Ba tube, at the left in Fig. 21-13, was the replacement for the BF and BO tubes in telephone practice. It operated with a filament current of 0.5 ampere at 3.5 volts. The Ca (Fig. 21-14) was the replacement

Fig. 21-14 (Left). Siemens & Halske Type Ca tube. (Reproduced from *Veröff. NachrTech.*, 1935, 5.)

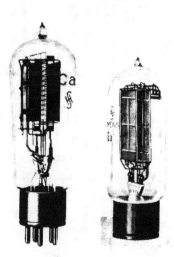

Fig. 21-15 (Right). Siemens & Halske Type Ea tube. (Reproduced from *Veröff. NachrTech.*, 1935, 5.)

Table 21-1. Telefunken Tube Nomenclature

GROUP OF LETTERS		GROUP OF FIGURES		LOWER CASE LETTER OR WORD	
Fundamental Letters	Additional Letters	First Two Figures	Last Figure or Figures		
RE = tubes for receivers	N = AC heated filament S = shielded grid tube Z = multiple sets of elements	Average filament current in hundredths of an ampere	Terminal voltage of filament supply (battery or transformer)	no letter	European standard 4-pin, or 5- or 6-prong German standard base
				d	European standard 4-pin base with side terminal for shield grid
RG = rectifier tubes	L = low tension for battery charging N = high tension for battery eliminators			s (or serie)	Special tubes for operation from DC power line with filaments connected in series
RV = power tubes for audio-frequency output or low-power transmitting tubes				Neutro	Special tubes for HF amplification having very low anode-grid capacitance
Example RE	S	16	4		d

for the OCK. The Da tube, shown at the left in Fig. 21-12, was the replacement for the CO. The Ea (Fig. 21-15) was the highest step of power output in which the oxide-coated cathode was still used. The output was 5 watts with 400 volts on the anode.

The system of nomenclature for Telefunken tubes which was described in Chapter 12 was useful up to about 1927. The rapid increase in the number of receiving tubes pointed out the desirability of a change in the method of designating new tubes in this class. The new system was designed to give more information on a specific tube and involved letter prefixes of up to four letters, followed by a three- or four-digit number, sometimes followed by a lower-case letter or word. This system is shown in Table 21-1.

The squence in which the early Telefunken receiving tubes appeared is a bit baffling because the designation numbers were not in consecutive order. The RE11 and RE16 were being made in quantity for military use in 1917–1918.[9] An improved version of the RE20 was available in 1920.[10] The RE26, RE33, RE38, RE48, RE58, RE73, RE76, and RE78 were also available in 1920, although they were not described in technical literature in detail until 1923.[11] The RE82, RE83, RE84, RE86, and RE97 were described in 1924.[12]

Data on other Telefunken receiving tubes were obtained from various books containing tabular information on tubes, and the dates given are those of the publication of the books involved. The tubes and the date of publication of the book are as follows: RE70 (1927), RE71 (1924), RE75 (1927), RE77 (1927), RE79 (1924), RE81 (1925), RE85 (1927), RE87 (1924), RE88 (1924), RE89 (1924), RE95 (1925), RE96 (1924), RE205 (1927), RE209, (1927), RE211 (1927), RE212 (1927). The RE11 and RE71 were electrically the same but had different bases. The same is true of the RE58 and RE85, the RE78 and RE79, the RE83 and RE89, and the RE84, RE88, and RE95.

Fig. 21-16. Telefunken RE1 tube.

Fig. 21-17. Left to right: Telefunken RE78, RE89, RE201 tubes.

The author has in his collection a sample of the RE1 (Fig. 21-16). Figs. 21-17, 21-18, and 21-19 show other tubes in this series, which apparently did not include the numbers RE101 to RE199. Presumably this RE series was abandoned in 1927 with the introduction of the new numbering system shown in Table 21-1.

Telefunken lower-powered transmitting tubes of the 1920s were made in quantities and many have survived. The first, the RS1, and the RS2, RS3, RS4, and RS5 have been covered in Chapter 12. The RS12 was in production (about twenty per day) in 1918, and

Fig. 21-18. Left: Telefunken RE83.
Right: RE209.

Fig. 21-19. Telefunken RE202 tube.

had an output of 20 watts. The RS13I was a 500-watt transmitting tube—the first of the RS13 series. In accordance with Telefunken nomenclature the Roman numeral suffix was changed whenever significant changes in design were introduced.[13] The RS13I became the RS13II, then RS13III, and next RS13IV, by which time the power output had increased to 1000 watts and the tube was redesignated RS18. This later tube evolved into the RS32 and still later became the RS42.[14]

The RS17 was a Navy transmitting tube, produced at the rate of five per day in 1918. Originally it had an output of 75 watts and was intended as a replacement for the RS4. It underwent changes in design and became successively the RS17I, RS17II, RS17III, and RS17IV. The output increased from 75 to 200 watts, and the tube was renamed RS19. With further changes it became the RS21, later the RS29, and finally the RS36.

The RS55, a small transmitting tube of this era, had a tungsten filament which required 3 amperes at 10 volts. With anode voltages of 400–700 volts, the output was 5–15 watts. This tube also underwent changes in design. The RS55 (Fig. 21-20) was later replaced by the RS57, and still later by the RS50.

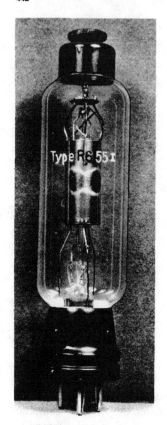

Fig. 21-20. Telefunken RS55I low-power
transmitting tube.

Fig. 21-21. Telefunken RE144
tube.

Fig. 21-22. Telefunken RE604 tube.

Fig. 21-23. Telefunken RGN354 tube.

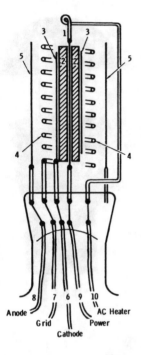

Fig. 21-24. Construction of REN1104. 1 = heater wire. 2 = insulating tube. 3 = oxide-coated metal tube (cathode). 4 = grid. 5 = anode. (Reproduced from *Telefunkenztg*, 1928.)

Following are descriptions of representative samples of receiving tubes produced later than 1927, whose designations are in accordance with the system shown in Table 21.1.

The RE144 (Fig. 21-21) was a receiving triode with a thoriated filament.[15] As the designation indicates, the average filament current was 0.14 ampere at 4 volts. The amplification factor was 10, mutual conductance 650 micromhos, and internal impedance about 16,000 ohms. It was a general-purpose tube for use in any position in a receiver, including that of a local oscillator.

The RE604 (Fig. 21-22) was an audio power output tube with a barium azide filament. The average filament current was 0.65 ampere at 4 volts. The amplification factor was 3.8, mutual conductance 3500 micromhos, and anode impedance about 1100 ohms.

The RGN354 in Fig. 21-23 was a half-wave rectifier for use in the anode power supply for receivers. The filament took about 0.35 ampere at 4 volts ac. The anode voltage was maximum 250 volts ac, and the maximum dc output was 25 milliamperes.

The REN1104 was one of the first indirectly heated cathode Telefunken tubes. Fig. 21-24 shows its construction. The heater was a straight wire down the middle of a ceramic insulating tube inside the oxide-coated cathode. Bifilar heaters were introduced somewhat

Fig. 21-25. Arcotron 201 tube.

later. The heater took 1.1 amperes at 4 volts and the recommended anode voltage was 200 volts. Under these conditions the amplification factor was 10, mutual conductance was 1500 micromhos, and the anode impedance was about 6700 ohms. This tube was intended for use as a high- or low-frequency amplifier.

The RES164d, one of the early screen-grid tubes, could be used either as a low-frequency amplifier or an output tube. The filament was of the barium azide type, operating with a current of 0.15–0.16 amperes at 4 volts. There was a side terminal on the four-pin base for the screen-grid connection. It had an amplification factor of 100, a mutual conductance of 2000 micromhos, and an anode impedance of 50,000 ohms.

Telefunken made the so-called bar tubes which appeared about 1930 and were named Arcotrons. There were two varieties, the Arcotron 201 (Fig. 21-25) intended for use as a resistance-coupled amplifier, and the Arcotron 301, a detector. Both operated with filament current of 0.25 ampere at 1.0 volt. The anode voltage specified was approximately 150 volts and the maximum anode current was 0.5 milliampere. The instruction sheet supplied with these tubes stated: "The direct tension applied to the metal coating (control electrode) of Arcotrons do [sic] not affect the plate current. For this reason normal plate current vs. grid tension diagrams cannot be given."

The Arcotrons were flat tubes about $\frac{3}{16}$ inch thick and $\frac{1}{2}$ inch wide. The control electrode was a sprayed metallic coating on the outside of the glass which flakes off with the passage of time, as can be seen in Fig. 21-25. These tubes were similar electrically to the Weagant tubes developed in the United States years before, but

Fig. 21-26. Loewe 2HF (left) and
3NF (right) tubes.

the Arcotrons were not satisfactory and were soon discontinued.

As in other countries, there were minor manufacturers as well as major ones. One of these whose products are of great interest to tube collectors was Loewe Radio A.G. of Berlin-Steiglitz. In Germany there was a tax on the use of radio broadcast receivers, the amount of tax being determined in part by the number of tubes in the receiver. The Loewe company capitalized on this condition, and von Ardenne and Heinert of this company designed a series of multiple valves. These valves were shown at the Berlin Radio Exhibition in 1926. The display included the 2HF and the 3NF

Fig. 21-27. Loewe Type OE333 radio receiver using 3NF tube. (Reproduced from *Wireless Mag.*, Dec.
1927.)

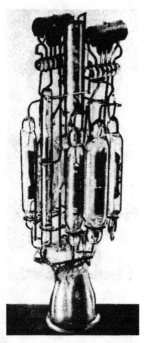

Fig. 21-28. Element assembly of Loewe
3NF tube. (Reproduced from *Wireless
Mag.*, Dec. 1927.)

(Fig. 21-26) and a radio receiver, type OE333, Fig. 21-27, which
was designed around the 3NF.[16] A view of the internal structure
of the 3NF is given in Fig. 21-28.

Fig. 21-29 shows two Loewe tubes, the LA74 triode and the LA77
screen-grid tetrode, which were made prior to the introduction of
the 2HF. The 2HF was essentially two LA77 tubes, with the coupling network in the same enclosure. The internal assembly is
shown in Fig. 21-30. Interest in the 2HF and 3NF was greatly stimulated by the low price plus Loewe's offer to repair any burnt-out

Fig. 21-29. Loewe LA74 and LA77 tubes.

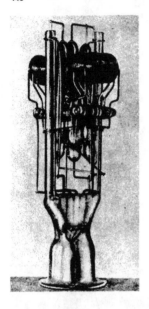

Fig. 21-30. Element assembly of Loewe 2HF tube. (Reproduced from *Wireless Mag.*, Dec. 1927.)

filament at a nominal charge, and at the same time replacing the other used filaments. The offer was made more attractive by the company's announcement that it had ceased to manufacture the earlier single tubes. The filament circuit of the 2HF required a current of 0.17 ampere at 4 volts. The anode voltage was 15 volts, and total anode current was 5 milliamperes.[17] The 3NF filament circuit took 0.3 ampere at 4 volts, and the anode voltage was 135 volts. The base connections of the 3NF and 2HF are shown in Fig. 21-31.

Sometime later, Loewe Radio introduced a much more advanced multiple tube, designated the WG36 (Fig. 21-32). This tube was enclosed in a metal shield and contained three units. Unit 1 was a variable-mu pentode used as a radio-frequency amplifier; unit 2

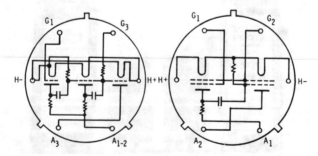

Fig. 21-31. Base connections of Loewe 3NF (left) and 2HF (right).

Fig. 21-32. Loewe WG36 tube.

was a triode used as an oscillator; unit 3 was a variable-mu pentode for use as an intermediate-frequency amplifier. Some idea of the internal structure of this tube may be gained from the X-ray photographs of Fig. 21-33. Two positions at right angles to each other

Fig. 21-33. X-ray photographs of Loewe WG36.

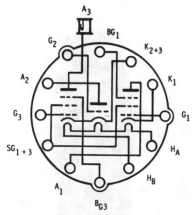

Fig. 21-34. Base connections of
Loewe WG36.

External Shield is connected to K1.

are shown. All the units had indirectly heated cathodes, with the heaters connected in series. The heater circuit took 0.18 ampere at 65 volts. The anode voltage was 250 volts on all units. The screen-grid voltage on units 1 and 3 was 100 volts. A diagram of the base connections is given in Fig. 21-34. The external shield was connected to the K1 cathode internally.

Dr. G. O. Spanner, GmbH, of Berlin, another manufacturer, produced at least two types of multiple tubes. The Delta Zweifach/4 (Fig. 21-35) as the name indicates, is a two-stage tube. Spanner also produced the Polytron-Vierfach-Röhre, which was composed of

Fig. 21-35. Delta Zwiefach/4 multiple tube.

Fig. 21-36. Auer receiving tube. (Reproduced from E. Nesper, *Der Radio-Amateur Broadcasting*, Berlin, 1923.)

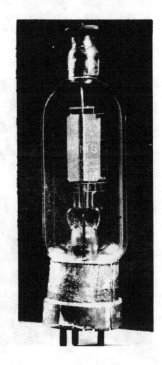

Fig. 21-37. Radioröhrenfabrik MS-30 tube.

four filamentary triodes, the filaments being connected in series. There were no coupling devices in this tube. The grids and anodes were brought out to base pins, as was the filament, so the tube had ten base pins. These were arranged in two concentric circles. The four grid terminals were in the inner circle and the four anodes and two filament terminals were on the outer circle. The filament circuit required 0.35 ampere at 3.5 volts. Units 1 and 2 were alike and had an amplification factor of 14, a mutual conductance of 600 micromhos, and an anode impedance of 24,000 ohms. Units 3 and 4 had an amplification factor of 5.5, a mutual conductance of 700 micromhos, and an anode impedance of 8000 ohms. Unit 1 operated with 60 volts on the anode, the others at 90 volts. Units 3 and 4 could be operated in parallel if desired.

An Auer receiving tube, designation unknown, is shown in Fig. 21-36. It has a bowl-shaped grid supported above a bowl-shaped anode. The arched filament is supported from above.[18]

The original Dr. Erich F. Huth, GmbH, became Huth Gesellschaft für Funkentelegraphie, mbH, in 1923. The latter was taken over in 1926 by Telefunken and Lorenz. The Huth LE244 was a triode with a cylindrical bulb and the usual European (so-called French) four-pin base. It operated with anode voltages of 40–100 volts. The filament took 0.08 ampere at 1.25 volts, the amplification factor was 4, the mutual conductance 350 micromhos, and anode impedance 11,000 ohms. The LE251 was also a triode with a cylindrical bulb and four-pin French base. The filament was 0.5 ampere at 1.6 volts. The amplification factor was 6.5, mutual conductance was 800

Fig. 21-38. Markings on Radioröhrenfabrik MS-30.

Fig. 21-39. Radioröhrenfabrik 201B tube.

micromhos, and the anode impedance 9000 ohms. Most of the later Huth tubes carried the trademark HUTH with the letters interlocked.

C. Lorenz, later C. Lorenz A.G., apparently entered the tube field about 1920. Their early tubes had horizontally mounted element assemblies. Their first satisfactory tube had an anode consisting of two parallel flat plates supported in a glass cylinder. The helically wound grid centered around the filament, which was on the axis of the cylinder. The filament required approximately 0.54 ampere at 3 volts.[19] By 1925 Lorenz was offering for sale a line of receiving tubes designated LV 0.1/50, LV 0.27/90, LV 3.5/220, LO 0.1/50, and M.O.G.[20] These were all receiving triodes with filament voltages ranging from 2 to 3.9 volts and filament currents from 0.06 to 1.1 amperes.

Fig. 21-40. Radioröhrenfabrik trademark.

Fig. 21-41. Radio-Röhren-Laboratorium Dr. Gerh. Nickel marking.

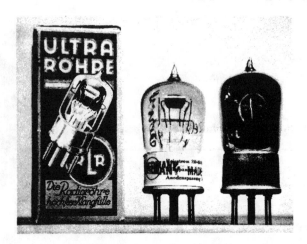

Fig. 21-42. Ultra UL550 (left) and U60 (right) tubes, with carton.

The MS-30 (watt) tube (Fig. 21-37) was made by Radioröhren-fabrik, GmbH, formerly the tube manufacturing department of C.H.F. Müller A.G., which was founded in 1924. Fig. 21-38 shows the markings on this tube. Note that the specific values of filament voltage, filament current, and total emission are handwritten on the glass, probably applied after the tube had been tested. The 201B in Fig. 21-39 was also made by Radioröhrenfabrik. The filament took 0.32 ampere at 4 volts. The amplification factor was 5.6, the mutual conductance 1000 micromhos, and the anode impedance 5500 ohms.

In general, the Radioröhrenfabrik's marking was that shown in Fig. 21-40. This company used the name Valvo in many of its tube designations. Examples are Valvo Normal, Valvo O-Reflex, Valvo Oekonom, Valvo Lautsprecher 201A, and Valvo Oscillotron. In fact, about 1926 Radioröhrenfabrik, GmbH, changed its name to Valvo, GmbH, and continued to manufacture tubes. Most Valvo tubes bore more conventional designations. By 1930 representative designations were H406, A408, and L412. Most of these tubes had 4-volt filaments. The Valvo name was dropped as part of the tube designation, but the name Valvo appeared somewhere on the bulb. Valvo was later taken over by Philips and is now Philips Valvo Werke, GmbH.

Radio-Röhren-Laboratorium Dr. Gerh. Nickel (later Dr. Nickel, GmbH) made tubes bearing the marking shown in Fig. 21-41. Nickel used the trade name Ultra for most of his tubes, although he also used Orchestron, Duotron, Sinus, and Dustron. He exhibited a series of push-pull valves bearing the name Dustron at the Berlin Wireless Exhibition in September 1926. Two of his Ultra tubes are

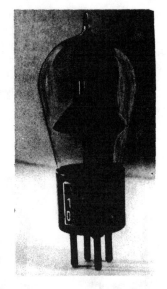

Fig. 21-43. Te-Ka-De VT107 tube.

shown in Fig. 21-42. The U60 took a filament current of 0.06 ampere at 1.1 volts. Its amplification factor was 8.5, mutual conductance 350 micromhos, and anode impedance 24,000 ohms. No electrical data on the UL550 are available. This company ceased to exist in 1930, and its rights went to Telefunken.

After World War I Te-Ka-De (see Chapter 12 for early work) went into production extensively. Most of their receiving tubes bore designations beginning with VT. The VT16, a triode, had a tungsten filament which operated with 0.52 ampere at 3.5 volts. The anode voltage was 20–60 volts, the amplification factor 3.6, mutual conductance 200 micromhos, and the anode resistance about 16,000 ohms. The VT105 had an oxide-coated filament which took 0.15 ampere at 1 volt nominal. The permissible anode voltage was 20–90 volts. The amplification factor was about 7, mutual conductance 200 micromhos, and anode impedance was 30,000 ohms. The VT107 in Fig. 21-43 had an oxide-coated filament which took 0.15 ampere at nominal 1.65 volts. The anode voltage range was 20–100 volts. The amplification factor was 6.8, mutual conductance 300 micromhos, and anode impedance about 25,000 ohms.

Schott u. Gen, of Jena, made tubes for a short time in the mid-1920s. Fig. 21-44 shows two of their tubes. The anodes are thick copper cylinders of large diameter in contact with the wall of the tube, and the cathodes are suspended by small springs.[21] The filament of the Type k tube took 1.35 amperes at 6 volts; the Type m took 1.2 amperes at 12 volts. Anode voltage was 200–400 volts.

A tube designated Der Club was made by Hochvakuumröhren-fabrik, of Wandsbeck, about 1926. It was similar in appearance to the American UV201A but had a four-pin European base. The fil-ament current was 0.33 ampere at 4 volts. The amplification factor was about 6, the mutual conductance was 2000 micromhos, and the anode impedance about 3000 ohms.

Fig. 21-44. Schott u. Gen tubes. Left: Type k. Right: Type m. (Reproduced from E. Nesper, *Handbuch der drahtlosen Telegraphie und Telephonie*, Vol. II, Berlin, 1921.)

REFERENCES

1. C. Nebel, "Die Entwicklung der Siemens Fernsprechröhre," *Veröff. Nachr-Tech.*, 1935, 5:215–226; see p. 219.
2. *Das Fernsprechen im Weitverkehr*, Reichspost Ministerium publication (Berlin, 1923). The section by K. Höpfner is entitled "Development and Present State of the Repeater Art in Germany."
3. A. Meissner, "The Development of Tube Transmitters by the Telefunken Company," *Proc. I.R.E.*, Feb. 1922, 10:3–23.
4. B. Pohlmann and A. Gehrts, "Die Verstärkerröhre der Fernmeldtechnik," *Siemens-Z.*, 1922, 2(5/6):282–291; see p. 290.
5. Nebel, "Die Entwicklung der Siemens . . .," p. 223.
6. B. Pohlmann and A. Gehrts, "Werdegang einer Verstärkerröhre," *Elekt. NachrTech.*, Mar. 1925, 2:65–74; see p. 71.
7. Nebel, "Die Entwicklung der Siemens . . .," p. 223.
8. *Ibid.*, pp. 225–226.
9. "25 Jahre Telefunken," *Telefunken Fest.*, 1928, p. 49.
10. H. Rukop, "Die Fabrikation von Hochvakuum-Röhren," *Telefunkenztg*, Feb. 1920, No. 19, p. 17.
11. Martin, "Telefunken Röhrentypen," *Telefunkenztg*, Sept. 1923, No. 32/33, pp. 51–55.
12. H. Rukop, "Moderne Empfängerröhren," *Telefunkenztg*, Oct. 1924, No. 38, pp. 19–38.
13. "25 Jahre Telefunken," p. 143.
14. F. Banneitz, ed., *Taschenbuch de drahtlosen Telegraphie und Telephonie* (Berlin: Julius Springer, 1927), p. 485.
15. G. Jobst, "Die Telefunken Rundfunk-Röhren 1928," *Telefunkenztg*, Oct. 1928, 9:29–34.
16. W. Reiss, "Valves as Complete Amplifiers," *Wireless Mag.*, Dec. 1927, 6:429–432. See also *Exp. Wireless*, Nov. 1926, pp. 654–658; *Wireless Mag.*, Dec. 1928, p. 444; *Wireless World*, Nov. 3, 1926, pp. 597–598; *Sci. Amer.*, Jul. 1926, pp. 69–70; *Radio News*, Oct. 1926, 8:362–363; *Pop. Wireless*, Nov. 13, 1926, p. 613; *Jb. Draht. Telegr.*, 1927, pp. 19–20.
17. *Wireless World*, Nov. 3, 1926, p. 597.
18. E. Nesper, *Der Radio-Amateur: Broadcasting* (Berlin: Julius Springer, 1923), pp. 264–265.
19. C. R. Forth, "Neuere Formen von technischen Elektronenröhre," *Jb. Radioakt.*, 1920, 17:174–178.
20. H. Wigge, *Rundfunktechnische Handbuch*, I Teil (Berlin: M. Krayn, 1925), pp. 159–163.
21. E. Nesper, *Handbuch der drahtlosen Telegraphie und Telephonie*, Vol. II (Berlin: Julius Springer, 1921), pp. 54–55. See also J. Groskowski, *Les lampes à plusieurs électrodes et leurs applications en radiophonie*, trans. G. Teyssier (Paris: Etienne Chiron, 1927), p. 135.

Chapter 22

The Early Days of Broadcasting, 1920-1930: *Norway, Sweden, Austria, Hungary, Australia, Japan*

This chapter presents limited information on the development and production of tubes in various countries other than those which have been covered.

NORWAY

In Norway, Ragnar Hansen, of Drammen, is the only known manufacturer of tubes in the 1920s. Though he was the exclusive supplier to the Norwegian marine, no records of his company are available, and few samples of his work remain. He made tubes up to 1000 watts. Figs. 22-1 through 22-6 are photographs of Hansen tubes. Fig. 22-1, a photograph of a tube in the author's collection, is the Gmb 2/250, about which little is known; Fig. 22-2 shows in more detail the markings on this tube. The Gmb 3/500 is shown in Fig. 22-3. Other Hansen triodes, designations unknown, are Figs. 22-4 and 22-5. The Hansen full-wave rectifier in Fig. 22-6 also has no designation.

SWEDEN

In Stockholm, Svenska Radio A/B manufactured tubes in 1926–1927. This company later became A.B. Svenska Elektronrör. One of their tubes, the TR6E, is shown in Fig. 22-7. No information is available as to its date of manufacture.

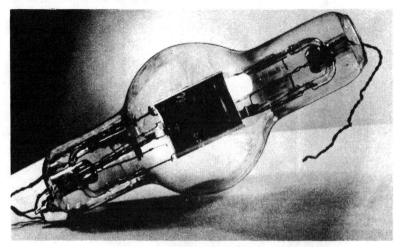

Fig. 22-1. Hansen Gmb 2/250 tube.

AUSTRIA

In Austria, a number of tube makers operated during the period 1920–1930. Unfortunately, their products did not always carry the maker's name. Such was the case of the Eagle tubes in Fig. 22-8. Neither the tubes nor their cartons carried any manufacturer's marking, but they were made by Joh. Kremenezky, of Vienna.

Kremenezky also made Orion tubes, two of which—the ND4 and L43—are shown in Fig. 19-23. The ND4 was an indirectly heated

Fig. 22-2. Markings on Hansen Gmb 2/250 tube.

459

Fig. 22-3. Hansen Gmb 3/500 tube.

Fig. 22-4. Undesignated Hansen triode.

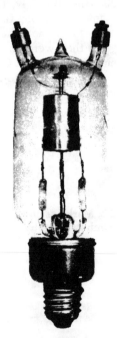

Fig. 22-5. Undesignated Hansen triode.

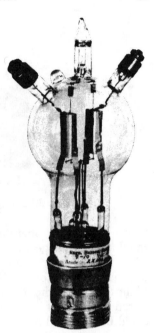

Fig. 22-6. Undesignated Hansen full-wave rectifier.

Fig. 22-7. A.B. Svenska Elektronrör TR6E tube.

Fig. 22-8. Eagle tubes, Fr12, La201, La206.

triode, the heater operating with 1 ampere at 4 volts ac., and the rated anode voltage was 200 volts. It had an amplification factor of 22, a mutual conductance of 2500 micromhos, and an anode impedance of 8900 ohms. It was the approximate equivalent of the Philips E424 or the Telefunken REN904. The L43 was an output tetrode tube with a filament which took 0.15 ampere at 4 volts. It could be operated on either ac or dc. The recommended anode and auxiliary grid voltage was 200 volts. The amplification factor was about 1.25, the mutual conductance was 1900 micromhos, and the anode impedance was 66,000 ohms. The L43 was the approximate equivalent of the Philips B443 and the Telefunken RES164d. The names and designations are etched on the tops of these tubes.

The Orion tubes were made in Austria but marketed in various

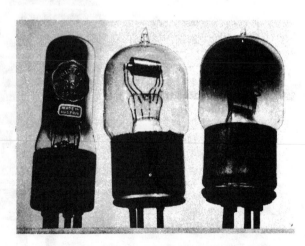

Fig. 22-9. Triotron tubes RS4, SV7, SV10.

countries. As noted in Chapter 19, one French merchant obtained his supply via Hungary. Despite the international restrictions on import and export trade in tubes during the 1920s, Orion tubes traveled far. The author obtained the tubes in Fig. 19-23 from a radio service man in Cape Town, South Africa. Kremenezky was still doing a thriving business in 1931, when there were four Kremenezky agencies in the Netherlands alone.

Triotron tubes were made by Radiowerk E. Schrack, of Vienna, beginning about 1926. Schrack also made Lilliput tubes. Three Triotron tubes are shown in Fig 22-9. The first series had dull-emitter filaments. The filaments were thoriated, although the base wire was not tungsten but a metal with a lower melting point, probably molybdenum.[1] The first series, operating at a filament voltage of 1–2 volts, included the RS2, TS1, and T10. The second series, operating at a filament voltage of 3–4 volts, consisted of the RS4 (Fig. 22-9), TS4, and ZE4. Schrack also made some specialized tubes. The OE4 was a resistance-coupled amplifier tube, the WE4 was an output tube with an ac filament, and the GE25 was a full-wave rectifier for supplying anode voltage. Other Triotron tubes which followed shortly were the TL, L10, S201a, S201b, SS, LSS, SV10 (Fig. 22-9), and LV3.

Czeija, Nissl & Co., another manufacturer in Vienna, was making tubes in 1927. These were apparently the same as the U.S. Western Electric tubes. Two of these were designated 215A and 216A, and their characteristics were the same as those of the Western Electric tubes bearing the same code numbers.

Nowack & Co., of Vienna, in 1927 made a series of receiving tubes. These were designated I, Ia, II, IIa, III, IIIa, PV1, PV2, and OS. All had thoriated-tungsten filaments. They operated with filament currents from 0.06 to 0.08 ampere with voltages from 1.8 to 5.5 volts. They also made a transmitting tube, the SE, with a tungsten filament which took 1.6 amperes at 5.5 volts. It required 220 volts on the anode. The amplification factor was 20, mutual conductance 1200 micromhos, and anode impedance 17,000 ohms.

Helikon tubes were also made in Austria about this time. Their designations were Victrix, Populair, Fortissima, and Miniwatt. They had thoriated filaments with operating currents of 0.07 to 0.3 ampere at voltages from 2.5 to 4 volts. Anode voltages of 20–120 were specified. The name of the maker has not survived.

Gustav Ganz & Co., of Vienna, marketed Ostar or Ostar-Ganz tubes in the late 1920s and early 1930s. This interesting series of tubes had indirectly heated cathodes with unique heaters intended to be operated at full line voltage, either 110 or 220 volts ac or dc. The heater power required was 5.5 to 6.5 watts. The heaters were made of tungsten wire and operated at 1100 °C. For the 220-volt

Fig. 22-10. Ostar EG50 110-volt
rectifier tube.

heaters, the heater wire was 0.015 millimeter in diameter and about
4 meters long, wound ingeniously. The Ostar EG50 110 volt tube
(Fig. 22-10) was a rectifier tube capable of outputs up to 130
volts dc and 50 milliamperes depending on the size of the input
capacitor of the smoothing filter. There was also an EG50 with a
220-volt heater.

The Ostar-Ganz L1525 (in center of Fig. 22-11) was an output
tube. It operated with 70–220 volts on the anode. Its amplification
factor was 5.5, the mutual conductance was 3000 micromhos, and
the anode impedance was 1850 ohms. The maximum output was

Fig. 22-11. Ostar-Ganz U920, L1525, and A520DG tubes.

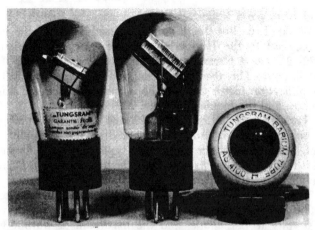

Fig. 22-12. Tungsram LD410, AR4100, and AS4100 tubes.

6 watts. The U920 at the left in Fig. 22-11 was a general-purpose tube with an anode voltage range of 100–200 volts. The amplification factor was 11, mutual conductance 3000 micromhos, and anode impedance 3700 ohms. The A520DG, at the right in Fig. 22-11, was a tetrode of the screen-grid type which had a close-fitting wire-mesh screen on the outside of the bulb. No information on its electrical characteristics is available. There were at least two other tubes in this series—the A520 and the W310—both triodes. They were intended for use in resistance-coupled amplifiers.

HUNGARY

Tungsram Radio Works of Ujpest, Hungary, made Tungsram and Sator tubes. Tungsram tubes were, for a time, assembled in

Fig. 22-13. Tungsram PP430 and
PV495 tubes.

England from parts imported from Hungary by British Tungsram Radio Works, Ltd., but the designations used were not the same as those assigned to the Hungarian product. The Tungsram LD410 (Fig. 22-12) was a filamentary triode, the filament taking 0.1 ampere at 4 volts. The recommended anode voltage was 200 volts. The amplification factor was 17, the mutual conductance was 1800 micromhos, and the anode resistance 9000 ohms.

The Tungsram PP430 in Fig. 22-13 was a pentode in which the suppressor grid was internally connected to the midpoint of the filament. It had a five-pin continental-type base. The filament required 0.3 ampere at 4 volts. The amplification factor was 60, mutual conductance was 1600 micromhos, and anode impedance was 36,000 ohms. The PV495 also shown in Fig. 22-13 was a full-wave rectifier tube. The filament took 1.1 amperes at 4 volts. The anode voltage was 300 volts ac per anode, and the maximum dc output was 75 milliamperes. The base was the four-pin continental type. Two Sator tubes, the S4 and the NSS4, are shown in Fig. 19-24.

Vatea tubes were made in Hungary by the United Incandescent Lamp and Electric Company of Budapest. In 1927 they offered for sale a number of triodes with tungsten or thoriated tungsten filaments. The WP3 had a tungsten filament which took 0.54 ampere at 3–3.5 volts. The anode voltage was 40–100 volts. The amplification factor was about 7.7, the mutual conductance 250 micromhos, and the anode impedance 38,000 ohms. The TP2 had a thoriated filament rated at 0.37 ampere at 1.4 volts. The amplification factor was 9, mutual conductance 300 micromhos, and anode impedance 30,000 ohms. The TP3 operated with a filament current of 0.065 ampere at about 2.9 volts. It had an amplification factor of 7.7, mutual conductance of 450 micromhos, and anode impedance

Fig. 22-14. One of the oldest inhabitants of Australia, expressing his satisfaction with AWV Radiotrons.

of 17,000 ohms. The TP4 was similar to the TP2 except for the filament, which required 0.175 ampere at 1.8–2.1 volts. Fig. 19-22 shows a Vatea DGP3 of somewhat later vintage. It is a space-charge tetrode with a filament which takes 0.06 ampere at 3–3.8 volts. The anode voltage is 4–15 volts. It has a five-pin continental base.

AUSTRALIA

In Australia, Amalgamated Wireless (Australasia) Ltd., after producing the Expanse B Valve described in Chapter 13, organized a subsidiary called the Amalgamated Wireless Valve Co. Pty. Ltd. At the end of 1924 this company negotiated a contract with the Radio Corporation of America to enable them to manufacture and sell certain types of RCA tubes in Australia. By 1927 they were making only four RCA types, one of which was the RCA30, but they were distributing fourteen Marconi and eighteen RCA types which they imported.[2] They did not start quantity production until August 1933, but even one of the earliest residents of Australia seemed to be enthusiastic over this company's products, as shown in Fig. 22-14.

JAPAN

There is little information available on the work done in Japan during the years 1920–1930. Mention was made in Chapter 13 of the Annaka AAB-5, but the maker's name is still a mystery. Fig. 22-15 shows one tube made in Japan (with its shipping carton)

Fig. 22-15. Japanese TEC tube.

Fig. 22-16. Japanese TWW tube, showing markings.

marked TEC. This may have been made by the Tokyo Electric Company. The tube shown in Fig. 22-16 has the script marking TWW stamped on the anode and a wTw monogram in a diamond-shaped enclosure etched on the glass. Fig. 22-17 shows another view of the same tube, which has two anodes, one flat and the other curved. The filament is between the grid and the curved anode. The filament and grid leads were brought out at one end, and the two anode leads at the other end. Except for the second anode being curved instead of flat, the structure is the same as the Negatron of John Scott-Taggart (Chapter 18). Possibly this was intended to be a Japanese Negatron. As to the TWW marking, it could be the maker's identification.

The Japanese tube shown in Fig. 22-18 carries the brand name EVER on the base and a trademark consisting of a capital T on the vertical portion of which there appears something resembling a winding. The bulb is marked "Made in Japan." The structure of the element assembly resembles that of the American 201A.

❉   ❉   ❉

How did Kremenezky's Orion tubes get to South Africa? The story of their acquisition—the scent, the chase, the chance of coincidence of being in the right place at the right time, the discovery, identification, and recognition—is a narrative familiar to every serious collector. It is as complex and complicated as this documented his-

Fig. 22-17. Japanese TWW tube, showing electrode structure.

Fig. 22-18. Japanese EVER tube.

tory of the development of the vacuum tube itself. Just as the collector may experience disappointment at the end of a pursuit, the reader may find an error in these pages in spite of all verification. May any such error or an omission serve as motivation for the reader to continue this research in industrial archaeology.

REFERENCES

1. H. K., "A New Dull-Emitter Tube," *Wireless World,* Feb. 17, 1926, p. 250.
2. L. McDonald, "The Receiving Valve Story," Amalgamated Wireless Valve Co. Pty. Ltd. pamphlet, undated, unpaginated.

Index of Tube Types

Numbers in boldface type indicate
pages on which illustrations appear.

Index

Numbers in boldface type indicate
pages on which illustrations appear.

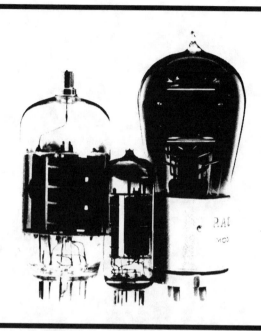